THE LONG JOURNEY

Parts Three and Four

THE CIMBRIANS

(Courtesy American Museum of Natural History, N. Y.)

PRIMITIVE MEN MAKING STONE IMPLEMENTS

THE LONG JOURNEY

THE CIMBRIANS

by

JOHANNES V. JENSEN

Translated by
A. G. CHATER

VOLUME II

McKINLAY, STONE & MACKENZIE
NEW YORK

MANUFACTURED IN THE UNITED STATES OF AMERICA

CONTENTS

BOOK ONE: NORNA GEST

BOOK TWO: THE CIMBRIANS

CONTENTS

LIST OF ILLUSTRATIONS

BOOK ONE

NORNA GEST

GEST COMES INTO THE WORLD

HE was born in Sealand. The first thing he remembered was a rowan tree covered with berries, which waved above his head, a lovely red revelation, and carried his eye up into a world of leaves and airy tree-tops, right into the blue sky, where great white things passed in a blissful depth; this was the first time his eyes saw the day.

Somewhere up in the blue there was something that shone and gave warmth; he turned his face that way and met a mighty white fire which glowed like a molten ring; dazzled, he closed his eyes, and then the darkness under the lids was full of strange living colours. When he opened his eyes again there were livid spots, ghosts of the sun, on trees and sky and wherever he looked.

His mother had laid him on his back under a tree at the edge of the wood, and she could see that the little one was beginning to take notice, he was so full of thought; wonder was depicted in his tiny features. He drew in his arms and legs and gave a frightened glance when a bird broke out of a bush and stayed for an instant fluttering in the air before darting in again; and no less fascinated was he with a little green worm that lowered itself by an invisible thread and curled in the breeze above his head. His mother laughed over him from joy and sadness, in the way mothers laugh—the little stranger couldn't make out at all where he had come to!

That was how he got his name. For he had arrived as a little helpless, dumb, strange person, on a journey from

3

one unknown world into another. His mother had been in a swoon when he came into the world, and the women who were with her were afraid she would never come to herself again; but when in her torpor she heard the little stranger cry, she opened her eyes and saw what a tiny creature he was; then she signed to them to give her the child and they placed it on her breast. It was as though the mother had been absent and would fain have stayed away, for when she woke she had not the look of a living creature; but when the new-born babe fastened itself upon her, the desire of life returned. Thus each of them came from an unknown world and they met in life. The little stranger had come on a long visit; Gest should be his name, and a welcome guest he was.

When once he had come he behaved in every way like a proper child. It was not long before he began to use his hands and thrust them out after anything that his eyes coveted; often he made a bad shot, but if he got hold of the thing, whatever it was, it always went the same way in a stiff curve right into his lips, and many a time his mother had to force open the little mouth and clean it out with her finger, until he had learnt to distinguish between what was eatable and what was earth.

Otherwise he spent most of his time sleeping securely in the bag on his mother's back, and he was well shaken up and ducked now and then, when she stooped down on the beach to gather mussels; this gave a savour to his dreams without disturbing his sleep.

He had scarcely learnt to walk before he tottered away from his mother's knee, one day after a thundershower, to grab the rainbow, which stood with one foot in the grass apparently close by; but the rainbow moved as he approached it, and when he had come right down to the beach it was hovering with both ends over the water; without hesitation he lifted his little leather apron and started to walk out into the sea; his mother had to hurry down and carry him ashore, shaking her head and full of laughter at the little man-child's precocity. It was evident that he had great aims. And in fact while still a boy he left his tribe of his own accord.

Gest's mother was a Stone Age woman, by name Gro. She was the mother of the whole tribe. The settlement swarmed with children, Gro herself had a number, but she didn't distinguish particularly between her own and the others', all of them were in her care. Wherever Gro saw a child with its little arms outstretched, she took it up and gave it a drink and then a sleep at her breast. She was the first up in the morning at the settlement and the last to go to rest; no one had ever chanced to see her asleep. The tribe held together of itself without coercion, thanks to her; among the men it was undecided who was at the head of affairs, and if a dispute arose it was seldom long before Gro was consulted. She was loved by all men.

Under Mother Gro's protection Gest spent his childhood, on a sunny strip of sand between forest and shore.

THE SETTLEMENT

GEST'S birthplace in Sealand lay well concealed, not on the coast itself but a little way inland, in a sheltered fjord on the Great Belt side.

Looking at this coast from the sea no one would have thought it inhabited; it had the appearance of a long, compact forest floating on the waves, so low did the land lie. Behind it, where the coast came to an end, another wooded headland thrust itself out into the sea, which might be a fold of the same island or another of the low Danish isles which floated between the Baltic and the Cattegat.

The sky above was in a movement of great clouds, like islands slowly wandering; isles in the sea and isles in the sky; the sea roared, the day showed white and blue with a primeval stillness, only gulls and seabirds wrapped the shores in a light sea-music; silently the seal came up with his wet eyes and looked towards land; a column of smoke rose above the forest, and the seal caught a smell he did not like, pinched up his nose and dived head first among the big weed-covered rocks at the bottom.

But inland where the column of smoke rose above the forest dwelt men. A shingly beach and a narrow belt of sandhills separated the forest from the sea. The outer edge of the forest was made up of low, tangled bushes and dwarf trees, which lay pressed close to the ground, held down by the wind, and were more impenetrable than a brier thicket; only little by little did the trees grow higher, as the outer ones screened the next; from the sea side the forest looked like an even, sloping roof rising landward from the shore, apparently less impassable along the top than among the trees. It was as though the land had turned its back on the sea.

But in one place by a headland a gap ran up into the land, not very noticeable if one did not know it; inside it widened out into a fjord, and here the forest opened up.

It was more sunny and still inside the fjord than on the windswept outer coast; the sun was on it most of the day, and in a bay the water lay quite shallow and smooth, bright from the sandy bottom shining through and dazzling with the reflection of the midday sun. This sandy bottom was one great oyster-bed.

The bay was enclosed by a beach of shingle and sea-weed, above which were low bluffs with bare gravel and big fallen boulders. Above that was forest. But un-like the forest on the sea side, which stooped and made itself thorny and impenetrable, the forest here rose into an airy, open vault with lofty trunks that stood like gates towards the bay. The great full tree-tops formed domes in calm sunshine; here the day was always calm.

Here were great crowds of gulls, the banks were white with them, where the tepid water was only a few inches deep; they screamed and quarrelled noisily all day long, flapping their wings and always on the move; they sat on the big rocks out in the bay and poured out their eloquence to each other till it roused echoes from the shallow water and from the forest and even from the other side of the fjord, where again there was a bluff crowned with domed and sunny woods. Above it all lay the blue summer sky with domed white clouds, which were mirrored in the bay and mingled their whiteness with the gulls'.

The still air held a thick warm vapour of fermenting seaweed, of salt water with the sun on it, of gaping mus-sels left by the tide and beginning to smell, of the gulls' white dung, and blended with it all was the green spicy smell of the woods, breaths of raspberry perfume and the scent of honey from the sunny glades within the forest, where wild flowers and grasses rose in a confusion of long stalks.

At evening the slightest sound could be heard. The seal came cautiously in from the sea and slid up on to a big rock out in the bay, flung itself on its side for a doze—and then it might be that one or more low trunk-like objects, each with something queerly alive about it, would creep out through the dusk. These were the hunters of the bay, who had caught sight of the merman and were trying to surround him. From their point of view the merman was favourite game, giving no little food, and the skin of him was specially coveted; it was worth trying to outwit him and get a harpoon in him before it grew quite dark. But if he smelt danger too soon and made for the sea, they stole back as quietly as they had come and drew their dugouts ashore. The women, who in joyful expectation had already made up the fire, were given to understand that it could scarcely have been a proper merman, but more likely a supernatural creature, since it had proved so entirely superior to human cunning.

A little way above the beach and up towards the bluff lay the settlement. There was not much to be seen; the dozen or so of dug-out canoes that were hauled up on the beach might at a distance just as well be fallen trees, of which a good many lay over the bluff, and the huts up on the edge of the forest could not be distinguished from it at all; they were lined holes in the ground roofed with turf and made one with the greensward. In summer most men preferred to sleep outside, by the fire, with a skin over them, spread on a couple of sticks; only the women and the younger children lived underground the whole year.

The days were spent on the beach itself, where the fire was always burning, when the men were not in the forest or out on the banks fishing. Here they went about their work and here they ate, seated on the remains of what they had eaten in years gone by; on the long and comfortable heap of empty oyster-shells and other refuse they were filled with the memory of their meals; here they were at home.

A penetrating, pungent and raw smell hung in the still warmth of the sun under the woods and the bluff, where there was almost always shelter, a greasy mixed smell of ancient fish and the fermenting remains of dead molluscs and seaweed, and of washed-down lime and soured sea-water, together with the smoke of the fire, the spicy juices of fresh wood, the hot exhalations of the embers and the stink of wet ashes, not forgetting the dogs or the human smell from bodies clammy with salt water and unkempt heads. You could not come near the settlement without a sneeze refreshing the heart; a good place this, here you felt at home.

The dish of food was the seat, close by was the open beach, which was a huge larder, the walls of the room were the mild summer breezes, nothing less, and the roof the great open sky.

It lay so calmly above the shallow tepid shore, where the domes and abysses of the clouds were repeated in the water; the tern dived silently in the noonday heat into its own reflection, sea and sky reposed in each other like twin worlds.

Far away below the horizon came a sound of thunder, short subterranean shocks like something moving in the earth's interior. It was as though there had never been anything else but midday and midsummer.

III

THE MEN OF THE STONE AGE

WHO were they? Were they the first men who set foot in the Danish isles?

In the myth of the Ice it has been told how the Ice Folk originated, the descendants of Carl; the first of them were mammoth-hunters, afterwards their lives were bound up with the wild horse and the reindeer, and at the time the latter was on its passage through Denmark it may well be that here and there a family of the primitive folk came into the country with their reindeer herds, but then they must have followed them out again and lost themselves to the north and east in the tracts which the reindeer still inhabits. In the age of the steppes Denmark was continuous with Asia; afterwards the sounds formed again around the islands.

The men of the Stone Age were seafarers. They came to the islands from the south, from the shores of the Baltic, where the Ice Folk had settled and become mixed with the natives, descendants of the Forest Folk; the oldest Danes originated from two sources.

If they themselves had been asked, the answer would not have been very satisfactory. Few gave a thought to the past or formed any conception of where they came from or how long ago it was, least of all the younger ones who had been brought up in the settlement and who only knew it and the immediately surrounding country as their world.

Some of the elders had legends, transmitted by their fathers and grandfathers, of which they sometimes talked among themselves, of a past when men dwelt in a land far

away, a voyage longer than from new moon to new moon
in dug-out canoes, through many sounds and along the
coast of one island after another; in that country the winters were said to be very mild, there were years when no
snow fell at all. The people lived on the banks of great
rivers and could always get fish. It was supposed to be
one particular man who had first found the islands in the
sea and settled in them; afterwards many followed him
and brought their families. In the beginning they used
only to travel out to the islands in summer and stay there
hunting and fishing as long as the weather was fine; it
was mostly young men who had pluck enough for the
voyage and knew the way; but when the nights grew cold
they rowed all the way back and wintered on the mainland.

In time they learned to get through the winters on the
islands too, either by choice or from having waited too
long and been cut off by the autumn storms; they found
that it could be done, and many families stayed in the
islands all the year round and never saw their old country
again.

The islands were uninhabited when the first of them
arrived, the game was untouched and in abundance, perfectly tame; you could catch the birds in your hand and
the deer came of their own accord and sniffed at the ax;
the hunters had not the trouble of going half a day's
journey from the camp to look for them, they lay down
by the fire, and when the deer came out of curiosity on
a brotherly visit they slaughtered them without going two
steps. But soon the animals knew better. By and by as
the hunting became more difficult there were fewer imi-
grants to the islands, nor did they all have such a kind
reception from the first settlers who had taken land; occasionally whole boats' crews disappeared without leaving
a trace. Finally the way thither was forgotten, and there
was no longer any one in the islands who knew the way
back; those who had sailed it and knew the sea-marks were

dead long ago. But nobody wanted to go back either, they were perfectly contented where they were, so long as they were left in peace.

The families became small tribes, scattered far from each other over different islands and with long intervals of coast between them, with no mutual acquaintance nor any particular desire for it; each tribe was sufficient to itself and not disinclined to regard itself as the only human community in a true sense, in contradistinction to all other quasi-human, totally inferior foreigners.

A position of this kind as the centre of creation was assumed, then, in their own comfortable conviction, by the inhabitants of the little hunting and fishing station within the bay where Gest was born.

They were not so numerous but that each knew all the rest individually, though they never attempted to find out how many they were. If a stag was brought down and each had his share of it, with as much shellfish added, the tribe might be fairly supplied, so that it was not such a very small family either, and the daily provisioning gave them all enough to think about.

The tribe's world was not a wide one. There was the bay and the stretch of fjord nearest it, and then the forest inland which was known in its smallest details, but no farther afield but that a man could range through it in a day and be back by evening. What lay beyond was pretty well unknown and for the present did not tempt further exploration. What they especially avoided was penetrating into the forest beyond the known tract; there was no knowing what might be in the interior of the country. It happened not unfrequently that a man came back to the settlement almost broken-winded with running and so terrified that his friends had to sit on him a long while to keep him down and bring him to his senses; this meant that he had taken liberties with the forest and had been scared by it.

The outer coast was seldom visited. Here the sea beat
upon the shore and was rough, and this was the way up or
down the coast to other settlements, whose inhabitants they
did not care to meet. With the nearest of these, who were
not so far off but that the smoke of their fire could be seen
from the entrance of the fjord, there was some intercourse,
though of a reserved nature. Curiosity with regard to the
foreigners was soon curbed; even distant tribes did not
look or behave differently from what one was accustomed
to in one's own settlement, apart from certain absurdities
which were to be expected of people who had learnt no
better. Within the forest the different hunting-grounds
met, with tacitly accepted boundaries; if foreign hunters
were encountered here both parties preferred to retire,
with a very formal stiffness of demeanour, whereas of
course the dogs on both sides instantly flew at each other's
throats. Often on their return home the hunters from the
bay had stories to tell of these strangers who had behaved
arrogantly, though without making any impression, while
the narrator was convinced of having conducted himself
with tact and of having inspired respect.

If then the ancient territory of the tribe was the bound-
ary of the forest side, the known world ended at the sea
on the coast. It was not open sea; on clear days from
the top of a tree a coast-line could very clearly be seen
on the other side, a long, low country like that they themselves dwelt in; but they believed it certain that that was
not the old home of their ancestors, no reasonable man
would go so far to sea in a canoe; more likely they had
come up along the coast from smaller islands lying to
the south of the one they lived on. For that it was a big
island they inhabited was maintained as probable by the
elders, though they had not themsleves made the voyage
round it.

When the hunters sat around the fire entertaining themselves with questions like this which lay outside every-

day experience, they might notice one of Gro's boys standing near, leaning forward and straining his ears, listening
with nose and mouth into the bargain; then perhaps they
condescended to throw a brand at him in fun, or he might
be allowed to stay, as the insignificant quantity he was.
This was Gest drinking in knowledge with every hole in
his head and hoarding up every legend he heard as a precious treasure.

Here he heard the first mention of a wonderful country
from which all men had come in the beginning; not the land
of the great rivers, which lay comparatively near, but a
land so far away that no mortal man could reach it, even
if he travelled all his life; it was so long since men had
left it that the tale had passed from generation to generation more times than any could count, and most of it had
been forgotten in this immense course of time; only an obscure memory of the legend itself and a few surviving features of it had been handed down. In that country, it was
said—but few could believe in the likelihood of its still existing, or ever having existed—there was never any cold
at all, clothes were not needed, the trees had breasts which
you sucked, and you slept in their arms at night! Of
course every one knew that the trees, even now, were sacred
and protecting beings, but the rest sounded incredible,
albeit no one had ever been able to forget the story. The
first men had been cut off from this country by a vast
Flood, wherein all of them had perished, with the exception
of a few who had canoes and could sail; from these the
Stone Age men were descended, and their canoes were
a sufficient visible proof of the truth of that part of the
story!

Gest listened, and what he heard sank into his soul.

He would have liked to ask questions and get to know
more, if only the direction in which the country was supposed to lie; but nobody would answer a boy, and no more

information came of its own accord. Then Gest gave a
quiet sigh and buried the fragments of his precious knowledge in his heart. Everything he knew he had to pick up
by snatches.

IV

THE WORK OF GEST'S HANDS

A SWARM of children infested the settlement, where the men chased them from one end of it to the other like the troublesome breed they were. The mothers on the other hand spoiled them and took their part, made great to-do with beating stocks and stones when the little ones fell down and hurt themselves, and found a scapegoat for their troubles by pretending to take big handfuls from the place that hurt and throw them into the forest; from that quarter they could always count upon sympathy. The third Great Power in the settlement was the dogs; relations with them were apt to be fickle, sometimes they fought over a bone or a piece of gut, dog at one end and youngster at the other; at other times they played together in sweet concord and slept in one another's arms at night; the smallest, who had scarcely begun to walk, tottered about with puppies in his arms; a large share of the children's time was spent in playing with the dogs. Otherwise they splashed about all day long in the shallow water of the beach, where they could come to no harm, or were busy digging in the sand and making all sorts of small scale copies of what the men did. The forest was forbidden, there the wolves might take them, and the men would not have them out hunting until they were big enough to be taken into their company; but then that meant the end of their childhood's world.

Gest was early to feel the narrowness of this world, but without exactly longing to be adopted by the grown-ups either; his relations with them were strained. Gradually, then, the plan matured in him of taking part in the men's life without asking their permission or becoming dependent on them, and in this he found an ally at critical moments in his mother Gro.

From the time he was quite small he busied himself with making all kinds of things himself, first toys, but afterwards regular implements such as the grown-ups used; he had his own little workshop beside a stone he had chosen just outside the settlement.

Here he sat through the long summer days making his first ax. He felt the want of an ax in everything he tried his hand at, and as nobody would give or lend him one he had to get one for himself. Everything in the settlement belonged to somebody or other and was not to be touched, and if it was not the property of one of the grown-ups then it belonged to the forest, or to the sea, or to the spirits; you could not get anything without giving something in return, and if you had nothing, why then you were thrown back on what you could make yourself. That was Gest's early experience.

Now a shed stag's antler had come into his possession; he had found it himself on one of his surreptitious rambles in the forest and picked it up, in the conviction that it had been placed in his path expressly that he might have it. He gave the stag a grateful thought and interpreted the fact that he had come upon it in the forest as a sign that the silvan Powers were also favourable.

Gest hummed to himself as he studied the antler and considered what the ax was to be like. His would-be playmates found his back turned, and one of the dogs who came fawning up to him was rudely pushed away by his elbow without so much as a look. The antler was long and slender, with not many tines, and when these were removed the whole antler could be used as a haft, with the handle at the thin upper end; the other, heavy end had a thick branch, which would have to be cut off at a suitable distance from the stem and hollowed out to receive the flint blade—altogether a complicated and difficult piece of work, but the day was long and Gest began to sing louder as soon as he saw clearly what he had to do.

As he sat singing at his work he heard with half an ear that somebody else was singing near him; it was a little girl called Dart, who had been Gest's playmate since they were quite small. Her mother lived next door to Gest's mother, so they had always been together. She had been given the name because she was so straight and slender, just like a dart, and when she was born she was covered all over with white down like the buds of a willow. She had bright, smooth hair like sunshine and was always smiling; she was the gentlest of girls. Like Gest she was fond of playing alone, but was always to be found with her little lonesome games somewhere in his neighbourhood.

He saw that she was busy picking bast fibre from the fallen branch of a lime-tree, just sufficiently decayed for the bark to come off easily without the bast being spoilt; she was separating the long pieces of bast into fine strips and laying them side by side on the ground, in silent rapture at the way the pattern was already coming out; she sang in her thoughts like a summer breeze, it was evident that she had some plaiting or weaving on hand.

Gest set to work at once, and it occupied him so deeply that for hour after hour he had no sense of anything else. First he hammered off the superfluous tines between two stones, as near to the stem as he could without spoiling it, the stumps were to be removed afterwards and the whole thing scraped smooth; then he began to hack off the thick branch in which the eye for the blade was to be set. This took time, he had to strike off one flint flake after another, and that too took time; Gest might well smash away at the blocks in the way he had seen the grown-ups do and as it ought to be done, but it was not every time that he got a useful flake, generally he had to put up with a fair splin-

ter, more or less oblong; and then he cut and hacked round
the hard horn and filed until the flake was so worn and
blunt that it could do no more, and yet he could hardly
see that the groove was any deeper. It was hard having
to wait till it was worked through and Gest's blood reached
boiling-point; no more song came from his lips, they were
tightly compressed as he exerted all his strength, quarrelling with the antler for being so stupidly hard, and with
his flint tool, which always broke if it was sharp and of
course would not bite if it held. He worked madly at
the groove till his arms ached and the palms of his hands
were cut by the sharp blades; they would have to be hafted
and he could scarcely spare the time for that; he borrowed
some bast from Dart, who made friendly remonstrances.
Gest seized half her work, wrapped up his flakes, and
sawed and cut and hacked for half a day, until at last the
groove was so deep that the branch could be knocked off.

Passionately he examined the broken surface, where he
now had to make a hole in the horn. Luckily the tissue
was softer in the middle, not so difficult to penetrate, but
he had to make special flakes for the purpose, and Gest
hammered and banged at the flint and a lot of it went
into splinters; The noise he made was enough to show he
was a busy and a wrathful man; and then he bored again,
blew into the hole and bored, with burning cheeks, his
hands trembling with impatience, but without giving up,
for the ax was already so far advanced that it spoke to
him, it was going to be a good one, it said, and he wanted
to have it finished instantly.

Shouts of triumph sounded from his workshop among the
boulders when the hole was done. The day was far gone,
Gro called to her youngsters from the fire, there was a
dainty meal of baked oysters, fresh from the ashes, steaming in their own salt water; Gest flung his food down, with
eyes on the unfinished haft in his hand, he ran to the brook
and drank, ran back and threw himself upon his work.

The most difficult and most critical part of it was still to come: how to shape a flint wedge that was sufficiently sharp at one end and of such a form at the other that it would fit into the hole and sit perfectly tight. But the flint did not split off at all as he wanted it, the blade would be irregular, even if the edge proved serviceable; he made one attempt after another, smashed up whole heaps of flint, but if it was as it should be at one end, it did not fit at the other, wobbled in the hole, was too large or too small. He was in despair at his failures and wept a little in his pain, with a burning oppression on his brows that tortured him; he smashed the unsuccessful wedge into little bits, ground them into the finest powder, it was to be destroyed utterly. He could not see for tears and anger, the hairs on his body bristled with defiance, and he began again, blew his nose and began all over again, more thoroughly this time, haste did not pay; he fought his way with deliberate force against the abominably refractory, the perfectly idiotic material; this miserable stone which laughed when it went to pieces was unnaturally stupid; but now he changed his tactics, made the hole a good deal deeper, since however he contrived it the flint would always wobble, and set to work to strike off correspondingly long and narrow blades. Of course the first one broke right across when it was nearly finished, that was what it would do! A roar escaped him, he dealt a furious blow at the fragments, hit one of his fingers and crushed it nearly flat; it turned first white and then blue, he quaked but then became viciously quiet, pretending it was not his finger at all, though it hurt atrociously. Quiet! he whispered, foaming at the mouth; over again, you wretched boy! And with a terrible calm, deeply hurt, he took a fresh block of flint and started again, with nine fingers and the tenth useless, swollen and numbed—and he got what he wanted, at last, just what he wanted!

Partly by design, partly by luck he succeeded in getting

a wedge of the right length and symmetry, so that with a little careful trimming of the edges and a corresponding adaptation of the hole it would fit in and ·hold fast. The ax-edge at the outer end was broad and substantial, suitable for every kind of work, but it would also be a powerful weapon if need were. Gest fitted the ax-edge at right angles to the haft; it was to be an adze, which would be better suited to the work he had in mind.

Now it was a question of the lashing, and this gave him trouble, he began to fear that the ax would not be finished that day, since for a really durable lashing you want fresh sinew or gut. He roamed all over the settlement, crept down into his mother's hut, but could not find what he wanted anywhere; no animal happened to have been slaughtered lately and there was nothing lying about that he could use, though there was plenty of carrion which the dogs were licking and tearing. Gest was disheartened; gloomy and sorrowful he wandered about, and went over to see how Dart was getting on.

She had laid aside her bast work and allowed some girl friends to tempt her to play with clay. They were up under the bluff where a trickle of water oozed out, ochre-laden, and stained the gravel red; here the women often came to decorate themselves and make their bodies attractive; Dart and the other girls also put on some colour, laying it on thickly wherever they could reach; the only undyed spot was between their shoulderblades. Then they dug clay from the moist bluff, fine clay which was to be found hereabouts, brought great lumps of it down to the beach, sat down on flat stones to knead it, flinging the hair from their eyes, and began to make pots. Water for shaping them they fetched from the beach in big blue mussel-shells. First they rolled out long strips of clay, which they laid one above the other in a ring; when they had reached the proper height they kneaded them together and smoothed them with a flat stone, until the pot was finished and could be put in

the sun to dry. Unlike the impatient Gest the girls took
plenty of time, lingering over their clay while they chatted
together and letting it grow beneath their hands as they
themselves grew.

With many a sigh Gest hung about, watching the girls'
pastime. But suddenly he went back to his own place with
long strides—eel skin!

Eel-skin, of course, if sinew or gut was not to be had!
Eel-skin was the toughest in the world—if he could just take
one of the canoes and pole out with it and get what he
wanted! But that was just what he could not do, and that
was what lay at the root of all Gest's plans, the want of a
boat. The canoes belonged to the grown-ups, and if you
touched their things you got beaten like a dog; Gest would
not ask for the loan and be denied like the other boys, he
preferred to do things for himself, and he put to sea
astride of an old tree-trunk which he had dragged down and
which would just bear him. The pole he used, a long
hazel shoot, he had ingeniously provided with a slit at the
upper end, and if he saw anything at the bottom of the shallow water, he turned the pole round and used it as a clutch.
There were eels enough and to spare in the tangled mass of
weed and more than once Gest got one in his cleft stick, but
they regularly got away again. Of course, the fork spread
out on the sandy bottom, and the more he pressed, the more
room there was for the fish to escape. The men's fishing-
spears stood leaning against the trees at the edge of the
forest, but it meant a thrashing that would make your head
ring for a long while after if you just happened to upset
them, to say nothing of using them. They had several
prongs with barbs of bone or stag's horn, lashed in a
bunch to the end of a pole in such a way that the barbs
were turned towards each other; splendid, but not to be
borrowed or imitated on the spot. Gest went ashore and
improved his cleft stick by giving it a lashing, so that the
slit could not open any more, and in the middle between the

two prongs he inserted a big, sharp fish-bone. Then he poled out again; and this time the eel did not escape when once he had got one on his pole, it was caught between the prongs and held fast by the point. It was a big, long eel and he had a severe tussle with it, even after its head was off. The trunk went round with him and he got a ducking out of his depth, swallowed a lot of salt water and was sick as soon as he had scrambled up again, but he never let go of the eel and he brought it ashore.

The skin he flayed off with the best of tools, his teeth, but then it had to be divided into several narrow strips, a difficult and tiresome work as long as it was wet. He went at it as hard as he could, but still had not finished when it was growing dark and all the children had gone in, leaving a whole assemblage of the girls' little jars drying on the beach. Not until it was quite dark had Gest finished his strips and put on the lashing, with one end in his teeth and his mouth full of eels' slime; when once the binding was dry it would be immovably fast. He woke in the night and got up, half-asleep, to feel whether the lashing would soon be dry.

Next day he was up early to test the ax; the blade was fixed so firmly that no human strength could move it, and to split the handle was impossible with that binding. He went into the forest and tried it; it lopped off hazel shoots as thick as his wrist quicker than you could say it. It almost went to his head; although he himself had made the ax he was not far from attributing supernatural properties to it. It was not for nothing that a stag had a share in it; that gave it swiftness and the power of fury; it was destined to be dangerous in the chase. And that a fish had contributed something to it would certainly make it powerful and lucky on the water.

But what it could do in the work Gest had in mind, felling heavy timber and boatbuilding, was soon to be seen. A little way from the settlement, at the edge of the wood overlooking the bay, an oak stood quite near the beach, a tall, straight tree with a perfectly faultless stem which one could see was just made for a boat. Years ago Gest had picked out this tree and had lost himself deeper and deeper in dreams of what a splendid canoe it would make. The trunk was about double the thickness of a man and longer than was needed; the canoe would not have much beam, on the other hand he could make it unusually long; it would be a fine and a quick sailer and would easily carry two people. The tree stood on the extreme edge of the forest just by the sea, as though it had come as far as it could of its own accord and was only longing to come far-ther. When his ax was finished Gest wanted to set about felling the tree, so that at last he might have a proper big dug-out like the grown-up men.

Almost since he had been able to stand upright it had been his ambition to sail; he used to wade about all day long in the warm shallow water, making sticks float from one island to another, for he pretended that the big rocks off the beach were islands; afterwards he hollowed out his sticks in imitation of real boats and undertook long voyages to distant shores, rocks far out in the bay, where the water came up to the armpits of the skipper wading alongside. In these games he always had the help of Dart, and they were so absorbed in them that they might really just as well have been transported to strange worlds; they forgot everything around them and had neither eyes nor ears when they were on a voyage. But now their play was to become earnest.

Gest had thoughts of emigrating. This was not quite clear to him, but all that he had picked up in childhood and all that he had lately turned his hand to led him in the same direction, like a fate.

It was no mean undertaking for a boy entirely single-handed to try to fell the big oak and set about shaping it, but not even this was the greatest of his difficulties; other

and weightier obstacles stood in his way. In the first
place of course he had no right to cut down the tree; it
was taking a liberty with the forest which could not be
allowed unless great services were rendered in return. In
the second place it was altogether forbidden to take fire
from the settlement, the fires belonged to the grown-ups;
they were sacred and he might not touch them. But without fire of course the work was hopeless.

The same morning Gest finished his ax and tested
it he took a brand from his mother's and began to build up
a fire close to the tree; as soon as the smoke was noticed
he had one of the men down on him, who took him seriously
to task and stamped out the fire, in doing which the clumsy
lout fortunately got his toes burnt. As soon as his back
was turned Gest nursed up the fire again from a brand
still smoking among the ashes and started afresh; this time
there was a regular commotion in the settlement, several
angry men came up, and Gest was dragged home ungently
by the ears. Gro appeared at the entrance of her house,
the men made their accusation with many words and
gestures, the dogs chimed in as usual when there was a
quarrel, barked and went for each other with bristling hair
—general excitement on the kitchen midden!

But the men soon let go of Gest, in consequence of something or other in the expression of Gro's face. The abuse
went on without anything further happening, and Gest
callously went back to his fire and got it to burn up for
the third time. And this time he was left undisturbed,
though he could hear distant growls and threats hurled at
him from the settlement.

The day came when the oak fell, after Gest with a great
deal of trouble had got it burnt through at the root; the
great tree heeled over with an ominous crack which could
he heard a long way off, a scream of its branches as they
were broken to bits and a booming sigh which shook the

earth as the trunk with all its weight thundered down on
to the beach. It woke the men out of their midday nap
and they began at once to make a row about it; they were
not going to put up with such doings from a boy who broke
the peace with all the Powers of the forest and the sky,
and Gro had to come out again to give them a piece of her
mind.

The children of the settlement followed the battle at a
safe distance, crowded together in a body, and watched
with wonder how Mother Gro quite by herself tamed all
that excited swarm of men, simply by what she said, and
with a smile on her lips too, while all the hairy men were
roaring with all their weapons about them and a look of
murder in their eyes. Just as they were on the point of
leaping on the blasphemer with harpoons, axes and bows
to make an end of him, the murderous weapons dropped
from their hands and they stood there looking like fools,
just because of some words Gro had uttered with a hearty
laugh; she must be full of witchcraft! What she had said
they could not hear, or it was above their heads, but the
battle was over, that was clear, and Mother Gro had won
without the slightest effort.

Now what Gro had to say to the men was this, that if
they wanted to put her youngsters to death they really
couldn't expect to find the passage of her hut open at dusk
any more; she was not going to have them running after
her and fighting like mad bulls for her favours and then see
them exterminate the offspring afterwards! Gro snorted a
trifle, this was just a little too strong!

The prospect of falling out of Gro's good graces was
more than any of the men could bear. One after another
laid his weapons on the ground, eager not to be the last;
there was a regular rain of lethal weapons. And as they
stood empty-handed and abashed, Gro gave them the parting shot, after enjoying a laugh at their expense; there
was one thing she would like to ask: was there a single

one of them who was certain it wasn't his own son he had
come so near killing?

At this the men hummed and hawed in a feeble way and
shook their heads like oxen. The baring of Gro's revelation taxed their minds, paternal feelings worked in them
with difficulty; there they stood, and the children in the
background saw them shove their beards into their mouths
and chew them with downcast eyes, while Mother Gro
laughed at the whole lot of them, but now with a more
genial laughter which they knew and which told them that
peace and reconciliation reigned once more among the
grown-ups.

But that day's sun was not to set without the band of
children being reduced in another way; the affront the
men had swallowed and the predatory spirit that Gro had
checked in one direction found vent in another.

The noisy and threatening commotion over Gest had died
away, the midday sleep was resumed and the warm day was
already sinking to its close when suddenly a roar burst
out again from the settlement; this time it was the men
who were laughing—not a pleasant laughter—and a single
thin little scream was heard in the midst of it.

It had been discovered from various signs that one of the
girls in the children's band was a child no longer, and instantly the signal was given for a bride-hunt. The man
who first made the discovery clapped his hands and began
roaring with laughter, and then all the men of the settlement clapped their hands at once, like a flock of birds
taking wing, and burst into uproarious laughter, a tempest
of merriment; the band of children broke asunder and the
poor little woman who had been found out knew what it
meant, made a dash for the woods and ran for her life—
and the whole crowd of men laughed and clapped louder
and louder, for she had done just the right thing, trying
to run away from it, run she should, ha, ha—and with

loud yells of the hunters and fierce baying of the dogs the pursuit began.

It might be short or it might be long, according as the girl was light-footed and knew how to hide herself; sometimes even the dogs let her off and would not follow the scent because she had been good to them. Who would be the first to reach the victim was hard to say beforehand; it would show who was the swiftest and fittest of the men of the place; but the hunt always ended in the same way, with the girl being caught.

Then the poor thing, who that very day had been one of the playmates in the children's flock, might be found crouching in the darkest corner of one of the winter huts, bleeding and trembling many hours after, with her head buried in her hair, inconsolable.

And with that she went over to the women's side of the settlement, was given a digging-stick and set to provide shell-fish for the hunters when they came home from the chase and yawned round the fire; she was never allowed to play any more.

From Gest's workshop at the edge of the wood came the sounds of the ax all day long, one summer day after another, enough to send any one to sleep who was lying in the settlement, so regularly came the blows of the ax; now Gest was at work.

Near him sat Dart with her sunny hair, not disturbing him at all; she was busy weaving her finest patterns, talking to herself, whispering and plaiting, happy as usual in playing alone. Only when a chip flew from Gest's ax and got her on the head would she look up with a chilly quiver under her eyes; Gest must be angry, quarrelling with his work and red in the face; yes, it was terrible how that boy carried on and made his own life a burden.

He was at work shaping the outside of the canoe, after the tree had been felled; he walked round the mighty

trunk like a little giant, attacking it with his flint tooth of
an ax, a hopelessly unequal fight by the look of it; the
trunk lay bare and heavy, resounding dully through its
immense wooden mass, of which the greater part had to be
removed; but Gest was stubbornly gnawing his way into it,
as though sick to be finished.

First he had made holes in the bark and pulled it off in
big flakes; then, when the trunk was bare and he could get
a better idea of the form, he made up a fire under the
root end and burned that away; he did the same thing up
towards the top at the length he had decided on for the
canoe: a piece of work which the fire could do almost by
itself, he only had to stand by and put it out with water
when it ate its way too far in.   And then came the shaping
of the outside, and here he had to hack at the trunk as it
lay, doing the best he could; it was to be more or less
pointed, of course, at any rate at one end.

This took many, many days, and Gest was perfectly silent
all the time; he hacked and hacked, chip by chip, sharp-
ened his ax again when it would not bite any more, which
delayed him for half a day at a time; young as he was his
toil brought furrows to his face and a hollow between his
brows; all the time he was ahead of his work with his
desire to see the ship finished as he had it in his head; he
pressed on with a passion which made him forget himself
entirely and become one with the tree-trunk, with the chips;
every one of them spoke to him with its individual nature
and offered its own tough resistance; he was absorbed as
though for all time in the astringent smell of the fresh oak
wood, which makes the hands black.   And at last, at last
the outward shape was as he wanted it.

Without a minute's delay he began on the hollowing out,
to which he had long been looking forward impatiently.
First the upper rounding of the stem had to be taken off
down to about the middle; this he did with the ax, a work
of many days, with blisters on his hands which turned to

sores and healed again; then he laid on hot stones and began the actual hollowing, with the consolation that the end
was in sight; but now he had to watch very carefully how
far the stones burned in and be always ready with water to
put out the fire in time. The burnt and charred part he
went over with the ax, then burned more and chopped the
surface clean; and so he went on till the oak was hollow
right down to the bottom like a long narrow trough. Now
it was all ready for the sea. Great shouts of triumph were
heard from Gest's workshop one day, as though somebody
was killing himself with joy, and though the men had tacitly conspired to take no more notice of the boy's doing,
since they had come to grief in trying to put a stop to them,
they could not help walking past the place, just to see how
he was getting on.

And there they found Gest silent, with the shouts of joy
sticking in his throat, standing dejectedly beside his completed craft. One thing Gest had forgotten to take into
consideration: how he was to get the trunk from the place
where it had fallen out to the water. It was only a few
paces, but the first time he had put his hand on the gunwale
to move it, he could feel that it lay as though grown fast
to the earth, immovable as a rock, as far as his strength
went. He had forgotten to put rollers underneath before
the tree fell! How could he forget that?

A couple of men came out of the wood where they had
been watching and asked him with an assumption of sympathy how it was the canoe wouldn't move? They were
nearly bursting with suppressed laughter; more came up, a
whole crowd of men with their beards all in a grin, and
all together they burst into immense roars of laughter over
the wretched boy, leaning against one another so as not to
fall; their amusement simply took away all their strength,
it was a long time since anything had done them so much
good.

Suddenly Gro appeared amongst them, attracted by the

howls, and she too laughed, Gest could see her laugh—but while she was still cooing, for Mother Gro always laughed like a big wood-pigeon, being rather short-winded with all her fat, she went up to the prow of the canoe, lifted it without more ado and with two or three tugs pulled the whole craft out into the water! When she saw it was afloat she gave it a little shove and waded back again, with a smile at her son, and watched the inconsolable sorrow in his face change in a second to joy, he was laughing through his tears.

"There, now you can take a hand," she said to her son in a singsong voice; she gave the men an offended glance, turned her back on them and went calmly away to the huts.

There the men stood. They saw the ground smoking where the stern of the canoe had ploughed a furrow, they glanced askance from there to Gro's back—never had they known that she was so strong! It was the strength of four men, nothing less!

They looked at her back as she walked; what a woman she was, massive and slow, her immense flanks and loins shook with every step, her knees turned in a little as was natural in a woman, her arms could not fall against her body but rowed freely in the air on each side, so big was she; she swayed as she walked—how beautiful she was!

But to think that she was at the same time so strong . . . the men looked at each other quite foolishly. One of them scanned the sky, trying to make out what kind of weather might be expected; another absently rolled a straw between his fingers; a third sneezed violently and blew his nose. Some of them had already stolen away, the rest went off in different directions. The affair was never talked of again.

But Gest had snatched the paddle which he had long ago split from a branch and hacked into shape; with a leap he was in the canoe, which received him with a grand wooden resonance and splashed the water under him; it lay perfectly on the water, proclaiming its nautical nature from the start, and a little later Gest could be seen sailing out in the bay in his bright new canoe with the paddle walking away first on one side, then on the other.

That was how Gest got his craft launched. A few days afterwards it occurred to one or two of them in the settlement that they no longer heard or saw anything of Gest. It takes a certain time to notice the absence of any one, if he has not been constantly under one's nose; at last it becomes clear that he is gone. Gest had vanished together with his new boat. Also the little girl they called Dart; her fair hair no longer showed up among the band of children either. The women knew of it first, then the men discovered it and felt injured at not having been asked; they put down the theft of the girl to that presumptuous boy's account together with his other sins. But Gro was able to inform them that Gest had indeed left the place and taken his playmate with him; Gro had not opposed it. That ended the discussion.

It was not long before the two children were almost forgotten, and perhaps Gest's name would never have been mentioned again but for an event which recalled his crime in a painful manner.

One of the men lost his life while hunting, in particularly striking circumstances. He had not returned at evening with the others, and on searching for him next day they found him impaled on the stake of his own pit, into which he had fallen in the dusk. He was still alive when they got him up, and was able to walk back to the settlement, holding his guts in his hands. Outside Gro's entrance passage he lay down, and she held his head on her knees till he was dead. He was one of the best hunters of the tribe and a merry, handsome man; Gro had loved him dearly and wept for him a night and a day; all over the settlement they heard painful subterranean wailings from Gro's house-grave, where she lay mourning in the innermost darkness.

Gro's sorrow shocked the other hunters which, to say the least, was unbecoming in her. The dead man had been a good friend and comrade, but still, when they buried him, they took good care that he should not walk; they heaped a goodly cairn on top of him. An excellent man he had been, but in future when Gro's eyes had a kindly look for one or other of them, it would not be on *him* they would light.

But as to the warning pointed by the accident, its cause, the men had no doubt. They said nothing about it before Gro; she was too dull to draw even the most obvious inferences and besides she was personally interested; but among themselves the event gave them a lot to talk about. For the case was perfectly plain: it was Gest's iniquity that had called down punishment upon the tribe, as they had very truly foretold; the forest had been outraged, and now it had taken its revenge.

But Gest had disappeared, and nobody but Gro knew whither he had gone.

V

THE THREE NORNS

THERE was a secret connected with Gest's birth, which Gro revealed to him privately before he left home.

When Gro had recovered after his birth she wished to have the boy's fortune told and sent for the Norns that they might take a look at him and read the omens of his destiny. Some of Gro's men had to sail after them, for they had to be fetched from another tribe up the coast, where they had been in the exercise of their calling. They had no fixed place of abode, but wandered about among the settlements on their momentous and at times somewhat dreaded mission.

They came, and they were three very ancient sibyls, rocking to and fro on their staves and nodding their noses with age; they had beards, but not a tooth among them; they were clad in old garments of fur that had not been off their backs for twenty winters; but they were wise.

Gro received them well in her cabin below ground, entertained them nobly and took special pains to put them in a pleasant frame of mind. The meal was oysters and mussels, taken out of their shells and put into a pot, all ready to gulp down; after that hard roe and wild pig's liver cut into strips and intended to be swallowed whole; and the drink was spring water well sweetened with honey. The old dames were pleased wih the fare and did it justice, they grew loquacious and told many a good story, brought to mind by the food, of hunting that had taken place before Gro was born. Gest's birth reminded them of their own childbeds and marriages, the merry outrages they had suffered on the part of hunters long since turned to dust; their children too were dead, they were homeless sibyls now, but they still mumbled with their toothless gums and hee-hee'd with pleasure at the thought that they had once been human and had known all that a human being has to bear. One's trials were not so bad. Ah, now they might walk alone in the forest; even the wild beasts puckered their lips at an ancient sibyl. Yes, indeed.

When they had eaten their fill and their eyes began to sparkle—the Norns' wisdom taking fire within them—Gro emptied out her bag on the floor and bade them consider the boy.

They found him big, placed a finger on him and declared him to be well bred, they opened his mouth and felt his gums, sharp already, forward with his teething. They all felt and nothing happened with the first two, but when the third had her finger in his mouth the boy gave a bite and the sibyl had to waggle her finger to get it out. Mother Gro didn't like that and made a note to punish the youngster, but in her heart she thought him a brave boy. After that they went over his limbs, poured out a wealth of experience; they nodded their appreciation, whispered together and nodded; yes, he was a proper man.

Then one of the sibyls got up and started to prophesy, talking wildly and singing a horrid incomprehensible song which made the whole place seem uncanny, but it was all with the best intention, a magic incantation against evil Powers of every kind, and she ended by predicting that the man-child would have much good fortune and would see more than most people. The second sibyl nodded several times, concurred entirely in this prediction, it was exactly the augury she herself would give, and Gro smiled with pleasure, took the boy by his heel and dumped him into the bag again.

But the third had not said anything, and when Gro gave her a questioning glance she could see that the old woman shut her mouth tight so that her chin and the tip of her nose came together; there was something smouldering in her eyes that boded no good. It was she who had been bitten so unfortunately.

As a matter of fact she had been displeased long before, ever since she arrived, though she had concealed it. The first thing she had taken offence at was that Gro had set nothing but soft food before them, as though to let them feel their toothless state. Besides which, Gro's person in itself was something arrogant and insulting to small, thin people; for she was as big and fat as a whale, with limbs of indecent size, on which account she was desired of all men, it was said, no doubt truly, considering their coarse taste; furthermore she was audaciously dressed for the occasion in nothing but a thin summer mat, woven with the utmost vanity in open meshes, a porpoise in a net couldn't be less concealed, an altogether too obvious contrast with other people's slightness and sharp angles. Round her neck she vaunted a loud ornament, a necklace of more bears' teeth than anybody could count, one for each of her men—as no doubt one would be right in guessing—and she didn't make any secret about it either, for when they were examining the child and the other two agreed that judging by certain signs he would be kind to women, Gro had laughingly remarked that she wished him as much luck of that kind as she had had herself, a piece of impudence that was enough to damp the spirits of a lonely person. Moreover Gro was proud, as you couldn't help seeing the moment you entered her cave; it was clean, Gro had swept it, as good as an insult to such as maybe had a couple of feet of filth and offal and overlaid children at home!

But the worst thing, the thing that offended the eye most of all, was that Gro had lighted a candle. Not like other simple folk a fire on the floor or a bowl of grease with a handful of moss in it, but a big dip, in her high

and mighty way, made as it seemed of tallow with a rush
for a wick, mad newfangled ways that one heard tell of
and a slight upon the customs of simple old people; to
say nothing of the light, nearly as bright as day, not being equally advantageous to everybody's appearance and
of a certain smokiness and gloominess being more the
thing when there was magic to be done.

All this hurt the feelings of the third sibyl, and therefore, when Gro frankly asked her what fortune she would
tell, the old dame rose and made ready to go, rocking
on her staff and dipping her nose time after time, neighed
to clear her voice and finally croaked out with a nasty
bird-like glance at the candle that for her part she couldn't
promise the boy any longer life than that of the candle
his mother had lighted over him.

Gro launched out for the mouth of the bird of ill omen,
but too late, the augury had been pronounced and the old
woman made for the door-passage, chattering. But before
she reached it she bent forward and spewed, bringing up
all the dainties on the floor, then tumbled on all fours and
crawled like a toad towards the entrance. Gro snatched
up the crock with the rest of the food and threw the whole
broth over her back; if the hag wouldn't keep the bribe
inside her she should anyhow take away the marks of it
behind.

Then Gro, like a raging she-bear, turned to the candle
and blew it out.

That solemnity ended in pitch darkness. But Gest's life
was saved.

And when he went away Gro gave him the candle-end,
well sewed up in a bladder bag with a cord of sinew to
hang round his neck; she bade him never to part with it
and to remember what it meant. Gest thanked his mother
much for the gift. And with that they parted.

VI

THE SQUIRREL'S NEST

AT the extreme end of the fjord where Gest was born
a river entered; the people of the settlement knew
it for half a day's journey or so from the mouth,
but higher up, where it lost itself in dense forest and
totally unknown tracts, they never went and never thought
of going. This was where Gest and Dart had gone in the
new boat.

At first he had intended to put to sea at once through
the bay and follow the coast to the islands and the great
far-off country he had heard the elders talk about, but
his mother dissuaded him. When they talked it over secretly she had proposed to him to travel up the river and
into the heart of the country and try to live there first;
afterwards he would be able to come back and set out on
longer journeys, if he still had a mind to it. Gro gave
him a look and screwed up her eyes, trying to recall Dart
and guess at the ages of the two; after which she advised
Gest to stay away two summers. And so they started out.

The canoe was long and crank and as Dart at her end
rowed just as well as Gest they made no little headway;
they had set out very early in the morning, before anybody was awake in the settlement except Mother Gro; by
the middle of the day they had left the fjord behind and
were up in the river, past familiar ground; from now on
the country was all new to them, perfectly safe from any
possible pursuit in their rear, whereas in front they might
expect anything as they travelled on.

When they felt well secured behind many projections

of the land and turns of the stream they rested for a meal,
which meant that they had to fish first. Gest landed to
get worms for his hooks; fish they had seen all the way
in the river, nor was it many minutes before they had a
catch; the worm had scarcely sunk below the surface when
a shoal of black fishes' backs darted up to it from the bottom, the hook was seized and dragged hither and thither
till the line stood taut and tore the surface of the water;
the first they got up were broad fish with big scales and
red fins; Gest killed the floundering fish in his teeth, got
his mouth full of fresh water and the sweet juices of the
fish; he ate on when he had once started, the whole fish
went rapidly in at one corner of his mouth and the cleaned
backbone out at the other; the long row had given him an
appetite.

Gest was delighted with his hooks; he had made them
himself out of fishbones with a cunning calculation, for
with fish are fish to be taken, and it was in itself a merry
thought that the fish should swallow its own bones the
wrong way.

At her end of the canoe sat Dart modestly turning her
back while she ate a little fish she had caught, for she had
manners enough not to let any one see her eating. None
of the grown-up women did so either, they took a bite now
and then in the course of the day, unseen, but never sat
down to a meal; no one had ever seen Mother Gro eat.

Fish were here in plenty, they were simply fighting to
get at the hook. Soon they had eaten their fill, wound
up the lines and paddled on after lapping up a couple of
palmfuls of the fresh river water, smelling of vegetation.

They rowed that day and the next through entirely
strange country, in and out with the twisting of the stream.
It flowed towards them with a broad, calm surface between
high banks of rushes which usually hid the view, lightly
ruffled and rocking in the narrow places where there was a
current, resting over deep pools in the bends, where little

eddies broke the surface over the depths, and clucking against the hollowed banks; the river had its secrets, they could understand. On turning a corner sharply they would startle some living thing below; a deep furrow ran in front of them with rings on each side, a big fish or the otter, or perhaps the river sprite; often the heron flew up from some place they had passed quite close and took to his wings with curved neck and spindle-legs dangling behind. The swallows dived in their flight after midges on the surface of the water; frogs or water-rats flopped in by the banks, and the snake swam in great curves from one bank to the other with its head and the two poison spots on its neck above water. A long way off the wild duck rose in flocks from the stream, the coot hid among the reeds or dived; once where the view was open they saw a herd of roedeer make off in great leaps through the grass, hanging an instant in the air at every leap. The forest spread its domed vaults far away on each side of the stream.

At its outlet into the fjord and far up the country the river wound between broad stretches of marsh and thicket, impassable quagmires, but gradually the valley grew narrower, the woods on each side drew nearer, and the land became a winding valley with meadows and scrub at the bottom and great compact forests beyond.

On the second day, when they had rowed so long and so far that they felt quite lost, swallowed up by the stillness and solitude of these new wild regions, the windings of the stream brought them right in under the forest on one side of the valley; the land sloped upward here and was fairly open with lofty trees. Something about the place attracted them, the sun was beginning to sink over the valley behind them, and as there was an opening in the rushes and a broad place which seemed of itself to invite a landing—the bank was low with a sandy and stony bottom and many tracks of beasts, no doubt a drinking place —they decided to go ashore here, drew up the canoe far enough to keep it from floating off, and began to look about them.

The forest opened to receive them, they were quite one with it and felt they must draw near, whatever it might conceal; with it they were now to live. They took each other by the hand and went in among the trees, slowly; the shades of the forest fell upon them, they heard it resound with their footsteps; vast and cavernous and lonely it was within.

There was a rustling in the bushes in front of them, they stood still with all their limbs a-quiver, seeing nothing, but somewhere farther in the leaves of the hazel trembled, an animal had broken through; they nodded and looked at each other, opened their mouths but found nothing to say.

Cautiously and with wary steps on the forest floor they then examined their nearest surroundings. Here the forest stood on a long slope which thrust itself out into the river valley; on both sides of it the meadow ran up into smaller lateral valleys, the forest as it were extended an arm here; it gave them a sense of security to know that this piece of it had its limits at any rate on three sides, and for the present they tried to make themselves at home.

At the bottom of one of the side valleys they found a brook, which joined the river lower down, and by following it a little way they suddenly came upon the source. It lay at the end of a cleft, a deep gash cut by the stream, like a portal opening upon the forest and the country beyond.

The source itself issued among rocks and twisted roots beneath a great forest tree and with other huge trees standing round about. It was a cool, deep hole with a floor of the finest sand, and in the sand was a strange pit looking as if it were alive, a mouth which blew the sand from its lips, stirred it with its tongue, made itself round and shot

up water from the bottom, closed and opened again, all
without the slightest sound; and you could hardly see the
water coming, so transparent was it all in the deep, clear
hole, but you knew by the sand in the pit being continually
in motion that water was coming up all the time; it domed
up and spread away down in the clear, clear depth with
the fresh water that was always coming up; it was the
underground spring that brought forth water and sent it up
from the bottom of the hole, keeping it always brimful
and running over to form the brook.

A strange and mighty gloom there was here under the
tall trees, which inclined towards each other over the
spring and talked together with their murmuring foliage
under the sky, where they shut out the daylight. Farther
on the forest rose darkly, trees and trees with their roots
down in the earth, losing themselves in an airy wall of
distant trees and shadows blended together, whence came a
solemn breath; but through a gap in the trees on the other
side you could look down upon the meadows, which lay
sunlit and open with the blue surface of the river winding
through. Under the trees lay a deep shadow, and in the
heart of the shadow was the source.

Gest and Dart plucked up courage and leaned over the
spring; its mirror gave back their faces and they took it
for a welcome and drank, mouth to mouth with the silent
water-giver below, the first long, sweet drink that this new
world offered them in welcome, laden with the country's
innermost taste of earth and pure coolness. They drank
and their faces were wet and refreshed, it did them good
within and without.

And when they had drunk they laughed and felt that a
miracle had happened; the feeling of oppression vanished
from their minds, they were as though new-born, a sweetness penetrated all their veins, so good was the water of
the spring. All at once they felt at home here, scarcely
remembering the settlement in the bay and all that lay be-

hind them, though it was only two days since they had left
it; all that had lost its reality, a new life and a new reality
had taken its place. Here they were and here they felt
they would remain. Such power had the water of the
spring.

Therefore, when they had drunk and been refreshed, they
thought they ought to make a gift to the source. The only
thing Dart possessed was the necklace of wolves' teeth
which she had had from her mother to guard her against
wild beasts; it was hard to part with it—her only possession and for the moment all she had on—but she decided
to give it away and dropped it into the spring. It was
well received, it sank right to the sandy bottom and lay
there. Gest had come into the new country just as naked
as Dart, with the exception of his amulet, which there
could be no question of sacrificing. But he felt in his
hair and took out a long awl made of bone, felt elsewhere
and found, not without bringing away a good deal of
hair, several bone fish-hooks, a good roll of sinew, some
flint flakes and other small necessaries; he offered them all
to the source, and his gift was also well received.

They had now entered into relations with the Spring
Man and felt that they might stay here and dwell in his
neighbourhood, until perhaps they would one day find
themselves on a good footing with the forest as well.

The forest, they could see, was bigger and loftier here
than they had known it in their former existence, and no
doubt it offered at least the same difficulties. At present,
however, it seemed to take no notice of them; it talked
endlessly to itself, as forests and old people do, and they
for their part had not the slightest intention of taking any
rash or precipitate action against any kind of visible or
invisible Power in the new country.

The first night they spent in their boat by the river,
quite comfortably; they drew the canoe ashore when it

began to get dark and fell asleep in it without a thought of danger, forgot everything and slept on undisturbed until it grew light again; but that sort of thing would only do once. The trees were safer.

They chose for their sleeping place none other than the lofty tree which had the spring beneath its roots. It was not easy to get up, the trunk was far too thick to clasp and the lowest branches were high up, but from a slenderer tree close by you could climb over into its top. Between the branches and the trunk, high, high up, there was a nook which would suit; when it had been enlarged with other lopped-off branches and a wattle-work of twigs it would make a comfortable and perfectly safe lair.

While Gest went up into the tree to cut branches and build the nest, Dart plucked grass, which she laid in the sun to dry; this was for lining it.

There was one who lived in the tree before them, a squirrel. It received Gest with mixed feelings the first time he came up; ran out on a branch and showed every sign of curiosity, sat up and raised its broad furry tail again and again, pricked up its ears and twitched its nose, quite unable to keep in hiding though it guessed the danger of showing itself. It approached in bounds and dashed off instantly when Gest made a move, chattered loudly from the top of the tree among the foliage; soon after it was there again, sitting up on its hind-quarters and scrubbing its cheeks, its beady eyes sparkled, it held itself stiff, came nearer and then again dashed madly off in two or three long bounds. The little man, whom Gest knew very well but had never before seen at such close quarters, was evidently much interested in his arrival and in doubt as to its meaning. When Gest began to chop away among the branches of the tree, the squirrel was right up in the topmost twigs, making a most abusive noise; Gest did not care to disturb it, not knowing what power it might possess here, but as he had no intention of doing it an injury he might surely be

allowed to come into its tree. He might always do it a
service later on in return. Gest lopped off the biggest
branches he could manage and put them in place in the
fork where the nest was to be, making them fast with a binding of honeysuckle stalks, and above them he laid sticks and
twigs, in the way the stork builds; soon he had a good and
secure lair ready.

The moment Gest began to deprive the trees of their
branches and help himself to withies and whatever other
growing things he wanted, he knew well enough that he was
taking liberties with the forest. The squirrel's behaviour
was worth noticing, perhaps it knew more about the matter
than one would expect from its size; it would be better to
do something to appease the forest at once. As soon,
therefore, as the nest was finished and he had come down
from the tree, he betook himself farther into the forest, not
liking it, but driven by a feeling of the necessity of
approaching it and trying to establish a tacit mutual understanding.

He walked up over the wooded slope that formed a sort
of forest promontory, came down into a valley on the other
side and over another hill; the forest closed in his rear, he
was now within the deep main forest and felt himself in
its power, but went on in a hesitating way in the vague
hope that something might happen which would bring
him face to face with the very spirit of the forest. But
nothing happened, and yet it was very near all the time.

A good way in he discovered a glade, and in the midst of
it stood a very big tree almost by itself, an oak; he at once
had the idea that this must be a mighty tree, it was old and
very thick with an immense trunk and long, gnarled
branches, its foliage made a whole wood by itself. Some
smaller, strangely black and crooked trees grew near it,
creeping along the ground, uncannily alive, with eyes on
their stems and queer limbs; of these he was afraid. But
the big old tree did not inspire fear. The whole of its

huge spread of branches was covered with the thickest foliage, and among the leaves grew acorns like a lot of green babies; the tree was with child, teeming with fruit; without doubt it was a rich tree and it must be the strongest in the forest. When Gest came right up to the oak he saw that the trunk was hollow, the tree had a gash in its belly, and at once he followed an impulse and placed his best flint knife, a half-finished ax of red flint and five good fish-hooks in the hollow.

It struck him as quite appropriate that the forest should have just those cutting tools he had used against it, and he went away feeling confident that now he might use all the wood he needed. But he ran the last part of the way; it was not good to have the forest at one's back when one was alone, and he did not stop to take breath until he was well out of it again.

Having got over this formidable visit to the forest Gest set to work in good heart to carry grass and leaves up to the nest. He made a regular little island of it up in the spacious tree, floating between heaven and earth.

The view was wide, on one side the whole winding valley with the river in its midst lay spread out before their eyes, and far away they saw the fjord they had come from reflecting the pale blue of the sky; behind it, a darker blue, the sea beyond the coast, which lost itself in a bank of mist. But on the other side the forest extended into the country, a green domed roof of tree-tops, woods and woods as far as the eye could reach. On the edge of the horizon the forest rose like a wave towards the sky, and at the highest point the forest wall was pierced, an opening between the stems through which the sky was visible, a distant blue gateway, with slanting shafts of light falling from the cloud above against the sun; they had the idea that this was the gateway to the wide world and that they would one day pass through it.

And when they had set their island in order up in

the tree they set out, sailed a long way up the river and made themselves acquainted with the valley farther in. It ran deep into the country, they could not see the end of it that day. They came across many new things, surprised beasts and birds that they had never seen before, and the river revealed to them more and more of its nature. It was full of fish, flashing down below when one of a shoal turned and showed its side; the big fish swam in the deep water, on the surface stickle-backs swarmed in dense little crowds. In shallows the pike stood still as a stick with its striped body and ugly lower jaw, disappearing in a cloud of mud if you came too near; the brown eel wriggled deep down at the bottom in the brown sun-warmed mud among the stalks of the waterlilies. Underneath the banks they discovered little caves deep down, where crabs hid; they were not difficult to get and were a very pleasant bite as a change from all the fish they ate. They left nothing untasted, every single thing had a soul which entered into their soul; the fresh muddy smell of the water, the strong breath of the banks made up of wet water plants, of sweet flag and curled mint; the meadow grass invaded the river, strewing its light seed in the stream among the swaying rushes, and over the meadows was a dense wilderness of fragrant plants and flowers surrounded by bees, a mist of honey wherever one turned the eyes; in the little groves of willows and bushes that grew in the quagmires the birds chirped lustily, here they were in safety with their nests.

The day was warm, the sun poured down upon the narrow boat, baking its timbers and bringing out a scent of tan; strong and fresh was the smell of the fish that lay at the bottom of the canoe in the sun, its occupants themselves had a smell of fire about their hair and the nearness of the water tempted them; they plunged in, ducked below the surface in the deep, cool water which pressed against their limbs, holding them up, got water in their mouths and water in their souls; good was the river. Afterwards they sunned themselves till they were scorched between the shoulder-blades, with cooling waterlily leaves on their heads. Close by on the bank the otter rolled in the grass, getting his coat full of thistledown and pollen; he darted a swift wet glance at the two unknown, sneezed and took to the water again like a snake.

In a bend of the river up on the firm ground they came across the wild sow luxuriously stretched on her side in a mud-hole with a litter of little pigs on top of her; she turned her small red eye as they passed but stayed where she was. The osprey swept down on a broad reach of the river, made a mighty splashing on the surface and took to its wings again with a salmon held fast in its talons.

Their voyage of discovery lasted the whole day, but before evening they were back at the spring and went to rest up in the tree before darkness fell, tired and fed and content with everything, on a springy, swaying couch of grass with sticks below. They heaped grass over themselves, especially over their heads, so as to be well hidden.

And here in their airy nest they fell asleep, insensibly swinging and held in the arms of the lofty tree, rocked to sleep without knowing it, delightfully warmed and cooled at once by the fresh grass. And in their sleep they glided into another airy, hanging world and were cradled, rocked and swung through infinite existences, warm and cool, in a profound and peaceful trance.

Above their heads, higher up in the tree-top, a forest creature watched over their rest.

That little man the squirrel had his house under the sky, up among the lightest of all the twigs, just strong enough to bear him and his house, but inaccessible to any animal heavier than the squirrel. Here he had patched together his nest, a summer house built upon an old crow's nest and covered over with a roof of twigs, leaves and withered grass, with a little door to it and lined inside with moss, all very dainty; and here he dozed at night, but only lightly, nothing could happen without his hearing it with his furry ears and being wide-awake in time.

That the two ridiculously big, tailless and naked, pink and altogether misshapen and unhandy man-things had now come and built their nest in his tree did not make him uneasy at first though he could not control his curiosity. Now they were there, and now he would see what would happen. To tell the truth, it was not the first time the squirrel had shared a tree with Man; though he did not exactly remember it, it was in his veins that he knew them. So now a couple of unprotected man-children had taken to the trees again, and the squirrel received them as one receives very distant relations, with reserve but with a deep-felt attraction; they came to be on quite good terms with one another.

The squirrel meant something to them simply because he lived in the tree, and they too meant something to him; since they had moved in the marten and the wild cat came there no more, nor the birds of prey which threatened the squirrel from above; they had a respect for the new inhabitants. The lynx came up to them one night, but then the squirrel made such a noise, behaving as if he had gone mad, that Gest awoke just in time to see a pair of greenish sparkling eyes quite close to him in the dark tree and to plant his flint ax between them. The lynx sneezed and dropped from the tree, and it never came there again.

In time they became very intimate, the squirrel grew so confident that he would come quite near, when the children had anything to give him, and take it out of their hands. To watch him eat was a great delight; he sat up and took the food between his fore-paws, with brisk and gusty movements, examined it in a flash, turned it upside down, took a quick bite and munched busily; his teeth went so rapidly that you couldn't follow them, he stretched his tail, munched, took another bite, it was a sight to see his long sharp front teeth working; they smashed up a nut or an

acorn so that the splinters flew; Gest watched the little
carpenter with admiration and would have been glad of
some tools like the four splendid little chisels the squirrel
carried in his mouth.

But when the squirrel was fed and wanted nothing for the
moment, it was fun to watch him hide what had been given
him in the first place he found, a crack in the bark, or in
his house; another time he would fetch out what he had
hidden, dart down the tree and start digging vigorously
somewhere at the root of another tree near by, where there
was not the slightest mark to be seen, and up he would
pull an old earthy nut which he had buried perhaps three
months before and just happened to remember. This
hoarding was something to follow, and Dart took the hint.

Dart loved the nimble little elf and often gave him things
for the sake of enticing him so near that she was just
allowed to touch his fine coat and feel his little warmth;
but as for taking hold of him, it was not to be thought of,
he was too quick and too sensitive for that, the least touch
of his hair sent him off instantly; tame he might be, but
he kept to his own air, visible but in reality a spirit of
the forest.

He showed what strength he possessed in spite of his
smallness when he had one of his flying fits, and these
would come over him like something very important that
had to be done—unless it was his play—without apparent
object he chased wildly from tree to tree, flew in long
daring curves like a bird from one tree-top to the next,
streaking like a flame along the thinnest twigs, and if it
was too far to the next tree he landed on the ground, gal-
lopped on like a red snake in the grass with his billowy
tail on high and in a second was up the vertical tree-trunk
again, throwing himself from branch to branch; in a
moment he was away in the depths of the forest.

It was such a temptation to follow him. Gest and Dart
were infected by the joy of his flight and made attempts at

climbing after him, laboriously from one tree to another, when the branches came near enough together; it was a very poor copy of the squirrel; they were too heavy, slow and careful, and never made anything of it in the trees. But the giddiness and the difficulty of getting from tree to tree without having to touch the ground had an attraction of its own which they could not resist; it was like a happy dream to see the world from the trees, the airy elusive view from above was at the same time something new to them and an obscure repeated experience; it gave them a kind of drunken feeling, they forgot all else, were simply in an eternal forest and eternal sunshine, an eternal summer, so long as they practised crawling about from tree to tree.

In this way they penetrated by degrees into the forest. On their expeditions, which became longer and longer, they could at any moment run up the trees if anything at all unusual appeared. They covered the distances on the ground but most of their observations were made from the trees, where they could look down and themselves remain in hiding. Thus the squirrel became a guide who gradually enticed them into the forest and made them familiar with it for miles around.

The nest up in the trees had been roofed over, after the squirrel's model, with a few rafters placed against each other and covered with leaves; there was just room for them inside, and the hut was hardly to be noticed from below if one did not know it was there. Here they were sheltered at night from rain and wind and all the evil things of darkness, here they were rocked into dreams and hushed to sleep by the murmuring trees and the airy soliloquies of the forest.

They went about in mats of bast which Dart's skilful hands had woven, rough things to wear at first and superfluous most of the day, but in the morning and evening they were glad of them. Dart adorned herself and was different every day, now with wild flowers, always some new sort

which she found in the forest or the bog, now with feathers
shed by the birds which she stuck in her hair; she beautified
herself with ochre, which was also to be found here by the
springs in the ground; but she was not alone in this, for
Gest was not above improving his appearance with a couple
of broad red streaks on his face. They were always
occupied, always had something on hand, no time of the day
was without its business or pleasure, if it was only plucking
the little pointed calyxes of certain flowers and sucking
the almost imperceptible drop of honey they contained.

They found honeycombs in the meadows and sucked out
the round cells with a straw, put them back again in the
nest and might afterwards return when the bee had filled
them anew.

But one day they had a visit from the wolf. It came
prowling down in broad daylight from up country, long,
gaunt and foot-sore, and on catching sight of them halted
underneath the tree they sat in, raised its forepaw and
seemed to have come just on their account. It raised itself
on its toes and spread its whiskers, with a bright look, an
expression quite sunny with kindness, and the children almost began to think they had wronged it. For in fact they
had never seen the wolf at close quarters and had perhaps
formed an entirely false idea of its nature. If they made
friends with it, it might be just as good to play with as a
dog, and they wanted a dog. It looked so like a dog.

Though tempted to come down and open an acquaintance they stayed where they were for the time being; for
if the wolf meant well it could easily come up to them.
Their grey friend kept walking up and down below, as
though in thought, licking its thin chaps and hanging about
much longer than one would have thought the acquaintance
was worth. The children amused themselves by throwing
sticks and bits of branch at the wolf, who blinked his

veiled yellow eyes and pretended to enter into the sport, feigning to bite at the things they threw and showing himself as ready to play as a puppy, though he was a bony and experienced old villain; he jumped skittishly and played with his paw, put on a pathetic air and tried a tender bark, curled his thin lips into what was meant to be an outburst of merriment, ingratiating himself so sweetly; and the children really felt the strongest desire to come down and pat this playful puppy; they looked at each other, shifted a little farther along the branch, in doubt what to do.

The tempter down below sported more seductively than ever, jumped off into the wood and turned his head to entice them to follow; but one thing struck the children as odd, they didn't think the wolf's smell was nearly as sweet as his laugh, whiffs of ancient carrion were wafted right up the tree to them, and the wolf looked as if you might hurt yourself against him, with his bones sticking out of his mangy grey skin; it was probably not worth while going down to him, and they stayed where they were.

When at last the wolf had recognized the hopelessness of waiting to captivate the couple, he dropped his mask and yawned like a pit with boredom, exposing four long rows of fasting teeth; hunger and murder were plainly written in his eyes. Then, after sitting on his haunches and howling, a bitter uncanny lonesome wail, he lifted a hind-leg against the tree, scratched up the dust with his feet and prowled off, long, gaunt and with drooping tail, never once looking back.

The couple in the tree looked at each other and turned white in the face; they felt that in broad daylight they had been visited by the *Night*. The wailing of the wolf was what resounded every night in the forest, nothing else; and what they had taken for the voice of the forest and half a world full of supernatural Powers turned out, when they saw it close at hand, to be nothing but a famished and disappointed old eater of carrion. So much had they learnt.

Gest followed the wolf with longing eyes till he disappeared in the forest—if only he had had a bow and arrow! Perhaps he could have shot the deceitful old prowler and given Dart a new necklace of wolf's teeth in place of the one the spring had. Without a doubt it was her having parted with it that had made the wolf so bold.

Next day Gest sat at a big stone near the spring that he had chosen for his workshop and made the place ring with the finest flint work. It was a delicate job he was on, arrow-heads, which you make by splitting suitable flakes across; a lot of them go to splinters before you get a few as they should be. Gest had a fancy to make himself a bow and arrows. He had been to the young ash trees for the wood, was wondering how he should get the string and thought of every place he knew of in the neighbourhood where there might be reeds.

Gest saw the bow as he wanted it and attacked the wood with his sharp flint; the slender ash shoot had to be carefully scraped so that the bow should be equally pliable at both ends; notches were to be made for the string; he could not wait till the thing was finished but worked as though possessed, longing for the string while still at work on the wood, with the arrow in his mind while he was on *that*; he had neither eyes nor ears.

Dart was at work plaiting and had to lend Gest some bast for a string; he called to her when he had got it stretched tight and plucked its first singing note with his finger while she listened, smiling the smile of the creator —didn't the bow sing well? By his side lay a bundle of reeds that he had fetched from the brink of the stream and peeled, long straight wands, they were the sort for arrows.

The day wore on and Dart got a lot of plaiting done, busily whispering to herself and with frequent casts of the head to throw the hair from her eyes; she went back to look at what Gest was doing but this time found him close and gloomy, uncommunicative, quite a different Gest; he had had trouble, the first time he pulled the bow-string hard and released it again it broke with a snap, it could not stand the sudden strain. No, of course, bast was no good, unless you made the string so thick that it would have a dull note and no spring in it. A bow must have a note or it has no soul. That his bowstring ought to be of gut Gest knew very well, for what is to reach the guts must come from gut, but here his plans led him in a circle; how was he to shoot anything before he had the means of shooting?

For the present then he would make the string of hair, and so Dart had to suffer, since her hair was both longer and finer than his own; laying her head on a stone she meekly allowed him to saw off as much hair as he wanted with another stone, and even helped him to twine the string.

It proved to be durable and gave quite a good clang. The fact that it was of human hair gave it a significance of its own, which other human beings would have to beware of, should they meet with any; but of course it held a fate for all other hairy creatures.

When the bow was finished Gest sat down and played Dart a piece on it. It sounded quite lovely, monotonous but lovely, and he lingered over the string while Dart lent her ear and delighted in the music. That was Gest's first harp. He afterwards became a minstrel.

But now it was a hunter he thought of being. The first arrow that was ready he shot straight up, and it rose like a worm against the sky with its little flint point, went higher than the highest trees, and when it had looked about in the blue for an instant it turned again and sought the earth head downward; it stood with shaft straight up, buried to the depth of a finger in the mould, when Gest after some search found it again in the grass.

He broke truce with the birds the same day. In time he became a practised archer. At first the bow was but short and the arrows of reed, but it grew with him and his arrows were of wood, long and tough. Gest had now taken up a thing to which there was no end, each new bow he made was an improvement, he grew and it grew, became long and powerful in its stroke, soon it was no longer a plaything with a little innocent clang; Gest's bow began to make itself heard in the forest with ferocious voice.

One night there was a gaunt old dog-wolf who left the pack and went on the prowl by himself; silently he came limping down through one of the side valleys towards the stream, impelled by a memory that was always running in his wolf's head, of a pair of pink half-grown man-children that he knew were to be found hereabout, and whose savoury tracks he came upon more and more thickly as he neared the river.

He was hungry, desperately hungry, though it was not so very long since he had had something; he was always hungry, always had been, hungry through and through and all his life long itching to eat himself up, a fallen creature who couldn't understand that the more he ate the more he was feeding his unquenchable hunger. Now there was a voice in his ever-burning entrails which deluded him with the notion that tonight he should regale himself with human flesh.

But just as he was prowling along with his nose to the ground and had got it full to drivelling of a lot of fresh scent, an inconceivable thing happened: the earth suddenly vanished under his feet, he sprawled in the air and hurt himself badly; when he reached firm ground again and on recovering himself after the somersault he found that he

was in a hole with vertical walls of earth on all four sides.
He tried to jump up again, but the hole was as deep as a
shaft, there was no chance of getting out.

So he sat there all night and had a view of a square of the
starry sky, until morning came and the square turned blue.
Then the wolf got uneasy and went round and round the
hole many times; he was so hungry that he felt an extra
wolf in his entrails, as though there were two of them, and
both dreaming a day-dream over again: of a couple of
pink man-children, not big enough to be judged dangerous,
but still a fair mouthful, just what a wolf could manage.
Twice he had filled his nostrils with the rich near scent of
their flesh, one night when they had unsuspectingly lain
down to sleep in the grass, but then they had unfortunately
raised such hideous shrieks that any one would have thought
there were hosts of humans about the place, the wolf
couldn't stand it, he had cut and run from a safe meal.
The second time was when they were sitting up in a tree,
from which however they had been too cowardly to come
down. The wolf was so hungry and his dream was so vivid
that he could almost see what he wanted so much to see.

And at that moment he actually did see them for the
third time, up at the edge of the pit, where they lay on
their stomachs with their hair hanging over their faces,
looking down, unpleasantly amused and holding their noses
in an impolite manner.

They knew him at once, saw that it was the same old rascal who had tried to get them to play with him in the
forest; he was running round himself like a shadow, glanc-
ing up and blinking at the light, and they saw him staining
the pit yellow with fear of what awaited him now. For it
had never occurred to the old murderer that one day *he*
would be faced by a violent death. They laughed at him,
and for answer he sat on his haunches and gave his carrion howl, hoping to make their flesh creep so that their
hearts might be softened; but it only made them the

merrier to hear the miscreant performing his own dismal elegy.

So then Dart got a necklace again. The teeth were very long but half decayed, the old rascal had had a diseased jaw. The skin stank and had chafed bald patches in the hair, but it would serve until they got younger and better skins. The nights were getting cold and they felt the want of more covering than hay and bast mats.

But from the wolf's guts Gest got his first real bow-string, hard and tough as though tempered in the fire, springy and yet so strong that no human strength could tear it apart. Neither the wolf nor any other beast was safe from one of the shots. Thus it came about that the old wolf's appetite was stayed, while Gest secured food for his own.

VII

LIGHT NIGHTS

INLAND on the edge of the horizon the forest rose like a wave, pierced at its highest point by a gap in the stems through which the blue sky was visible, like a gateway to the wide world; through this Gest and Dart passed one summer day when they were out roaming; they had broken into a run, the distance had passed into their souls and they went on running.

The day was both warm and cold, the sun gave heat but there was coolness in the breeze; for the first time that year they had thrown off their clothes, crept out of the nasty old sooty skins, which lay like a cast-off larva, and had rushed naked out into the sun and the air, but the air was cold, though the sun baked them; they ran and running made them hot and red all over, they cooled themselves in the breeze and felt thin and airy as the wind and burning like the sun, air and sun united about them, the cool young woods united about them, the blue sky and the swelling white clouds foamed and swelled over them; they ran, were caught up in the air, they flew—now, now they would go to the end of the world!

Running they came up to the highest point in the forest, an opening with a few big trees at the top of a hill; from here they could see far into the country, more green forests, valleys unknown to them, a new horizon with distant forest portals, and towards it they ran, ran on and on, up hill and down dale, without once looking back, they were the air and the sun, they were the wind, they were the wide world!

Gest ran in front, bow in hand, and as he ran he shot his arrow, which flew before him, leading him into the strange country; he saw it climb towards the blue vault of heaven and raise its point against the clouds, and Gest was with it on high and sought the ground with it, ran till he found it and shot it again upward and forward. His shot carried far, with a mighty whirr of the bow each time; the bow was long and heavy, the twin to his arm in strength, and long and slender was the arrow with a double-barbed flint point, akin to the lightning-stroke and winged with stork's feathers to make it go high; it was his longing, it went before him in a leap between heaven and earth, as he himself leaped.

And thus they ran on into Sealand, into widespread waving young forests, with here and there a glade and a hill, where glimmering aspens blended with the shafts of sunlight on the horizon. They saw what no man had yet seen, lakes in their primeval stillness surrounded on all sides by the walls of the forest, heights clothed with heather and juniper which gave a view of new forests and new blue sounds, stretching far into the country from the sea. And they came upon wide grassy plains strewed with big stones and framed afar in waves of warmth, with a scent in the stillness of wild wormwood, a web of larks' song as of everlasting fountains in the air, alder woods and streams where that wet man the beaver splashed about swimming in the shadow of the woods with his gnawed logs—and again the open country with rolling wild pastures and rocks, flowers as far as the eye could see, and above it the airy swallows weaving their flight in and out, up and down, and above them again a hawk high up against the blue, hanging and diving in its flight. . . .

At the hawk Gest shot his arrow and ran, flew after it through the long grass, with a swish of his own hair . . . and as he turned he saw his playmate come running after like the wind, almost without touching the ground, with

her long hair flowing out in the air like a flame and her
necklace of wolf's teeth flung the same way, a bunch of
wild flowers in one hand and a pretty feather she had
picked up in the other, her mouth wide open, she ran, she
flew . . . and then Gest saw that it was no longer "Little
Dart" but a long-legged young maiden with fair arms who
came flying like a summer breeze over flowery grass.

But she for her part saw that it was no longer a boy
running before her, but a young hunter holding his head
high on a strong pair of shoulders; she heard his cry, a
hunter's halloo to the sky, and on he ran, shot and ran
again, leaping above the grass like a stag to catch a scent
—she shook her hair, filled her lungs and followed him,
and so they lost themselves running in the wilderness, in
a shimmer of sunlight they vanished on distant plains.

The fox came up on the top of his house between blocks
of stone and sniffed with his nose in the air after the
couple, when they were well away, scenting a drama.
What strange creatures were men! He had seen before
now a lot of men running after a woman, but here it appeared to be a great hulking youth seeking safety in flight,
pursued by a maiden. Uf, the fox cleared his nose, men
were strange things! He turned about and disappeared
with his brush after him between the stones.

Empty, in primeval stillness the wide plains lay, wrapped
in the song of larks above and the high summer note of
bees among the flowers below; the clouds pursued their
airy life, the sun marched on in solitary might, the long
sweet summer day reposed in itself, until its being had an
end.

Sated with shining the sun sank behind hills. Then with
the dew the larks came down from the sky, falling obliquely out of space and hovering an instant over the long
darkening grass, before they slipped down and vanished in
their nests, sated with song.

Green and cool was the world; for a brief while sheer

silence, while darkness grew among the stones and blended with the evening mist; the stars came out, chilly and small. Soon other evening voices made themselves heard, the twilight hooting of the owl, a wandering beetle's ticking in the gloaming. From dark groves came a long-drawn enchanted note, the night raven's, and from swamps and pools the cool dream-chorus of the frogs was heard on every side.

And the day was gone. But it did not grow dark; in the north where the sun had gone down the day still slumbered, the sky shone light, fields and forest lay in a gloaming, and the white clouds could still be seen with their sleeping summits reaching up into the night, a blue night; the bushes filled with mist, and out of them came white nocturnal forms. Soaring free the moon rose grandly over the edge of the earth, with a dazzled stare at the other side of the sky where the sun had vanished; a great calm white star attended on the moon. Far away echoes sounded confusedly among the woods—the wolf barking at the moon, angrily, with a snap in his voice from annoyance at the marvel. But the moon lived her round life up in the sky, rising and soaring in her solitude, advancing over still lakes with her mirrored image and staring blindly upon sleeping woods and sleeping heights in the distance.

Somewhere far up the country by a tarn among birches a fire was burning; far around the animals sniffed and stood still before open moonlit glades between the groves, not daring to cross over; never before had fire been seen in these vast uninhabited tracts; a smell of roasting—what now, were they to be burnt and eaten? Clear flames rose from the fire and the smoke was visible in the light night; now and again a black upright shadow passed in front of the fire, there was no doubt about it, man had come with his hot arts.

Now it was Gest and Dart who had lighted their evening fire here and delighted themselves with its warmth after

running all day in sun and wind. They had not lost heart;
naked and taking nothing with them they had run from
home that morning; they did not know where in the world
they were, but the thought of turning back never occurred
to them. The night had no fears for them, it was so light,
and they had the fire. Gest kindled fire with the first two
sticks he came across and made free to miss out a good
many of the mysteries connected with the act, not even forbidding Dart to look on at it; anyhow he got fire, it smoked
and glowed in a moment beneath his strong hands; a full-
throated song did duty for the incantation, and when the
blaze flared up he threw a brace of birds into it, sacrifice
and supper in one. The great fire ceremony and the sacred
meal were now celebrated every day. Gest had left all
his tools behind in the winter house; the nearest sharp
stone had to serve for the present as a knife. When they
had finished eating, the feathers, beak and claws together
with the picked carcase were given to the fire, which
seethed with satisfaction; then they broke off branches and
built a booth for the night.

Thus they returned to the simplest way of life, older
even than what they had known where they came from;
they began again at the very beginning, in freedom and
alone. And the light nights held them, they stayed out
the rest of the summer, quite forgot their home by the
spring and the settlement on the coast; they moved on and
slept in a new place every night, saw new worlds, became
like the birds, like the flies, like the light—nothing but
flight and light, outside time, animated only by one another.

The love-star shone above them, as it shone above the
innocent who cleave together and evoke vital warmth and
multiply upon the green earth; they lost themselves among
them, among birds that sat on their eggs and deer with
new-born young, and swallows that rustled together on the
wing, and dragon-flies on their bridal flight, two and two

like *one* winged creature, and cuckoos that played at hide-
and-seek and gave their cry wherever they might be, and
hedgehogs chasing each other in the twilight, and snorting
buck hares—everywhere an enticing, calling and crowing,
a mad miaowing of the wild cat in the moonlight, a
tortured scream from the rutting lynx—but drowning all
the rest came the bison's roaring challenge from one end
of the country to the other like the voice of a deity from
heaven, multiplied by echoes and swelling through every
valley.

The fox spying upon the human couple seemed off and
on to have a fly in his ear; never before had he come
across such joyous people nor heard such wild, meaningless songs as they sang while they were tearing about.

In the autumn they came back to their home by the
spring, sunburnt and matured, and resumed their life there.

The spring welcomed them with its familiar, intimate
voice, they looked at their reflections in it and remembered
the childish faces they had seen there; they were now gone,
and in their place had come a pair of well-developed young
people who could scarcely find room side by side in the
mirror. On Gest's face a beard had sprung out, he was
now a man. More beautiful than any other earthly marvel
was the cleft of Dart's young breast as she gazed at her
reflection.

Deep down in the source, at a giddy depth, they saw an
eagle soaring on his wings in the abyss; they looked up,
the same eagle was soaring sky-high beneath the clouds;
the reality was linked with its image in the source.

Their house stood untouched as they had left it but
had nearly collapsed; they rebuilt it and lined it with
great stones to keep up the walls. With wonder Gest
found his tools again, weighed his old ax in his hand—
to think that he had once hewed out a canoe with that
fingernail of a thing! Now he struck big, heavy ax-heads,

slender but nearly a foot long and hafted in proportion.
The bow he had with him was twice as long as the old
one; he had taken to carrying spears now when he went
hunting, long flint-tipped poles that were dangerous even
to the biggest game when he got within throwing range.

There was no difficulty about providing all they wanted
for the coming winter; Gest was more intent on making his
things agreeable to the eye than on their mere usefulness,
which had been well proved; he would spend months
grinding an ax to get it perfectly smooth all over, and
he set about it with extreme persistence, sitting the whole
day long before a big flat stone and working the piece of
flint backwards and forwards as far as his arms could
reach, pouring on sand and water and grinding, pressing
and grinding, till the stone was hollowed out and the flint
too began to feel it, but slowly. Gest was strong and the
work made him stronger; many, many hours, day after
day he ground away, dumb with passion, nothing but a
tight-shut, immovable beard to look at as long as the fit
was upon him, and he did not give up till the last trace
of flaking was effaced from the flint, even though for the
sake of symmetry a layer had to be taken off the whole ax;
in his mind's eye the tool was perfectly smooth, and it
had to be made so. His spear-points he made quite round
in section and absolutely straight, he had no love for them
until they were perfectly rounded and straight.

Dart was just the same with her things; it had come
upon them as a sort of flowering of their nature, this desire that everything they produced should be well done,
just as they saw it in their mind's eye and not otherwise.
Dart decked herself over the source, mirroring her loveliness and thinking out new and graceful trappings for it,
trying and turning the skins on her person, this way and
that way, before she cut them out and joined them into a
new skirt. She talked to herself about it half aloud, spread
out the stuff on the ground and pondered over it; she

plaited and invented new patterns, plaited everything she saw, her hair too; and Gest had to fashion a comb of bone, with many teeth, to comb it out with. When it began to get really cold she sewed fine otter skins together and made mittens of pole-cat's skin turned inside out, which she decorated on the outside with scraps of many-coloured fur.

But the smallest and finest skins Gest could bring in were tanned by Dart with special care and laid aside; and when she was making pots, which she decorated and covered with the richest designs, she made for her own amusement a whole lot of little jars besides, like a row of children the big pots had got.

In the course of the winter Dart gave birth to her first child, her little bud, and now there were three of them in the nest, the first feeble whimpering of a new life was heard in the cave underground, a little human supplication never to be forgotten.

It was a hard winter, the snow lay late, and the house by the spring was snowed under in a great drift and lay buried for weeks, while the world above it lay buried in darkness. So long had winter lasted that summer was forgotten. The memory of it remained, but summer itself could not be recalled—it had always been winter. Even the river was frozen over, and Gest went out on the ice, wrapped to the eyes in furs like a bear, and speared eels. The muddy fish tasted distantly of summer slime and fresh open water; summer was a long way off.

But now a springtime had come to them in the dark days, a little harbinger, tender and defenceless like the very earliest spring flowers that come up with their bulbs under the snow and hang their white bells in the moist wind; like the furry buds on the willow that raise a smile of spring to the thawing clouds and the first powerless sun; Dart had repeated herself and produced a bud just like herself when she was little, with a white nap all over, downy and sunny-bright about the head, a little girl too, the smallest, sweetest and liveliest little woman in the world. Gest had a catch in his throat, a change was wrought for ever in his heart when he lifted the warm little creature in his arms for the first time and saw how tiny she was. She was a bud, and Bud should be her name. Gentle as her mother she was, only uttered a few little whimperings when she came into the world and then sank back into the long sleep from which she had come, like the long sleep of spring, lingering in repose before it comes out as spring.

It was a wondrous child, strangely fair, silent and full of life. Gest fitted another string to his bow-harp, the two he had did not suffice to express her nature, in the new one he put her soul, a high, delicate, joyful note. During the long winter days he sat playing to his Dart and his Bud and singing songs, till it seemed as if the narrow underground cave were filled with sunshine and the notes of birds, the summer wind and the quiet talk of leaves in fresh-clad woods.

And even as he sang this all came about, the loveliest spring broke in upon them that year, when at last winter's time was past and the storms had raged out and the showers were spent and the sun grown warm.

The first green day, with warmth on the sheltered side and yellow flowers in the grass, Dart took her Bud up to the spring and let the surface of the water kiss her, that she might have its strength and be pure and inexhaustible as it was; she held her up to the sky and gave her to the daylight, held her towards the forest and prayed that it might shelter her; and then she laid her down under the big tree by the spring that she might touch its roots and acquire fecundity. And as she lay there they could see the wonder of the earth reflected in her clear eyes. The little hands shrank shyly from their first touch of the world—but then what things they were she saw! a great frog took a huge leap and hopped right over the Bud—

no doubt a happy omen, but what *was* she to think of it!

But it was not long before Bud showed a predilection for devouring not only frogs but anything else that moved within her reach, and from that time forward she behaved like most other marvels in human form of the same age.

Spring passed in blissfulness and song, and summer once more established its summer eternity, high summer, mid-summer, a dazzling realm full of sport and good days; winter came again, and winter too was good.

But when another spring arrived the little girl could totter by herself out into the air and stretch out her small hands to the sun and forest. And that spring the family broke up their home by the source and prepared for a long journey. Gest wanted to see the world. He had made up his mind to go down the river, out of the fjord and on along the coast in search of new countries. In the course of the winter Gest had built a new canoe, bigger and broader than the old one, out of a real giant among trees, but boat-building was only an amusement to him now with the big sharp-ground axes he had.

When all was ready and the season come, they set out proudly with all they possessed and desired to possess in the roomy new boat. There were Gest's new weapons, bow and arrows, lance, and his good tools, all they re-quired of skins and clothes; and there was Gest's harp which had grown out of his bow and become his friend; there was his firestick, for which the bow had again had to adapt itself; Gest passed a slack bowstring around the fire-drill and turned it by drawing the bow backwards and forwards with one hand while holding the drill in place with the other; it never failed, whether he mumbled or sang to it. They would be able to cook food in the boat, Gest had made a fireplace of earth and stones amidships, he was thinking of voyages where perhaps they would not have a chance of landing every day; the hearth was to go afloat with them. Fish-spears, hooks and nets they took, of course; where one can float one can fish.

At her end of the boat sat Dart, and the paddle in her hands was a work of art, decorated with carvings and ornaments by Gest in the long winter evenings; and at the stem of the canoe he had carved an image which was supposed to represent a squirrel; it was to go in front and bring them luck.

Round her neck Dart wore a necklace of many rows of animals' teeth, all of them picked eyeteeth, a costly piece of work which held within it the souls of all the beasts Gest had brought down since he became a hunter. At her feet in a nest of skins sat the Bud, blue-eyed and holy, in an ermine hood and holding in her hand a bird's bone inside which her father had put little pebbles, so that it rattled enchantingly when she waved it in the air like a sceptre; it was a thing to scare away evil spirits. And in the prow of the canoe sat Gest broad-shouldered, dipping his double paddle in deep, slow strokes that made the boat jump forward each time.

Thus they set out. Against the stream they had come into the country in distant days now almost forgotten, when all was beginning; downstream they went now, back to the fjord and bound for new shores. Gest's nostrils expanded at the thought of meeting the sea again.

The voyage lasted a couple of summer months and took them round Sealand, as it turned out at last, for they lost their bearings on the way and were not quite clear about how the world was pointing.

They sailed out of the fjord by night, silently and in mid-channel, saw nothing of the people of the settlement and had nothing to say to them either. Gest had always had an idea in his head that he ought to have the coast on his left hand when he came out of the fjord and wanted to follow the land in the direction of the unknown foreign country the Elders talked about; he sailed that way and they soon came into pretty rough water and hugged the coast as closely as possible. They knew that there was land on the other side, but it was no part of Gest's plans to try that way, and besides the water seemed too wide. So they kept along the coast in the hope sooner or later of slipping out of the country and finding their way to the great rivers the old men prosed about.

But the coast proved to be indented with many bays, several times it ran up into extensive, branching fjords, and as they always sailed in the immediate neighbourhood of land they had to take all the ramifications before they got out into the open water again; it was a long voyage, they turned completely round time after time and lost all direction, but in the end they left off worrying about where they were going. There was no hurry, they supported themselves on the way, lay still and fished, and Gest went ashore to hunt where the land invited thereto. They saw a great deal and had many strange adventures, though none of a fateful nature.

The coast was everywhere pretty much alike, low and with woods or bluffs down to the sea, in some places sand-hills; dense, close forests inland wherever they came. As a rule they could see other coasts or islands on the far side of the water, sometimes fairly near, but they still followed the land from which they had started, with the coast on their left hand, as Gest knew he ought to do. Now and then they saw smoke rising from the forest or in the neighbourhood of the coast, and then they proceeded cautiously, hiding in the daytime and only passing the suspicious places at night; they had no mind to encounter men.

Thus they lost themselves in the world and became experienced travellers, having their eyes opened by constantly seeing new shores. At last they came again to a fjord that ran up into the country; there were many of them, it couldn't be denied, and this one was not particularly broad; Gest considered whether it would not be best to cross its mouth and sail on beyond, but decided after all to follow the land; there was no knowing whether it was closed at the end or perhaps might be the very opening he was looking for.

But what was their surprise on going a little way up the fjord to see it open out into a bay with shallow water and masses of seagulls, shores and headlands opposite that seemed familiar; strange how it resembled their native fjord which they had left in the morning of time! Could it be possible that two fjords, with at least half a world lying between them, could be so exactly alike? Absolutely the same woods with their bent trees creeping up from the beach! And with the same settlement inside the bay— they swung round a headland and at once saw smoke, boats hauled up on the beach—and now at last it dawned on them that it *was* their native settlement to which they had returned by unspeakably roundabout ways. They had simply sailed round the whole country, and as it was an island, that could only end in bringing them back to their starting-point.

They were well received. The meeting was really cordial, without a trace of bitterness on either side. That the old quarrel was forgotten and not to be dug up again was a matter of course, now that the tribe's prodigal son had come home and had made himself famous as a seafarer. So at last it had been proved, by actual circumnavigation, that Sealand was an island. Well, wasn't that what the Elders had always said? And it resulted of course from direct observation that the face of the earth was circular, that could be *seen*, the earth was an island in the ocean, as everybody had naturally supposed, and now it had been proved. Which was the more meritorious, to supply the tangible evidence by a voyage, or to sit at home and think the whole thing out by inner sagacity, was left undetermined; both parties had every reason to feel respect for each other.

Gest found his mother Gro unchanged. She did not walk much now, preferring to have things brought to her; people she wanted to talk to had to be at the trouble of calling on her. Dart and her Bud were presented to her on arrival, and she pronounced herself appreciatively about the child's condition and obviously good nursing, paying at the same time a handsome tribute to the young mother.

After the inspection was over Dart mixed gaily with her friends, young mothers who had been children with her but had had babies while Dart was away; and she had to lift her Bud in the air and measure it against all the other buds to see which was biggest. There was a great difference, some of the young mothers' children were short and fat, others more in the form of a ball, but Dart's Bud, though plump, was slighter and more slender than any of the others. Great was the joy at that end of the settlement on meeting again; it now appeared that Dart, though she had never breathed a word of it, had always had great longing to see other women she knew and to exchange motherly wisdom with them.

Gest was duly received into the company of the men of the settlement, submitted without turning a hair to all the bloody and cruel ordeals prescribed before one could be initiated into the men's traditional mysteries; it turned out that he knew most of them pretty well beforehand. Gest soon became one of the foremost hunters of the tribe.

(Courtesy American Museum of Natural History. N. Y.)

IT WAS A HARD WINTER AND THE SNOW LAY LATE

See page 66

VIII

THE VOYAGERS

BUT he could not keep away from the sea. On the voyage round Sealand the clouds had got into his soul, they had passed over him like great creatures of the air with outspread wings travelling through the sky— where were they going? It was plain that they were carried along by the wind, for they always went the way the wind was blowing—where did the wind come from, and where did it go to?

If the wind could take the clouds with it, why should one not commit one's self to it in a boat? Gest began experimenting with a sail in his canoe, a mat stuck up on a pole to begin with; it bore but little likeness to the spacious clouds, but still he drifted along the same way as they, not so slowly either, it was clear that he was on the right track.

The Elder's shook their heads at Gest's sailing freaks, they had heard the like before but never wasted any trouble on it; but he got several of the young men of the place to join him and together they made prolonged trials with sails in their dug-out boats, first inside the bay, then more and more boldly out in the open sea. They soon reached the limit of sail the narrow canoes could carry, they capsized easily, and of course they could not be made broader in the beam than the thickest tree in the forest; so they tried putting two together and connecting them with cross-spars, or they gave the canoe an outrigger, a trunk floating a little way from its side and fastened to it by several wooden stays; this gave a boat the power of carrying as much sail as if it had had three or four times the beam, and without taking anything off its way.

With new and complicated craft like these the young men made longer and longer voyages to sea, as by degrees they assured themselves that it was perfectly safe. The Elders had no desire to sail in winged ships of this kind; their motto had always been that you ought not to go farther from land than you could reach bottom, better to pole than to row; ships with sails were immodestly conspicuous at sea, you drew attention to yourself; it was more manly to row than to let the wind do the work; and finally it might look safe enough with that outrigger in the water to prevent the boat capsizing, but then the very safety of it was a challenge to the Powers both above and below, the stormy as well as the wet ones, which might involve fatal consequences.

As always happens in a conflict between the impetuous new generation and the circumspection of its elders, they separated. One fine day the young men went off on a longer voyage than usual, they had hinted at the coast over on the other side, and they never came back. The Elders had carried the day, they stayed in the settlement where they had always lived, and presumably the youngsters had come to grief; at all events the rash skippers were never again seen in Sealand so long as anybody was alive who could remember them; they were dead, or the world had swallowed them up.

They had as a matter of fact gone over to the other side; Gest and his companions discovered Fyn and found settlements there pretty much as at home, a similar population of shell-fish-eaters, friendly rather than ferocious, few of them cannibals and none at all supernatural as might have been expected. They had a merry time there, but as they had set out in search of new and strange things it was not long before they put to sea again. With very much the

same result the young sea-rovers visited one after another
all the rest of the Danish isles.

Thus they cruised about the Baltic waters until at last
they found the great continental rivers, ascended them and
penetrated far into Central Europe; they fished their way
on, and when they could no longer float they went ashore
and turned hunters, shot their way on through wastes and
dense forests, came into wild mountain tracts, until they
found rivers again on the other side; then they turned fishermen again and sailed thousands of miles into Asia, lost
themselves on boundless steppes and became reindeer hunters, were carried northward through sparse forests and over
frozen swamps to the Polar Sea where the sun was almost
lost. Here they hunted seals and made themselves boats of
skins for lack of timber, found their way along the cold
coasts to the outlet of other mighty rivers, which carried
them back as fishermen thousands of miles into Asia again,
and once more they turned hunters in new wild forests and
made their way across other mountains of terrifying steep-
ness which raised snow-capped walls to the clouds between
heaven and earth; but where the mountain goat could go
they too found foothold and food—namely the goats;
these mountains they conquered in their turn and came
down into the warm valleys with rivers that drew them on
to the south; the great tiger showed his stripes as he turned
among the reeds on the bank; naked they now sat in their
boats and the sun opened gates of fire above their heads.
Thus they reached the warm countries, through the tropical
jungles and out of them again, to the borders of Asia on the
south and east, the whole immense circuit of the coasts,
and northward again to the farthest arctic islands in ice-
bound seas, where they took to seal hunting again; from
there they passed over to the American continent and found
the moose, lived in forest and mountain, made themselves
bark canoes and bored their way through rivers and lakes

into the interior, came out upon immense prairies and hunted the buffalo; tropical America swallowed them and kept some, just as some had stayed behind wherever they went, but others emerged again and spread over the bleak plains of South America; on to the south they pushed and could not understand how it was this time that the farther south they went the colder it grew. Here they hunted beasts like camels which they caught with a noose, and their wanderings only came to an end at the extreme point of South America, on cold, gloomy winter islands not unlike those they had come from in the beginning; here some of them settled, in a sort of consciousness that they had arrived at the world's end and yet to all intents and purposes were back at their starting-point, no way forward and no way back, discontent taking the place of longing—and they are there to this day!

But others found their way from Asia to great islands in the ocean and pushed on south of the sun, became snake-eaters and pursued beasts that hopped; their souls too were closed, they had come into a pocket of existence and had forgotten who they were. And others again set out at random upon the South Seas, committed themselves to mighty billows in their miserable outrigger canoes, riding half in the water with naked feet which the sharks snapped at; on *them* they lived, fishing their way on, and came to little palm-wreathed islands, smoking volcano summits, in the immeasurable ocean, remote and forgotten by Time, like the seed that floats on the wind, whose fate is never known.

It was the great Stone Age migration which Gest and his companions had been caught up in, and which absorbed their instincts long after they were dead; new hunters and fishermen, generation after generation beyond all count; they were a part of this human wave which spread in ever-increasing rings, until it was cast up on the farthest shores of the uttermost sea.

Nor were they the first, for other waves had gone before, a procession of generations, the early Forest Folk that had lived before the Ice Age, whom the cold had driven out and who now hid themselves, shunning the daylight, in the hot vaults of tropical jungles in the heart of Asia and Africa; all the distant, widely-scattered border folk, who generation after generation had thrust each other on towards the extreme coasts of the continents; their waves broke over these wherever they went, peaceably or in conflict; and the march went on, the ages passed.

But at last there came a time when Gest bethought himself, went over in his mind the long way he had come and was homesick for the place he had set out from. Many generations he had followed, and they were all dead; there alone he could not follow them, for he could not die, he was the very spirit of travel. He did not even grow old, so long as he was on his wanderings. But now he had a longing for an abiding place.

He was on an island in the outer ocean, the farthest of them all, hundreds of leagues from the other islands, when this despondency fell upon him. The deep sea ringed about the island on every side with a succession of long, slow-rolling waves; he was in the centre of the ocean swell, and over his head leaned a palm-tree with its top full of fruit, like a breast with many breasts; then it came upon him that he could not stay, the old unrest which hitherto had always set him off on his travels, but he did not move. He was homesick for the big old tree by the spring in Sealand and the northern stars, and so violent was his longing that he could not bear to think of the same endless journey back again as he had come. Then he determined to die and took out his candle, which he had kept so long, and lighted it.

It was a strange candle, it burned quickly, but the present and eternity were in its flame. It was as though time had not gone by, there was no time, Gest had his whole life about him at once, far-off things were near, Mother Gro, whose hands had fashioned the candle, was with him, his beloved Dart was beside him, breathing into the flame; the only unreal thing was that he had ever been parted from them. For a brief moment he had turned away, and now he was at home again. Then he felt so glad that he no longer had any wish to die, and hastily he blew out the candle.

After the dazzling light black darkness fell. But even as he sat in the dark he could feel that he was in a different atmosphere, he no longer heard the long roaring thunder of the surf on the reef of the island; all was still, and close at hand he could hear the tinkling sound of running water.

Little by little the dawn spread around him, and he saw that he lay beneath the cool foliage of lofty trees. A distant ring of hushed music surrounded him on every side, the cool nocturnal witchcraft of the frogs; it was a clear night, and above his head were misty stars, the old familiar constellations. For he was in Sealand, where he had always been!

The grass where he sat was cool and the night refreshing; he sighed out all his sighs in a single sigh, sank back with closed eyes and slept on Sealand's breast.

IX

THE RICH VALLEY

H E woke at the sound of his name, a laughing voice that asked what kind of a guest this might be. . . .

On opening his eyes he was dazzled by the sun, and close by in the pale green wood he saw a woman.

For a long, long time he looked at her. Well what kind of a guest was he, where was he, who was she?

Gest could not take his eyes off this wonderful woman; he knelt in the grass and looked at her. Was she supernatural, some friendly forest deity? Strange were her garments, a dark brown woven skirt of cunning workmanship, and a tunic, neither of skin nor of bast, made to fit closely to the body and arms. In her hand, with the frugality of women, she held a long stick that chanced to have a crook in it, and at that moment Gest discovered a new marvel—behind her in the wood moved several cows of a kind that he did not recognize at first, neither bisons nor deer but a sort of cattle; and they did not seem to be wild, grazing quite quietly among the neighbouring trees; from one of them came the sound of a bell every time it moved, from some hollow thing or other on its neck; what was it, were they her animals, were they supernatural too, how could they go about so peacefully together? She must be a great sorceress, since she could put a spell upon the beasts; but she was no sibyl to look at, neither old nor ugly, quite the reverse.

His staring at last put the young goddess out of countenance, she laughed and would have turned away, but he hastily reached out for her skirt; it was real, his hand could feel the thick, soft stuff. She stayed still, silent and with a smile on her lips, a smile he knew—it must be Dart! Was it Dart?

She shook her head at his question, understanding his language; and he too understood what she said, though their speech was very different. What was she called, who was she?

Well her name was Skur, she was a cow-maid and a thrall at the homestead yonder—she tossed her head in the direction of the wood.

Thrall? Homestead? Cow-maid?

Gest asked no more; riddles multiplied with each fresh thing he was told. Cautious observation was better than exposing himself by too many questions.

Thus the conversation dropped, but they still looked long at each other and a liking grew up before they were aware of it; to him she was not of this world, a wonder in human form, with Dart's warm smile and yet not Dart, and she could hardly resist his obvious admiration. Slowly they began to walk in company, she with head bowed as though to warm waves breaking over her, he rich of soul and uneasy already with the fear of losing her.

From the first they were a pair. They influenced each other powerfully, he as a stranger, she as a mystery; but even when they had come to know each other better they remained a pair; it made no difference that she was a mortal, nor was she disappointed that, though a stranger, he was a man like other men.

They spent the lovely spring day together in the forest, and Skur taught her friend how she tended cows, he helping her, though as a hunter it took him a long while to get used to such a tame sort of game. She ruled her cows with gentleness, kept them together by her voice and made them go in the direction she wanted simply by leading the bell-cow, which all the rest followed. Gest examined the bell and found that it was a hollow piece of wood with a clapper in it, very clever and pretty work.

In the evening Skur drove her herd into an outhouse in the wood, a fairly large building of logs, strikingly well squared, with walls of faggots and a roof of rafters thatched with straw, all very proper to look at, a big and sumptuous abode, thought Gest, even for men.

And here Skur milked her cows.

Gest was silent while this went on; he expressed no astonishment but looked on and took note of what he saw, he was always ready to learn. So she squeezed the milk out of the cows with her hands, and why not?—adroitly catching the jets in a pail; he could scarcely control his curiosity about the pail, which was not made in one piece but built up of several staves, with a hoop of withies round it, an extraordinarily neat piece of handiwork. The cows willingly let themselves be milked, they stood chewing the cud and puffing, warm and fragrant, the whole house was full of twilight and the sweet smell of milk. When Skur had filled her first pail, with her forehead pressed against the cow's belly and seated on a three-legged stool, she rose and put the pail to Gest's mouth; he drank the foaming drink, full of vital warmth, shyly and with deep emotion.

Skur poured the milk of all the cows, many pails full, into shallow round tubs which she put up on shelves in the cowhouse, and when she had finished she came into the doorway, where there was still daylight, with a cake and began cutting bread.

Gest tasted and ate, quite incapable by now of grasping any more. A food made of kernels, he could tell that, baked into a lump and sweet, and while he was still eating and thinking he had never tasted anything so delicious, she put a new food into his hand, cheese—??—he looked at it, smelt it, ate and shook his head with the deepest gratification. But then the knife—the knife; what was it that cut such thin slices and was so narrow? The knife was of bronze. Gest sighed, the riddles overwhelmed him, there were too many of them. Wait a bit, let us see, let us think. Much wisdom was required to penetrate so many hidden things at once!

And indeed it took Gest a long time to get quite familiar with the way things were. The place he had come to was his native valley, but everything was changed. He must have been away a very long time, a thousand years or so; he had left in the grey Stone Age and had come home in the middle of the Bronze Age. All those who had shared his wanderings had remained at the same stage while they were on the way, with them motion had taken the place of growth; here, where people had been sitting still, they had become different men. Gest was a long time finding out merely wherein the difference lay, but he never felt at home with it.

They were the same people as they had always been, but new generations, without the smallest recollection of the past which Gest shared with them; and they had multiplied, the valley was inhabited from the coast up along the fjord and the river and far inland. Gest never associated with any but Skur, the first he had met.

Amongst all the other things that were new to him Gest discovered that Skur was unfree, that is to say she was owned by a man in one of the homesteads of the valley who could put her to any work he chose and in all else disposed over her lot. In Gest's day there had been only one kind of folk, now there were two, masters and thralls, and to the latter class Skur belonged.

She was living alone in the woods when Gest found her, tending the cows and making cheese from the milk while the summer lasted; she slept in the pen with the cattle, and nobody asked any more of her. For the sake of her working efficiency care was taken that she was left in peace; girls that were to run after the cattle had to be kept apart, like those that were set to tend the fire, one thing at a time;

they were decent people at the homestead she belonged to. On her own account she kept a cudgel just inside the door in case any hunters or young fellows might be prowling round at night. But she was no hater of men, and now without much reflection she had given herself to this strange guest, because he wanted it so badly and it was to be he. They shared the light nights, and Skur's springtime came to her.

It was Dart and yet not Dart. She had Dart's loving mouth but not her slender form, and her hair was not fair, nor black either; red it could not be called, it was something like the colour of peat; but for that matter she had hardly any, it had been blown off her, she said. But for the shortness of her hair she made up in the length of her fidelity, a warm dumb soul that swelled once for all with gratitude for being loved. Heavily built she was, looking almost dangerous in her strength of limb, but with a blameless heart, a fountain of generosity and cheerful withal, full of latent tenderness and happiness if only the sun would shine on her.

Gest saw handsomer and grander women later on, for the daughters of the free men of the valley were dazzlingly beautiful, flocks of tall, fair, sprightly maidens, with a sea of hair flowing down their backs and a wealth of ornaments, flashing new bronze rings on arm and neck, sometimes gold, and a bronze sun in the middle of the pliant tunic, not too great an ornament for a slender girl's waist; they were garbed in costly homespun, thick, heavy woollens that had taken masses of yarn, a fortune in themselves and beyond question burdensome in summer, but they had to be worn; to make up for it they naturally had nothing on underneath. The latest fashion was not to gather the skirt together with the belt, as was the natural thing to do when it had been thrown round the body, but to fasten one end high above the other, so that there was a pleated edge in front, like a basket of folds in which they carried their proud breasts, decently concealed but with outlines that could not be hidden, beneath the smooth woollen bodice; this was the custom of the valley and every one followed it. On the head, when their hair was not fluttering free, they wore a little network cap, full of the golden hair which hung imprisoned therein like a heavy lump of light weighing upon the neck.

A sight not to be forgotten was to see the young daughters of the freemen being driven in bronze-mounted cars from one homestead to another by their stately sword-bearing fathers, behind little shaggy snorting steeds and followed by a cavalcade of young mounted spearmen.

But Gest kept to the homely bondwoman who had appeared to him in the glory of a goddess when he saw her for the first time and who had since enriched his heart in simple human wise.

Not only were the people changed and their way of life quite different, but the country itself had undergone great changes in the time Gest had been away.

The first thing he looked for was the spring up in the valley where Dart and he had lived. It was there still but did not give much water, and the deep source itself was overgrown, the greensward had closed over it; the mirror and what Gest and Dart had seen therein was no more. Now the source came out of a wilderness of weeds on the ground, many little springs that trickled and ran together to form a thin stream. And the river where it ran out was now nothing but a brook.

The big deep river which ran with a swift current up to the top of its banks had shrunk and lost itself in winding intricacy through the meadows, choked with waterplants and vegetation; the meadows themselves were drained and cleared by human hands, and up towards the sides of the valley he came upon large open spaces of purely arable land, glades in the forest which had been

cleared and made fit for agriculture; here the crops of
the year grew in green wind-stirred plains, like the wild
grasses Gest had known inland, but here was all the same
kind of grass which was cultivated for the sake of its seed.
And in the midst of the green clearings stood the homesteads.

Elsewhere the forest remained the same, where no gaps
had been broken in it, extending dense and pathless into
the interior, and the game was as before, though scarcer
and more timid, as Gest learned by experience.

Only the bisons had vanished from the forest; some of
their blood had passed into the tame bulls, who resembled them but were much smaller. But deer and wild pig
were still there. Now tame swine were kept on the farms,
besides horses, sheep and other domestic animals that were
not indigenous to the country; the migration of domestic
animals was an obscure saga in itself. The disappear-
ance of the bisons made the woods quieter, the great roar
to greet the sun was no longer heard in the valley. But
a memory of it was preserved in the shrill note of the
lur, the great bronze horn which was heard now and then
in the valley and meant either a sacrificial solemnity or
war, some sanguinary encounter between lords of the soil
who could not agree and marched against one another
at the head of their men.

People were more relentless now than they used to be;
then they had been full of threats, noisily calling down
slaughter for a week or so, without bloodshed; now they
stabbed and then without a word, they had lengthened
their knives; nobody now seemed to feel the smart in his
own breast at the bare thought of wounding his neighbour. So when the lurs woke echoes in the valleys there
was blood in their note. It was as though the bisons' mad
onslaught at pairing time still haunted the air. In their
very curves the lurs recalled the bisons' horns, which had
been blown before they were imitated in metal; but that

was so long ago that even the population of the valley had forgotten all about it; so long had Gest been away.

But if the voice of the primitive bull had passed into the signals with which the free owners of the soil called each other to single combat over disputed land, the primitive cow reappeared in the tame cattle which grazed in the woods and shared their peaceable disposition with the quiet folk who owned nothing and were set to tend the beasts and till the ground. If the thralls had been asked whence they came they would have answered that they were born to it. And where were they born? Probably in the turf-pit or the pigsty where they lived. But for that matter they never showed any discontent. Thus the life of the valley had assorted itself.

And it was populous, restless both to the eye and the ear, a bustling traffic along both the roads which ran from the coast inland, one on each side of the valley; hardly a day passed that one did not meet some man on horseback or driving along at breathless speed; and it was not as in old days some man one knew and whose business one could guess by the look of him, tell what he was hunting; now they were all strange faces, nothing was to be read in them, and their errands might be of the most various kinds; life was a complicated affair now, it was impossible to survey it any more.

Besides people flying along the roads a thrall might often be seen at work in the fields, or a herdsman; the wild animals had of course fled from the valley but in their place you saw the tame ones. An everlasting sound of men and their companions came from the valley, the barking of dogs from every side, the neighing of horses and distant cries, the shriek from the hub of an ungreased barrow, crowing of cocks—foreign birds that spread their feathers here and grew thick-voiced and impudent; tame geese that shot their necks at a wayfarer and wanted to bite, poor wretched poultry, now bound to earth and fat of throat, robbed of the music of the clouds as in the days when they were birds. From the homesteads, from the women's quarters, stole the cat, another foreigner, creeping on tiger's paws in the dewy grass with its snake's eyes, on the hunt for the innocent native field-mouse. There was always some movement, always some buzz of sound in the old valleys, once so silent, if it was only the hum of the children's toy mills which they stuck up in the breeze on the palings. Yes, wealth and life had come into the valley.

Gest preferred to keep to the forest. At the top of the valley, round about the source, it was fairly untouched but was not the same forest, even the oldest trees were other than Gest had known; the tall old ash by the spring was gone and in its stead there grew a little grove of many smaller ash-trees, perhaps ground shoots of the big tree in which Gest and Dart had once had their nest. Of the house in the ground where they had lived there was not the smallest trace, turf many centuries old covered the spot. The forest murmured, but with a different murmur from the old.

And what of the settlement on the bay inside the fjord? Not a soul lived there nor had done for generations, there was not a trace of human habitation; only a long low ledge above the beach, overgrown with wild plants, showed where the settlement had been. There were still fishermen, but they lived out on the coast in quite different conditions and had no traditions about there ever having been a fishing station inside the fjord. They had clincher-built boats and went sea-fishing in the Belt.

In a harbour in the fjord, by the beginnings of a town, lay great sailing craft, so big that the canoe, which had sunk into a dinghy, looked like a tiny baby beside them, as it lay made fast by the painter. Yes, those were ships, and Gest hung about them a long while at a distance, studied them almost in fear, circling round before he

ventured little by little to approach, the wonder of them
was too much for him all at once.

They came and went between foreign lands! Some of
them were so big that they could take twelve or twenty
men, besides cargo! They expanded the soul with immense vague ideas of the distant realms they came from,
entirely different regions from those in which Gest had
lost himself; they were the mysterious countries from
which all this wealth had come to the valley, the metals,
the domestic animals and the knowledge of agriculture—
and Gest kept silence, said nothing even to himself if he
could help it; had not life cheated him after all, in
spite of his travels and all that he had seen?

This traveller and discoverer might now turn and begin
again, travelling and discovering in his own home, so
had time slipped from him. Was there any part for him
in this entirely new world on the old soil?

The valley and all the conditions of life in it gave him
a silent answer, as he gradually made his way into things
and learned to understand them. The homesteads were
closed to him. They spoke with their open green corn-
fields, but they were fenced in, the husbandman owned the
land together with his family, and the woodland around
they owned in common with other families, up to the
boundaries where other ownerships began, other groups
of families in other valleys beyond the forest; everywhere
the whole island was as thickly populated throughout its
valleys as here. The boundaries only met in the midst
of wide uninhabited forests, but on every hand the right
of proprietorship was vindicated, whence it was that the
lur spoke now and again and the long stabbing sword sat
so loosely in its scabbard. So there was no chance of
Gest getting any land, since he had no kin.

The landowners lived on their estates in log houses of
heavy timber, many different houses grouped together and
fenced in; they did not object to visits, they were armed

A HUNTER OF THE STONE AGE

Neolithic man—restored according to Prof. Rutot of Brussels

and feared nobody; how to get past the shaggy bandog
that foamed and danced round itself by the yard gate
was the wayfarer's own business; the master of the house
was gracious enough to a wanderer, especially if he had
some stories and could tell them or was gifted as a
bard. He was liberally treated and offered shelter, in
the loft or in an outhouse, according to his appearance,
but next day it was understood, quite reasonably, that
the wayfarer must move on.

Gest for his part soon found his place. Who he was
and where he came from nobody knew or cared, and he
never touched on that himself; but it had got about that
it was he who had taken up with Skur the cow-maid in the
woods; nobody took him to task for it, but still people
seemed to recoil a little stiffly when they saw him. For,
apart from the fact that as a stranger he had involuntarily
chosen his own position, he had begun by committing a
little breach of the law, a depreciation of the girl's value,
not yet visible but presumably to be expected before long,
to the injury of another man's property.

They were not mistaken. Towards the end of the summer Skur began to lose her breath when she had to run
after the cows. By that time Gest had also made up his
mind about his position and seen that there was no place
for him here. At first a certain curiosity made him quite
favourably received at the homesteads, for he played the
harp remarkably well. The fine freemen's daughters were
carried away by the waves of an undreamt-of world rushing over them in his music, but their dilated eyes went
beyond him, they had visions but saw him not. And if
they did see him their eyes froze up and their nose gave a
jerk as though it caught the smell of the cowshed.

Gest did not envy the lords of the land. They lived
amid a wealth of which greed for more made them un-
aware. Dry bread was no longer good enough, they cried
for added delicacies; supporting one's self alone in the

woods, as men had been able to do in old time, was a lost art; even the thralls talked about being hungry if they hadn't a loaf in their fists, and that in a mast year!

Gest could easily have made a living, if they had but allowed him room. He would willingly have been a fisherman, but found that his catch would be taxed and he would have to pay rent to the owner of the shore rights, and that was not to his liking. Within the fjord where the ships lay a number of unattached people had taken up their abode, owning no land but supporting themselves in various ways; here, for instance, dwelt the bronze-smith who made all the fine weapons and ornaments of metal. After watching his work a few times Gest caught on to the handicraft and had a taste for it, but when he had made himself a good ax and a knife his inclination was exhausted: working for others, even for pay, seemed to him an ignoble lot. Wherever he turned it was obvious that he would be dependent on others.

So for the present he took to the woods with Skur, thus making his crime complete. As a robber he was free as a bird, as he had been once before.

But this time things were not so easy. No doubt he could live as a hunter in the forest, but in the long run it would be hard to keep in hiding, even in the thickest and most remote parts of the island. Swineherds passed through, or other hunters came prying about; a fixed dwelling was not be thought of, and without one you could live in summer but not in winter.

So Gest once more fashioned himself a craft on Sealand's shore, in an out-of-the-way place where he could escape discovery for the time, and when the birds of passage began their flight he too set out and sailed with Skur to other shores.

X

IN SWEDEN

THE couple felt by no means poor and abandoned as they left the coast of Sealand behind and steered for the unknown. Gest had fish-hooks and bow with him as he always had, and as to the bronze knife and ax, he had to go and hide himself in order to enjoy these possessions to the full. To him they represented his share in all the glories of the rich native valley he was now leaving. Perfectly astonishing it was what these new implements could accomplish. And he had well noted what it meant: the fine big log houses that were closed to him might be made real elsewhere and bring him the right to the ground whereon they stood; he too would become a landowner and had made a note in his head of all that pertained thereto.

He laughed again and again as he told Skur of his good fortune with the two bronze things. He had himself cast and forged them to gain a knowledge of the nature of the metal, and he had paid for his instruction, everything had to be paid for; but he had also paid for the metal, and that was dear, there was a lot of weight in the ax, and what did she think he had given for it all? A stone, just a little bright stone that he had picked up once on his travels and kept because it was red; that bronze man's eyes were like hot coals when he saw it and he would have loaded him with more metal than he could carry simply to get it—well, some people were fools. And Gest roared with laughter over the crazy fellow who had handed over an ax and a knife of bronze for a little stone!

But Skur was not devoid of possessions either when she left the country, for she had in the boat a little bag of seedcorn which she guarded as her dearest treasure; it was to rise again as a cornfield in her new home, if the Spirits of the soil were willing and Heaven gave its blessing; and in her arms she held two young kids, a pair, they were hers, and she took them with her when she ran away. She would have liked to take her cows too, but they were not hers, and besides there was no room for them in the boat. The kids gave her trouble enough, they were afraid of the water and wanted to jump overboard, and at last she had to tie their feet together and lay them down where they could do no harm.

It was not long however before they could land on another coast and let the kids have ground under their feet for a little while every day, and afterwards they got their sea legs and stood up in the boat without having to be looked after. Gest left Sealand on the side opposite to his valley, over against the great land of Sweden which he knew of but had never before visited. He crossed the Sound in its narrowest part, in fair weather, nothing even for a heavily laden canoe, and when he was across he turned northward along the coast in the direction of the low mountain chain that lay like an outpost in the sea; it was his object to look for a river that might lead him up into the country. Southward he did not go, since he knew that the whole of Skoane and the coast towards the Baltic was well populated, and, as in all his travels, it was not men he sought for.

Wherever along the coast they saw smoke or other sign of habitation they passed by, if they could, or lay concealed till nightfall; they entered the first river of any size they came to after rounding the promontory and found its banks apparently uninhabited, but after travelling up it for a couple of days they saw entrails drifting with the stream and turned, seeing that there were men higher up.

In the next, which ran out farther north along the coast, they again found men; they came unexpectedly upon a skin boat in a creek among rocks where they themselves had put in to hide, but the people in the boat were more frightened than they, shamming death and lying immovable at the bottom of their boat so long as they looked at them, with the whites of their eyes showing and their mouths wide open. They were little people, there were two of them, with coarse black hair; their mouths were long and pink at the corners, they were very greasy, had salmon in their boat and were evidently fishermen. None of their gear was of metal. Gest decided not to go up that river either.

But the next again, which was a big, fairly rapid stream, did not look much frequented; great fallen trees lay rotting and untouched everywhere along the banks, few if any landed and lighted fires here, that was easy to see, and up this waterway they voyaged for many days, deeper and deeper into the country, among a maze of forests, no lofty trees, but slender, light and open woods, mostly birch, with bogs and glades between, rocky ground with scattered blocks as high as houses, and here and there firm rock. The country was wide and open but with stretches of valley and turns and heights which gave a view, a paradise for game, and in primeval stillness, entirely after Gest's heart. He felt that here nature was younger, here he would stay.

Far up the country, where the river narrowed but still abounded in fish and where there were tracks of elk on the bank, they sought a lodging one night under some huge rocks which projected one above the other so that they formed a shelter; here they stayed, and this was their first house in the new country. The kids climbed the rocks as soon as they were put ashore, clambered up as high as they could come above the house and seemed happy, they too felt attracted by the country. Gest began to look

about him in the forest with his bow and felled trees for
a dwelling when he was at home; matchless his new ax
was; Skur found a level space near with a soil of mould
which could be made useful for a crop when the worst
of the stones were cleared, and she went to work at it
without delay, with her giantess's strength, carrying off
big and small stones and building a fence with them round
the cleared space; it was a couple of score of paces each
way and neither round nor square; that was their first
farm.

The forest was uninhabited on every side for many miles
around; on his long hunting expeditions Gest made sure
that he had that part of the country to himself. At a
distance the forest was bounded in one direction by great
lakes, which he had not examined closely; in another,
many days' journey away, the land ran up into long, low,
rounded hills, masked by snow late in the year—the cold
corner of the country; from that quarter he fetched a
reindeer when he wanted one.

The elk was found in the forest in his immediate neighbourhood, the broad scoops of its horns, like immense
hands with outspread fingers, showed among the foliage
in the wet, low-lying forest swamps. He did not scare
them, they should be allowed to live undisturbed by the
bark of dogs; Gest hunted without a dog and usually went
about the forest as quietly as the other animals. Once
or twice a year he took a bull, when it was necessary, and
as a rule without its knowing anything about it; the lightning struck, it had the shaft in its body and fell, without
so much as having time to feel sick; one had to live but
not to do harm. Therefore Gest never had to go far for
food.

At home he was a carpenter and raised a fine log hut
under the lee of the great rocks where they had first made
their camp. He learned husbandry from Skur, and in

the course of years they extended the farm with many small fields, all well fenced with the stones they had cleared off them; in time they grew more corn than they could consume. The pair of goats became a herd. They themselves had a flock of children.

Gest was at home here. Above his head the wind passed through the wide forests, came far away with a rustle of the trees, tore along and lost itself far away in other rustling trees; the birches straightened themselves, shook all their leaves and were at rest again when he had gone by; it was the Wind God who was abroad, invisible, the cold one, the never-resting. But Gest stayed.

Over his head stood rowan-trees bathed in sunlight. Here was work for him to do; he carved wooden spoons for all the mouths there were to feed as time went on, fashioned wooden bowls for Skur of gnarled birch roots, enough to keep him busy most of the winter. Everything they possessed was made by themselves.

Gest thought he might almost call himself a lord of the soil, when a few years had gone by and they had houses and outhouses round the yard, with not a few fields about it, irregular in shape and up and down according to the lie of the land, with big rocks in the middle of the corn, but productive and always capable of extension. Of domestic animals they still had nothing but goats, and for years Skur sighed for cows, to say nothing of sheep, for goats' hair is not the same thing as wool; a pair of horses was Gest's constant dream; but all this came of itself when the children were grown up.

Skur's children, red-haired, freckled and hardy every one, were born here in the hut under the great rocks; outside its door the world displayed itself to them, a stone-fenced plot with many little houses where they took their first steps in the open and made playmates of the kids; afterwards the world expanded to the tilled fields, and then came the river and the forest; they were not very big when they began to roam on explorations as far as they dared go.

The heather received them and spread rough couches for them to lie on in summer days, with a scent of spice and the revelation of a bird's nest, well-hidden, mossy and wadded; the raspberry brake took them into its sunny cover where only their red shocks of hair showed up, whortleberry and bilberry offered them banquets in the rocky glades with fallen trees and cushions of soft moss, and here they annexed land, like the little men they were already, taking possession with a broad gesture of a tuft or a stump with lots of berries on it, if they had found it first; on such occasions no regard was paid even to kinship and the right of the first comer was always respected.

All things that crept upon the earth crossed their path and each received its own welcome: the ant, that little creature so murderous for its size, the choleric bee, the caterpillar, furry and arched as it crept its little way, the spider cunningly hoisting itself from thread to thread in its web, the black slugs that left a trail of slime and shortened themselves when touched; they learned to know the birds and greeted friends wherever they went in the forest, each tree received them with its living soul.

And the seasons changed about them, the hard winters, darkness and snow piled against their doors to the height of a man and barring the forest; but even this taught them delights, they dashed downhill on an improvised sleigh and went hunting with long strips of wood under their feet, made short work of the wolf, which sank to the bottom in the new-fallen snow, while the hunters gaily slid along the top.

Then spring came upon them with its marvel of the thaw, the bright sun, that great wooer, and the humble trees that received his kisses and began to swell with buds; song of birds and warm nights; then the long sweet sum-

mer days with the goats in the woods and the love-smitten
cry of the cuckoo in the valleys with the impudent laughter that followed it, like a frivolous forest divinity; the
short light nights that buried a treasure, never fully known,
in the soul and every year added a new treasure to it.
The harvest, when they garnered in reverence the ripe
corn on their little irregular fields and chased the fox out
of its last corner; the autumn's great time of nuts and
berries and the wild apples which deceitfully tempted, red
on one side, but were as sour as a kick in the mouth.
Most things in this world they tasted and made a wise
choice, wherefore they grew—and so they were grown up,
at one end of the line, while the last were still small.

They were hale and strong as giants, the boys with
shoulders that they had to turn sideways to the doors,
not to mention ducking their heads, but then that was the
only thing they bent the neck to, Father's and Mother's
house door.

These tall fellows sat still as mice, wooden spoon in
hand, around the supper dish, waiting decorously while
Father made his usual little speech about the wonder of
the corn and its unrivalled blessing; but then they fell to
with a ring of the spoons on their sound teeth; down went
the groats, bruised corn boiled in water, and they were
nice enough partly to conceal their greediness, did not encroach on their neighbour's lawful section of the dish but
met in the middle like well-bred children, until there was
nothing left.

And the girls grew strong, swung the quern wherein the
corn was bruised to groats, and sang a quern song, in the
summer scent of the sweet grinding corn; they got a
powerful swing and grew rich in bestowing nourishment
and receiving intense joys.

Gest's and Skur's children put an end to their solitude
and isolation in the forest; strong as had been their par-

ents' desire to be alone, the young people's yearning for the world outside and the society of their fellows was a natural force equally irresistible.

The sons found their way through pathless forests, a journey of days and days, to inhabited places, where they appeared in the new-created majesty of primeval men to tame women who in *their* eyes were altogether too desirable and delicate to tread the earth; they simply *carried* them off, after tearing down the maiden's bowers where they were kept and thrashing those who had the keeping of them. They came home in transports with bedraggled maids and were either allowed to keep them or went off sulkily to clear a space for a new home in the neighbourhood, if the maiden was too ragged-looking and did not find favour with the family; in this way one or two new farms sprang up as offshoots of the old one.

Skur's daughters looked after their goats capitally in the woods, but were negligent of their own personal security; they met rovers who had tracked *them* from afar, gods to look at, young swains who did not beat about the bush; and then there was more offspring about the place, of which no more was to be said but that they came and Grandfather had to make a wooden spoon for another mouth. But some of the rovers didn't let the girls go when once they had had their arms round them; they became sons-in-law and perhaps got a pair of goats as a dowry with the marvel of a freckle-nosed girl who had captivated them in the woods, with help to clear a farm near Gest the Old. Thus with the years a whole hamlet arose where before had been nothing but wild forest.

The sons, who had used their eyes and pried right down to the rich inhabited tracts to the east and south, had thoughts of improving their way of life. They had grown up from childhood on Mother's hearth cakes and goat's milk cheese, dried elk's legs hung in the smoke over their beds, and there was always porridge, better food was not to be had and there was always enough of it, but variety has its charms and what one sees other people enjoying one would like to share; the boys made long trading expeditions, since they had to fill up their spare time, and brought home new domestic animals, not without great difficulty; they were several weeks conveying a couple of fowls up into the wastes from inhabited places, awkward poultry to keep alive on the way, for they couldn't walk all that distance and when carried they scratched and were apt to peck nasty holes in one's hands.

When after a great deal of trouble they got them home and went and looked under them, they were rewarded by crowing instead of eggs; the chickens grew into cocks with spurs and combs, they had been taken in and sold cocks instead of hens! Well, well, then they would have cockcrow about the place, that was the proper thing in the morning, the same as other folks; and on another journey they brought hens and were careful not to complain about being fooled the first time; no need to expose one's weakness, but they looked more carefully this time. So now the cock spread his plumage on *their* midden, and pancakes were going when Mother was kind.

One year the boys came home after long wanderings afoot, dusty and tired but happy, with a couple of sheep at their heels. This time they had taken care not to be cheated the other way about; one of the sheep was to be a ram, and a ram it was. The women could depend upon getting wool now. And there stood the sheep, docile and used to the tether, far-travelled, with yellow eyes in which a black worm seemed to be alive, dumbly chewing when given anything to eat. A new note was heard in the forest, the baaing of the ewe as she stood in the wind alone, the ram's *molm, molm, molm,* like a bitter soliloquy that

was not meant to be heard but could not be kept entirely
to himself. Next spring the bleating of tender lambs was
heard in the yard about the houses.

Little by little all tame animals found their way there.
Gest himself saw to the bees, caught the wild swarms and
made hives for them, protecting them in winter with roofs
of straw; their summer hum resounded deep in his soul.
Soon the beehives took an important place on the farms;
they were given a sheltered nook behind the houses, the
beginning of a kailyard.

A great event it was when at last the first cow arrived.
They had waited a long time for that, many preparations
had to be made; first payment had to be got together, in
skins, the hunting of many winters. The sons had gradually become experienced traders and had an idea of prices;
if they were tricked now and then it was always a question
who came off best in the end. People might take liberties
on the sly with these shaggy, innocent country lads from the
backwoods, in the far-advanced places down country
where they traded; thus they were once persuaded to give
a whole stack of squirrel fur for a sewing needle, just one
needle, of bronze, with an eye in the middle; but the boys
dashed home rejoicing through the forest, many days' run,
with the needle, and in spite of the price they delighted the
women with their find. Even Father Gest's eyes brightened
when he saw it; his own priceless treasures, the ax and the
knife, had not propagated, and this little thin baby of a
needle was after all bronze.

But at last they had collected skins enough to buy the
cow, a load, for many men and many journeys forth and
back; it took the whole summer to complete the bargain
and it was late in the autumn when they got home with
the cow. She moved slowly and got sore hoofs, so that
they had to let her lie down before evening; she had to
graze rather a long time every day; they had to go a long
way about where the forest was impenetrable; it was a te-

dious journey, the cow's forehead was wrinkled with fatigue, but home they came with her.

It was worth all the trouble to witness Mother Skur's joy when the cow arrived at last. It could be seen that she was getting old now, she fell to trembling when after missing them for years she again for the first time took hold of Sister's warm horns.

But with this one cow they could not go very far. A bull was wanted if they were to have calves and milk, and the outspoken sons of Gest let fall a remark about the duties of sons-in-law . . . and well it was that they had them, for this was a time for united effort, for saving and getting up betimes in the morning to scrape together all the furs and corn a bull would cost. But when they had got it, at an unmerciful price, a perfectly unreasonable profit to the seller, they nevertheless thought they had done well and that it was the seller who was the fool, for with these two beasts they had bought not merely two head of cattle but the whole world of live stock at once, calves and their byres full of as many cattle as they wanted for all future time.

In a similar way they got horses. The whole place was in a fever the day they were expecting the two who had been sent out for them. They came riding home, proudly, with legs tucked in, for their steeds were small and they were tall fellows, but the display had its effect. The womenfolk were out with barley-bread in their hands to receive the dainty animals and put them in good humour. But out with their bits first, shouted the boys to their ignorant sisters; a nice thing to go and spoil their teeth through not knowing any better!

And there they were, the shaggy little nags, standing with their legs together and getting restive, well broken in eating bread with their gentle, short muzzles and covered with harness to the eyes; now they too had come. The children stared wide-mouthed; the tales of the grown-ups about the strength and speed of horses had led them to imagine that they must be as big as houses and provided with wings. But the reality soon made up for their dreams.

On the other hand the grown-ups suffered a certain dis-illusion; it turned out that they had had another little trick played on them, not as regards sex, that was right enough, only one of the horses was not satisfied with grass alone but ate wood till the splinters flew, was quite capable of chewing up a whole log-house starting at one corner, if he was allowed to go on; and the two men who were respon-sible for the bargain went about looking glum with vexation, for how could they tell by the look of him that the horse ate houses? But they would get their own back; if such tricks were transmitted they would have many a vicious crib-biter to bring to market in return, be sure of that!

Now the family at Gestthorp had all that a husbandman could desire. Swine they had long ago driven in from the forest and put into sties, the bandog foamed at the yard gate, and geese plucked at the grass with curly necks down by the pond. With the coming of the horses they had reached the summit of their ambitions, the mark of freemen, they had attained the dignity of horsemen and had it in their power to drive. Hour after hour the sound of chop-ping, broken by pauses of reflection, was heard from the workshop of one of the sons; he was engaged in building a car, balancing on the horns of the difficult problem of making a wheel round.

All the boys had inherited skill in different kinds of hand-icraft from the old man, to which title Gest now had to submit; one worked cleverly in wood, another became an inventive smith; hunters and powerful bowmen they all were. But from their mother they had the innermost secrets of agriculture and cattle-breeding.

Work on the farms becamse distributed entirely of itself. Strangely enough Gest the Old, who by nature had been a hunter and a passionate carpenter, came in time to drop these occupations, which he left to the others, while he kept to fishing which he had more and more to himself.

He loved to lie out in the river alone in his old canoe, the same one that had brought him and Skur into the country, in a dawn of the ages which their children and grandchildren knew not.

And in it he left the country. Alone, working his double paddle, with his back towards them and facing ahead, his kindred saw him one day set out to fish, as was his custom. But he never returned. His sons searched for him and came home sorrowful; they had found neither the canoe nor the old man.

The river had taken him, he had gone into the current which bore him along, out of the country, towards the sea. Now they were orphans.

For Skur was dead.

A few weeks before the young people of the thorp had lost their mother.

One day she turned pale; for the first time in her life the old woman felt ill and took to her bed, still without assistance, leaning on the table and the solid stools as she made her way through the room, but when she had put herself to bed she found she was more helpless than any of her babes had ever been. The heavy body which had given life to so many could no longer keep itself alive. She smiled calmly upon the room, searching for her husband with her eyes, but he happened not to be in; she felt for him with feeble hand, turned her face to the roof and grew paler; she was dead when they fetched Gest. They had been inseparable, living in concord all their life, and yet she was to die alone.

Gest made his beloved's last bed of a tree from the forest, a great living green tree which was to share death with her, their souls should fare together. He hollowed it out like a boat, with a melancholy fancy of the stream of time—

towards what shore?—and laid her in a mound with all that had been hers, that it might remain with her. Skur's best cow and a pair of goats were given her in the grave, and beside her pillow Gest laid a little bag of seedcorn; as she had come, so should she go. When the tree in whose stem she was buried turned green again, its evergreen leaves should wave over her beasts and over a cornfield.

The young families of the thorp had lost their venerable mother, the mother of them all. But to Gest it was a young maid who had died, he never remembered her otherwise than as she was in her warm youth. He could no longer live in the spot which she had left, she had gone and he set forth after her.

Downstream—ah, an easy task—he glided with the swiftly rushing river, away from the brief life which he had built up through so fair an adversity, the only thing that endures.

XI

THE ISLAND OF THE DEAD

AND then again he sought new shores, old but not aged, serious but unbroken, with a great empty place in his soul, severed from life's import but with a world before him in which to find it again.

He was alone, torn out of all that had been nature to him, only himself on his wanderings, alone with the ancient eternal solitary things, the waves, the blind stare of mountains and lands, the clouds that look down without a face, the trees that hold their peace, and the backs of the dumb, downward-working rivers.

He passed along the Baltic coasts in his old single-handed craft, found the great rivers and fished his way on as once before, with no joy of recognition; and when they could carry him no farther he landed and turned hunter, concealed himself in the densest forests and took to the mountains to gain the source of new rivers on their farther side. But this time he was not bound for the East, towards the sunrise, the morning path of all beginnings, where he had been before; he would go down to the South, to the noonday shores, and see how time went there.

A vague hope drove him on, the hope of finding again what he had lost. But neither was sheer curiosity quenched within him, he still thirsted with the soul of the primitive man after making the world's last promontory and last billow his own.

For it had not escaped his observation that while he had been away for thousands of years in the East and to the south of it, beyond the ken of the old world, that world had made vast strides in arts and forms of life; he had left home as a hunter and come back as a hunter but found the people he had left behind enriched and supported by the land where they had remained settled in the interval, with tame animals and agriculture in full bloom, no longer a few scattered tribes but a numerous, prospering and vigorous people. And yet it soon became plain to him that this was only a Northern, secondhand expansion of a progress which must be still richer elsewhere, whence it had come. Nobody in Sealand was at all clear about where they had their bronze, their corn and their domestic animals from, but they knew that all these glorious things came from the South and had their origin in southern lands; from that quarter they still derived all that they could not produce themselves, a constant stream of new things and new views of things, so that must be where the mountain of wealth stood, from which all gifts proceeded. Towards the same quarter the birds of passage migrated in autumn; it was said to be always summer there.

Some even asserted that death was altogether unknown there, not only did the natives enjoy perpetual life, but it was thought possible that all the dead, even from other parts, assembled there, a spacious thought which it was not given to every man to grasp. Far up in the North were found folk with southern influences who were so convinced of this that they no longer buried their dead according to old custom, but burned them upon a pyre, in the faith that they would come to the sun's coast if they were committed to the fire and the path of the sun. Sometimes they gave them some birds of passage on the pyre that they might show the soul the way.

To all this Gest did not know what to say. For his own part he had been content to lay Skur in an oak canoe, for that was a well-tried mode of travelling, even though it might take longer. This about the soul having first to pass through fire and then up into the path of the air was a thing his mind refused to understand, though he could not reject its possibility. Gest's own immortality gave him hard and fast ground to stand on; as regards dying he shared his former Stone Age contemporaries' direct conviction that of course a man continued to live for all eternity, unless he had the misfortune to be killed or bewitched by wicked people or fell into a sickness that was not to be driven out; such things unhappily befell every one, an exception was hardly known, but for all that it was just as certain that a man would keep his life for ever if the causes that threatened it were removed. And Gest himself was a case in point. But what was the explanation of other people's death, whether as some said it was a transition to further existence of another kind or in other realms, was not at all clear to him. So what else was there to do but to visit the coast they talked of and see with his own eyes what there was to see?

Gest found the countries in the interior of Europe very populous, but he avoided inhabited places, leading the life of an outlaw and making his way unobserved through many realms to the mountains in the centre of Europe. In lakes among the mountains he came upon people who lived in houses standing upon piles, whole towns on the water; they did not seem to wish for visitors, the bridges to their towns were carefully hauled up; so much the better, they would have to be longsighted if they noticed *him*.

Few men ever saw Gest while he was travelling. There were his tracks, big tracks and far between, he was as long-legged as the elk, but he himself was seldom seen, he was already a long way in front when his tracks were made out. Up over the eternal snow on the mountains, immense slanting snowfields which went right into the region of clouds, where vultures hung, his tracks lost themselves, and no one who traced them could tell where he had gone; downward they turned on the other side, no one could tell where they came from.

Once down on the other side Gest built himself a boat
in a lonely mountain wood near a watercourse that promised to become a river, and if any one heard him at work
he may have thought it was a supernaturally large wood-
pecker hacking away, the bird of Time; but when it ceased
Gest had vanished without a trace down streams that
marked his passage with a wake and blotted it out again.

He lost his way in the mountains and came into bypaths
that did not lead directly to the South; a tributary of the
Danube caught him up, and from that he came out into
that great old winding river, a highway in antiquity; here
was much navigation in many kinds of craft, and a great
diversity of people, a traffic beyond compare, not a day
but one saw a vessel or was seen by one; so much the better, where the whole world scraped sides, one toiling up
stream, another riding easily down, nobody took notice of
an extra nutshell; so many a greybeard dropped his lines
in the Danube.

The more unseen from the very fact that they saw him,
Gest swept on alone, a bearded face closed to the world;
he drank of the river, a fresh and muddy, tepid drink, rich
with the many lands it had soaked up on its way;
he made his frugal little fire ashore among the rushes and
broiled his fish, different creatures here from those in
the North, some with sensitive feelers around their mouths,
others powerfully protected with armour on their skin,
but like all fish they swallowed the hook and by their
greediness made a meal for others. Thoughtfully eating
Gest looked towards the sunset with sober eyes, like many
another numbed old fisherman.

And if a harp was noticed in his boat that was nothing
to be surprised at; what seaman does not divert himself
on board with some melodious plaint, borne upon the
wind, profound homesickness when he is in foreign seas,
restlessness incurable when he is at home and misses the
waves so sorely?

Thus Gest fished at his ease through outlandish realms, caught glimpses of horsemen in kirtles of violent colours with horses' tails and feathers on their heads, clad as it were in galloping fire and crested with folly, and he heard them shout; deeper he plunged his oar into the Danube and swept on, came out into the Black Sea and paddled about there, landed in Asia Minor and became a poacher, wandered in the desert and found river sources again, this time the Euphrates, and came into a cedar-wood boat down into Mesopotamia, where he dwelt for many generations and witnessed great and marvellous things.

Then he went down into the Persian Gulf, round the south of Arabia and into the Red Sea; turned westward, through deserts once more, and took to the Nile, came down into Egypt and remained there for many ages.

At last he drifted out into the Mediterranean, visited all its shores and islands, from shore to shore and from island to island, all round the sea. Every sign told him that he was now on the coasts of the Sun, and he stayed there until they had no more secrets for him.

They were rich countries. No misty legend in the misty North gave any real idea of how blue the sky was here, ever blue, it was a boon merely to be alive, and in a bountiful climate there flourished one happy and industrious people after the other. Gest watched them go their way through the light and filled his heart with their destiny.

He had seen the powerful people, delighting in the chase, in the country between the rivers, their ruthlessness in war and their enterprise, all their abundant irrigation works to make the corn grow; he saw the same thing in Egypt, and now he knew where corn came from.

Bull-worshippers they were on the Nile, as they were in Crete, all domestic animals had their home here or had been tamed in these luxuriant lands; and from here the sheep had tramped, tethered by men, all the way north, till they were penned in a mud hut beneath snowdrifts through the long winter and had to yield their wool to clothe the hairless Northerners; that is why the ram mutters through his nostrils in the evening breeze, complaining of his treatment. The goat lived on the mountains in the Mediterranean lands, therefore he still climbs every knoll amid level ground in the North, gathering all his feet, as though on the world's highest summit, and looks about him without giddiness.

And what these first creative people had founded, Gest saw carried further and raised in richer fulness and greater freedom by the happy Greeks; nothing they could not do, no bounds to their joy.

Long ago on his way south Gest had chanced upon arts and objects that were still quite unknown in the North; things that were but tentative fragments there he found as complete and already ancient civilizations in the South, so slow was the spread of the new on its way from South to North. They had iron in everyday use while those in the North still kept to bronze; they built marble temples and adorned them with perfect statues of the human form, at the time when the Danes poured blood upon black idols, a block of wood with a hint of a head, in smoky huts of turf.

And yet they were the same people, at root the same race. As Gest had followed the early Forest Folk, preglacial man, on its Stone Age trail eastward to the uttermost seas of the earth, so he was now taking part in the migration of the Ice Folk, only so far behind that they had become changed in the meantime, a richer and happier folk, unrecognizable. They were the descendants of those the cold had hardened, Carl's and Mam's people, White Bear's and May's people, who had gone south in waves, one generation after another, while the rest of their kin stayed behind in the North; and from these first great joyous seafarers, who left behind them marvellous skipper's yarns among the Greek islands, were descended the Greek Gods and Heroes.

For that which in the North is held fast by cold, rigour, adversity, bursts into flower in the South and grows into happiness and liberal arts. And as the wave, dashing against the shore, sends back many little waves, from land, so did a rebound of the emigrants' fortune reach the North arousing others there, who made for the South with new fettered forces and souls in bud ready to burst into flower. Thus culture came from South to North, where after all it had its tap-root.

Other conditions helped, more favourable than in any other part of the world or in any other age; in the Mediterranean countries the peoples of three continents were intermixed; from Europe the Northerner came down to blossom out, from the East the Asiatic, Wolf's and Tchu's people, to settle instead of wandering, from Africa the warm primitive folk seeking coolness, and coming together they released each other's forces and flourished in common, in a beauty which found expression in Greek sculpture and has never been surpassed since; in memory of a happy people on a happy shore there stands for ever the human figure in its marble nudity against a blue background, the Greek beneath his sky. So powerful was the expansion that it outlived the age, persisting in the spirit even after the conditions that had supported it had ceased to be.

Gest saw the sun of Rome traverse the heavens; he lay in the Tiber as a poor, unknown fisherman while the great imperial galleys passed in and out like overweening monsters lording it with three tiers of oars one above the other, marching back and forth in perfect time like so many legs, a fettered slave at each, such was the power of discipline; and out of the Tiber he slipped in his old canoe when the mob roared in the streets and Rome began to crumble.

Now he would soon have accomplished his mission, for which he had travelled so far and so long.

It had not turned out according to his hopes. No, his mission gradually faded away, as he came farther and farther on.

What he had set out to find was the Land of the Dead, and he found long summers, dwelling-places beautiful as those men had dreamt of, a nature imperishable, but nowhere did he find the dead.

The most likely place, it seemed to him, for them to dwell in would be an island, a place surrounded by the sea where every one could not come to them; he therefore sought out with special diligence all the islands of the Mediterranean, and they were many; but the inhabitants of all of them were natives, people lately born and with a pronounced stamp of the soil. Not everywhere was a man equally well received; on far-away islands where the natives were deficient in decency you could see them a long way off coming down to the beach, sharpening their knives on the rock, their home seeming to serve them as a whetstone; this showed no great development of wit, since they give a stranger a chance of becoming suspicious and turning back in time. Now Gest had not exactly expected the dead to appear as spirits or to behave in a particularly amiable way, they would be as they had always been; nobody doubted that the dead might be dangerous and voracious, but one thing was certain, they did not slap themselves on the back and make rude gestures at a seafarer in their disappointment at his turning away instead of coming in to them. These were men, entirely unpurged by death.

The same might be said of the inhabitants of the great populous islands who had more civility, they were all new, hearty people, open-mouthed, thirsting for tales, themselves overflowing with loquacity, eager for chaffering, with a fancy for female slaves; they were alive enough here, this was not the Isle of the Dead.

Finally, at the very last Gest found a little insignificant islet, far out in the sea and uninhabited; it was not the one he was looking for, but it was the last, there were no more to fix his hopes on; and here he stayed, settled down with all his memories.

It lay in the midst of the blue sea, the top of a sunken mountain, with the beautiful ever-blue sky above it; at its highest point it had a sort of shallow cracked bowl, a dead crater, overgrown with a heath of lavender, where grasshoppers played in airy solitude. Somewhere in a rocky valley grew a thicket of laurel and myrtle, a grove of carob-trees flourished by a little spring, on their fruit Gest lived; a rock close by canopied a sheltered nook, here he slept. Lizards sported upon the stones in the sunshine, they were his delight. On the steep cliffs sea-birds brooded and wrangled the day long; it sounded like a note of music, and the sea lay about the island like a harp. A sail might rise into sight far out, but only to turn off and sink into the sea farther away. The porpoise gambolled in the deep clear water just under the island, scratched itself on projecting rocks far down, blew voluptuously on the surface and plunged down again. Otherwise the island was still. Gest talked little to himself, shook his head from time to time. This was good.

In the face of the rock Gest hollowed out a little vaulted niche with portico and ornamental pediment, like a tiny temple, the work of several years, but he had time enough; and in the temple he set up a little idol he possessed, a piece of Greek work, the figure of a woman, the only one he had loved on these shores.

Wonderful were the Greek girls, whether they shone in holy calm, with all the folds of their clothing falling quietly to the ground, or whether in noble frenzy they kicked a leg free of the chiton and made a hook of it to catch the Wine God; of all things they might be guilty, save only of the one crime: lack of grace. Gest had looked upon them all with desire, they had been his delight; but only one had he loved and she was not alive, she was made of baked clay and less than a hand in height; it was she who now stood within the rock above his dwelling and received his daily prayer, ever and deathlessly the same. She was a tall and slight young maiden with strong and slender legs, perfectly nude, with her clothing laid beside her on a vase, and her hands were in her hair, tying it fast before she ran, for she was a racer, swift, swift as a flame, as the wind; she was the wind, she was in the air, she was woman, she was youth!

With such worship did Gest refresh his heart. It was not laid to rest thereby. When he had lived here for some ages, listening to what sea and sky said and listening inwardly to what he might have to say to himself after long undisturbed contemplation, it resulted in this, that he had indeed chosen solitude, but not altogether of his own will; it was rather solitude that had chosen him. He had been left alone because the others had gone from him. But was it not true that he had once himself fled from the place where he should have stayed?

Ay, that was the sum of life: first one is in advance, then one is left behind. As a young hunter he ran from life, and when he became mature and was rooted in existence, it ran from him.

He had lived long enough. Of what use was immortality if it could not be shared with others?

So, after calm reflection Gest lighted his candle for the second time in his life, in order to die. He had no wish to live when life had lost its savour.

There was only a stump left, the length of a finger, and it burned quickly. Gest felt himself aging as the candle burned, and that set him free from pain.

It was day when he lighted the candle, but it filled the

whole world with a yet more powerful, unearthly light, he was in light, and with him was all he had lived, all ages returned and rested in the moment; with him were Dart and Skur as though in one person, the same love-dazzled smile; with him was the wise Mother Gro, herself the essence of all love, and all his children; time and distance did not divide them, he was his childhood, youth and manhood again in one, in the same light; he had lost none, was not alone, only in his being was there truth, it was immaterial and untrue that he had gone away, not reality, he was again at home—and then the love of life returned, it was still too soon to die, a good stump of the candle was left, quickly he bent forward and extinguished it.

He was sitting in darkness when it had gone out and noticed already that he was in a different air, colder, refreshing to the soul; instead of the hum of the sea there was another hum over his head, from great trees; he heard birds, but they were not the same.

Slowly the darkness gave way and instead of the rocky island in the blue Mediterranean he saw trees about him, rowan-trees; he was in a forest of lofty blowing trees, above them the sky hung low like a continuous roof of grey chasing clouds.

He was in Sealand, it was autumn, in the thin foliage of the trees the storm tore with a mighty, open note, and the falling leaves swept like a fire up and out of the forest; rooks and crows were pressing up against the wind with tempestuous cries, scattered flights of plovers came down and tried to collect where slopes gave them a lee. It was one of the year's flitting days, the birds were being blown out of the country, the woods were groaning, cold jets of wind poured into the chambers of the forest among the open trees. Nature's harsh breath fell like a great, chilly streaming body upon exposed, light-forsaken Denmark. In their passage the clouds opened a rent and let through a cold streak of sunlight, the pale afternoon gleam of a frightened and freezing day, looking backward in its flight.

Ah! Gest blends his freshened sigh with the blast, with an autumn heart; now he is at home. The wind is on the way, and it draws on to winter, but he will stay—he will stay, he too will draw on to winter.

XII

THE WANDERING SCALD

ON winter evenings a strange tangled clang was heard, blending with the whistling in the doorways and the blast without—music—Norna Gest? —and if the outer door was thrown wide, he stood there, in the light of the hearth fire, against a background of raven-black darkness, tall and stooping, as though he bore the night on his back, with swathed legs and wrapped in skins, his harp in his hands. Norna Gest, was come.

He had but to pluck the strings once, it sounded like suns and stars, and the whole homestead came to life, the young people filled the doorways in a glow of expectation, and even the goodman of the house, whose dignity bade him stay within, could not restrain himself but came forward with eyes dilated and fair words on his lips; Gest was come!

And then the old man's long, heavy wanderer's pike-staff was placed to rest behind the door, and he himself was led up to the high table next to the master, together with his harp. Tales and the outer world made their entry into the hall that evening and stayed there many evenings, so long as with fair words, full mead-horns and downy beds they could make the scald comfortable and persuade him to stay.

But they knew they could never get him to rest quietly for more than so many days, even though they sent the children to beg it of him. His wanderer's staff knocked in its corner at night and was getting quite bent from wanting to go, he would say; they could look and see if it

117

wasn't really bent; Gest would have to go and walk it
straight again. Thus he jested, but one day he took his
leave, and they saw the tall form with the harp on its back
swing out of the yard gate; he walked slowly, with a swing,
gave himself time, but it was surprising how quickly he
got over the ground. Gest was gone.

Half a year or a whole year after, they heard him playing outside their doors again. He came and went just as
inconstantly and just as surely as the seasons.

Gest had taken to roving, he was always on the road like
the sibyls, he was a traveller, with no hearth of his own;
this had come about of itself when he returned to his native
land, there was no longer a home for him, but he was the
friend of the homes, and as he could not be in all of them
at once he had to divide himself among them all and go
visiting from one to another. All the year round he was
travelling through Sealand, but there were also years when
he did not show himself at all; then he was down in the
South in foreign lands, or his wanderings took him up into
Sweden or Norway; and when after a lapse of years he
showed himself again, the sound of his harp was more
varied than before and there was no end to the tales he
could tell. He was homeless, but all the world's lays and
legends had their home in his memory.

When Gest came home from his long journey to the
South, where he had sought in vain the Island of the Dead,
he was very lonely; no laughing young herdswoman waked
him and asked who he was, he found himself alone in
the forest, and when he made his way out into the valley
he scarcely knew it, and not a soul knew him. It was his
native valley, but it was greatly changed.

A thousand years or more had passed over it since Gest
had been here last; even the oldest secular oaks were not
even acorns when he left, no trees were the same. The
clans were different, with no living memory of the clans
from which they were descended, and yet they were the

same people; the big red fishers of the Stone Age as well
as the sturdy husbandmen of the Bronze Age lived again in
them, but their tradition did not even go back as far as
the Bronze Age, they were now living in the Iron Age and
had no conception of men ever having lived another sort of
life.

They knew not who they were who reposed in the great
stone-set chamber graves of the Stone Age, and yet they were
their own earliest ancestors; giants had raised these stones,
it was thought, or they were the home of the elves. They
themselves still buried their dead in mounds, but without
burning them as in the Bronze Age; they no longer believed in fire but had other complicated ideas about the
Powers, no longer seeing them directly in Nature; they
had become gods, persons, not very unlike the doughty
sons of men who worshipped them; they made images of
them, just as if they were to be seen, and regardless of the
fact that by doing so they exposed their impotence. Gest
never became an adherent of Odin, but he believed, as he
had always done, in the weather.

Their ideas about the realm of death were not clear to
him; they appeared to imagine two, one good and one bad,
and you didn't enter into the good one, as might have been
supposed, by assuring to yourself a long life with possible
continuation beyond the grave, but by an abrupt conclusion
of it; you had to get killed, to fall in battle, then you
were sure of being admitted to the good country, of whose
whereabouts they had only a general, embellished idea, no
definite directions for the journey being available. But
they still gave the dead a few important possessions when
they buried them, so the early belief in immortality seemed
to persist, though only in their customs; the belief Gest
shared, namely that there was no inherent necessity for dying, and that one was there so long as one *was* there.

The new faith had a sanguinary effect on the morals of
the valley; they fought more, human life had fallen in

value, since the proper end of it was presumed to lie beyond the grave, albeit nobody had ever come back and confirmed this presumption; but as the noble life one was to enter demanded a noble death they slew one another with the utmost cheerfulness and hoped to meet on the other side for renewed mutual slaughter and resurrection. Frequent death evidently meant happiness and glory to the majority, whereas an unviolent end was associated with shame and gave admittance to the other kingdom they believed in, a dark and mournful one. Longevity, which one would have imagined to be the thing aspired to, was thus a questionable fate, and Gest never sought an opportunity of mentioning his age, which for that matter concerned nobody but himself. He was no confirmed adherent of the bellicose Northerners' religion but was glad to add it to his scald's repertory.

Human nature is undeniably a queer thing: although the valiant Northerners took special delight in exposing themselves to death, in the hope of a speedy sequel, they nevertheless did everything humanly possible to prevent their being killed, surrounding themselves with armour, whole shirts made of iron rings, impenetrable to cuts and stabs alike, helmets to cover their heads and great shields; they made it quite an art to get through to their vitals. And this art never rested; as fast as the protection grew strong, the weapons got sharper and more mercilessly ingenious; they went for one another with big sharp iron axes and tempered swords, as though they would cut down trees; a battle was a noisy affair, the clash of iron against iron could be heard far and wide.

And their numbers were great, fearfully great, no longer a few bands of franklins who went out and settled a dispute—they still did that; but by the side of this ancient form of warfare a new one had grown up which threw that of the franklins into the shade, a different body from that of the actual landowners—the *Army*. But this was all a part of other great changes which had taken place in Sealand.

At bottom they were to be traced to one main cause, the increase of the population. Gest's native valley alone was so thickly inhabited that you could go through it all the way from the coast into the heart of the country, the best part of a day's journey, and never be out of sight of human beings, whether that was a comfort to you or gave you a headache.

This increase of the population had naturally taken place in the first instance at the expense of the forest: as human beings became thicker, so it was thinned out. In the Bronze Age the clearings had eaten their way on both sides of the valley as great open spaces; now the case was reversed, the forest only showed in as many patches as there had formerly been clearings, and the rest was all open cultivated land, neatly divided into fields by fences and dikes of the stones taken off the ground and crowned at the top by the sharp, bare ridges on which stood the barrows of many generations.

Not till one had gone a long way up the country did the edge of the forest present a closed wall, and from here it still extended as a vast connected whole towards the interior of the island. But even far within the forest there were open glades with clearings and green fields; settlers who had started farming on their own account in a strange place and there laid the foundation of a new thorp. The old scattered homesteads in the valley had become villages with common cultivation among many distantly related families.

Just inside the entrance of the fjord lay a town, with a harbour full of longships. It was not a big town, only a street of thatched houses, but its inhabitants lived a life of their own, were neither husbandmen nor warriors but were allowed to carry on some kind of trade or handicraft; quiet, cautious folk who offended no one, liberated thralls or strangers from foreign parts, useful and unobserved; they had dived into their town and waited for what might befall them.

Up at the end of the valley, opposite the town, dwelt the Earl. Who was he? If you asked the franklins, then his importance was shown merely by the respectful tone in which the free men spoke of him. He was Earl. A freeholder was of course a freeholder here in the valley, but somebody must be acknowledged as a superior, somebody there must be to lead them in war and to take the tax from them in peace time, which was due for the use of the land —to whom?

To the King presumably. The King lived on the Roskilde Fjord and so could not personally manage the whole island, though a contribution was due to him from every homestead; he appointed the Earl to administer his rights, and there were many earls in the island, one for each district. In their origin they too were franklins, but on a large scale; they were descended from families which had early seized upon much land and had brought great estates under cultivation; thereby they acquired the means of keeping a great body of men who might secure them in the possession of what they had taken and add more to it. From one of the oldest and most powerful families of earls the King himself was descended.

The Earl at the head of the valley owned all the broad meadows there, a great tract of forest and many farms. On the largest of these he lived himself, with his retinue of armed warriors, whose only work was fighting and who were bold, impudent fellows, juggling with their sharp swords and certain of escaping the garners of a straw death. Where did they come from? Well, they were the surplus of the homesteads, the many sons who could not all have land; they took the Earl's pay, entered the King's service or banded themselves together under a leader and sailed abroad in ships after land wherever it was to be

found and could be had cheap—after the death of the
owners, which they saw to.   That was the Host.

The earls did not cultivate their land themselves, for
that they had churls, the peasants who occupied their farms
and had become dependent on them; they themselves were
taken up with the King's warlike affairs, and they spent
their time in pomp and prodigality after the fashion of
foreign countries, heaping silver upon their women, who
were always fair and lovely.

At other times when there was no slaughter on hand they
hunted in their woods, not for subsistence but for the sake
of hunting, for the graces of the sport, on horseback; they
were horse-lovers and trained hounds to set upon the game,
they blew horns and filled the forest with noisy alarms, the
galloping of steeds, the many-voiced baying of the pack,
hallos, with the whacking of trees and shouting of a whole
countryside pressed into the service as beaters.   Their handsome ladies galloped with them, sitting sideways as though
they could not bestride a horse, in flowing robes of silk and
linen, falcon on hand; the whole hunt a proud spectacle
for the eye and a joyous uproar in the woods, but enough
to make an old food-hunter shake his head, one who had
been used to steal about alone with the utmost quietness,
losing himself in the forest stillness, when he wanted to
bring home a head of game.   The stag was there to be
hunted, true enough, but hunting and noise—!   Several
score of people raising a din, and many of them on horseback, all after a single scared beast in the forest—it was
not a thing to say aloud, for the Earl was a mighty lord,
but the old man shook his head that evening over his
supper of dried pork; he could not understand the world
any more.

And amid all this pomp the King's hunt was the most
magnificent.   He had the right of hunting in *every* forest.
At the King's court was assembled the greatest host, the
pick of the freemen's sons from the whole island, and if he

called to arms all the earls had to join him without delay with the host they commanded and with the muster of the freemen whom the King had at his disposal. This was when war was on foot and other lands with other franklins were to be brought under the King's tribute. All the waters of the realm, the channels between the islands, were in the power of the King; here he passed with his fleet, holding his lands together or making raids on foreign shores, when raids on his own were to be avenged.

Even the connection formerly existing between the individual and the Powers had been taken over by the mighty lords. The sanctuary stood in the Earl's burgh, he was the priest and received offerings to the gods on behalf of all. But the King again was supreme among the priests; in the eyes of the vulgar it would almost seem that he was the god and the gods in his own almighty person.

Thus then the population had increased and spontaneously arranged itself in layers, one above the other. In the middle were still the free tillers of the soil, but they were not what they had been; they ruled with an unrestricted hand over their thralls, who in their turn visited the cattle with human oppression or mercy according to their humour. Above the franklins stood the Earl, and his tolls were willingly paid for the sake of keeping his friendship. But if you saw the Earl and the King together— they were indeed two peers, but one of the peers was nevertheless so much the greater. The Earl's eyes were raised high, but never higher than the King's chin; over his head the King looked out upon the whole realm. That is how things were.

But among them all moved Gest the Old, equally welcome everywhere, and felt as much at home with one as with the other. He arrived on his wanderings at the town on the fjord and was greeted with joyful recognition, like the stork in springtime, by the humble folk there; and Gest poured of his music and of his visions into their souls

in return for his good reception, slept in their houses and
found honesty, the treasure of life, in their inquisitive children. He went about with them in their workshops and
lent an observant eye to their trade, the work of ship-
builders, which had absorbed the cunning of so many generations, a craft he could never tire of keeping pace with;
he blew the smith's bellows for him and kept it going with
its puff and sigh, heard the fire roar with its blue abysses
and watched the smith toss the slag from the iron before
he began to shape it on the anvil. The cooper's work fascinated him, and hard it was to leave the joiner and the
refreshing smell of wood in his workshop. The wares of
the small tradesmen had many things to say to him.

Gest would stray in the thralls' mud huts behind the
homesteads and stay there the whole day, to the astonishment of the people of the house. They discovered that he
stood and watched the girls at the quern and sometimes
helped them, adding the power of his stiff arms to the
supple turn of their young heifers' strength on the same
handle; he saw the malt run into the quern and fly from
the stones as flour; he traced the sunny fragrance of the
corn which yields its summer as it is crushed, a sweet,
bewildering odour of sunshine; and then maybe the old
man would sing over the quern, a song of malt and sunshine which was afterwards handed down and preserved
the thoughts that had moved his heart.

He was seen in the byre with the milkmaids, where he
listened to the splash in the pail and might be offered a
drink straight from the cow; there were some comments on
the old man hiding in the dusk of the quern-house with
the maids or among the cows, but Gest took the joke in
good part, he knew what men and women were but he knew
too what he was. Ah, the kindly striding fairies of the
outhouses might every one of them be his daughters!

From the despised dwellings of the thralls Gest betook
himself to the hall and was a freeman among freemen,

talked farming and helped himself from the porridge bowl
with the sons of the house; at the Earl's he held himself
erect and looked the Earl in the face, fell to with his children and held the hand of the smallest in his own, feeling
the warmth of the young blood communicating itself to
his veins and there too meeting life; to the King's hall he
came as a kinsman, increased his stature as a scald, a
natural thing where all was great; much honour had he
from the King, and weightier than gold were the strophes
Gest laid in the scales of time to the King's honour. Where
would Rolf Krake's fame have been without his scalds?
Gest had been with him and with all the kings of story,
with Charlemagne and with the Varangians in Russia, with
the sons of Gunhild too, he was at all the courts of Europe
with his story-telling and his harp.

None saw him grow old or remarked his age, for he
lived longer than memory lasted from one generation to
another. So long as the North was Northern he was there.

Of course every one could see that the old man was very
old. He had habits of his own, which no one within
remembered time could have taught him. The old vagabond did not care to be indoors, even in the most magnificent houses; when there was a chance he preferred to go
outside, even on cold days, and there was the curious thing
about him that instead of staying by the great hearth the
old man would be seen lighting his own little lonely fire
out in the open, where he sat and warmed his hands over
it. In food he preserved the simple taste of a vanished
age, was well satisfied with a handful of raw grain and a
drink of water; he was clever with his hands but strangely
enough disinclined to use better tools than an old worn
sheath-knife; often he would pick up the first stone that
came and use it when he had anything to scrape or cut.

His harp was of his own making; it was very handsomely
ornamented with carving and was a strong harp, suited for
travelling in every kind of weather. It was made of a

moderately thick block of wood with a branch growing out
of it at right angles; between this and the stem, which was
hollowed out, the strings were stretched, a good number of
them, each with its soul of music, every one a world in
itself. If he did but strike the strings in order, from the
deepest up to the very shortest of all, it was like flying up
the stairs of heaven, the rainbow in music, blissful to listen to; but he had a magical power of playing about among
the strings, up and down, and coaxing all the secret worlds
of the soul out of his hearers thereby; he was practised
in the most fugitive and tangled mysteries of the heart,
which music sets free. Beloved and almost feared was
Gest's harp.

The favourites among his songs were those which treated
of the Volsungs, the wild obscure lays of the Migrations,
which Norna Gest's Saga puts into his mouth; but the
Migrations and Gest's part therein form a story of their
own, which shall here be related.

The first men followed the game as hunters and fishers,
and in that way spread themselves over the earth. Then
as cattle-breeders they were still nomads, moving from one
pasture to another; only when they took to agriculture were
they bound to settle and stay where their corn grew, the
plough and the ox-team, back and forth along the furrow,
became the measure of their life; if the world had a message for them it had to come to them, they were the boors,
the dwellers on the soil; the flower of their life came in
the last part of the Stone Age and the Bronze Age—the
family, the homestead, the rich quiet valleys hidden in the
forests.

But then came Iron, the forest fell before its thin, greedy
axes, and the country was laid open; the fields gave nourishment until the people became so numerous that there
were no longer fields for all; and then the iron turned
not only against the forest but against one's neighbour;

blood was sown and the harvest was war, the sword took
the place of the plough, and faces which before had turned
inland towards the heart of the country were now directed
outward, like a ring of ripples running into a crest in the
centre and then spreading out again in new rings. The
world had come to the husbandman, but the warrior went
out to meet the world. And then the Migration began
again. The viking raids of the Northerners rushed out like
a damned-up wave and made for the South.

In the centuries following the fall of Rome all the Ger-
manic tribes of Europe began to arise from the soil, which
had made them strong, and go adrift, pressing upon one
another and working their way above and below, like the
flow of the ice in spring; this was the great Migration, of
which history has preserved accounts, meagre and half
unreal, and yet nothing was more destructive and real than
it.

We are told that the initiative of the great rising was provided by Attila, king of the Huns, when he broke into
Europe from Asia, and that the thrust communicated itself
from one people to another till none kept its place; the
cause lay deeper and was of older date, but *it* gave Attila
the chance of bringing Asia and Europe together in a
maelstrom, the great wreck of the gods at the opening of
the Middle Ages, the cleavage of races; and of this wild
drama Norna Gest was a witness.

In the midst of the Migrations Gest walked like a man
in a whirlwind, saw forces spend themselves in a storm before his eyes, while he himself stood in a calm; he had
absorbed all wanderings and all movements, the elements,
into his being and there laid them to rest; he was North
and South, East and West, the soul of all change, just as
he was the world of childhood and had penetrated all old
age. Himself no longer in ferment, a force proceeded
from him made up of all the forces he had collected and

balanced in himself; this was his force as a scald. And as
a scald it was that he aroused Attila.

He had come to his court, far away in the uttermost
confines of Asia, and had sung before him, had been made
to tell all he knew of Europe and its princes, and to all this
the Mongol King had listened inquisitively but callously,
unfeelingly. Then Gest had sung to him of the Northern
woman. That brought him in danger of his life. The
more the Asiatic heard of the tall, fair, freeborn women of
Europe the wilder he grew, setting off at a gallop, shouting
to his myrmidons to take off the singer's head; it was in-
tolerable to him to think that any other man should even
have seen and be able to describe what Gest described; but
he took him into favour again and waved off his guards,
for he wanted to hear more; and he heard the rest of the
song, and galloped off, steaming, with flaming eyes like a
stallion, altogether beyond control.

And his gallop infected the hosts, the myriads of Asia,
they poured in from the steppes and overthrew kingdoms
everywhere in Europe; Attila would possess all Northern
women, he had the daughters of freemen brought before
him, hosts of captured women, bright and fair; but their
fairness was not for him. He made them his wives by
force, loaded them with crowns and rings of wrought gold,
as thick and heavy as their rich maiden plaits; he had them
killed when they were cold and would not smile, though
he knew that their soul was all warmth and smiles when
they loved; and at last he saw that they would not love
him. They hardened in adversity, white and dumb, took
their fate with indifference, as they would have borne a
sickness or a hardship, despising life itself but never yield-
ing, just like their tall and hated men who laughed at the
swarthy weakling when he had overpowered them, twenty
to one, and had them flayed alive; he could get the better
of them but never bend them.

And there the despot found his limit. He could take hundreds of Northern women but did not get a single one, for they would not have him. But to be such that a single one would have him, he would have had to be another, and then he would not have been Attila. Therefore he went like an avenging scourge over Europe, burning everything down, since he could not become other than he was. Until a wise and penetrating woman, Ildico the Burgundian daughter, hatched his ruin, pretended she would be his, the first sign of willingness he had found, and strangled the happy bridegroom on the wedding night.

It was long before the ground swell left by the storm of passion the Hun King had raised came to rest. New tragic factors were added, for waves from Asia and Europe had now dashed together and could not quiver down to rest until they had broken and mixed and had become themselves again, though changed in their nature. The great, complete, tragic natures perished. The power of *gold* wore out the ties of friendship and blood, the Nibelungs' *Hoard*; grasping men, and women whose unkindness was a heritage from bloodthirsty fathers, extirpated each other, as the Edda laments:

> Brother bringeth
> brother his bane,
> cousin with cousin
> breaketh kinship.
> Never a man
> spareth another.
> Hard grows the world.
> Whoredom prevaïleth,
> ax-time and sword-time
> —shattering shields—
> wind-time and wolf-time,
> ere the world waneth.

Yes, even in those days they expected the destruction of the world!

Through the bloody storms of the Migrations strode Norna Gest. The memory thereof lived in the Volsung lays, like the night howling in the doorways, when all the living voices of the day are silenced.

Norna Gest's death is recorded here as it is told in his Saga. When Christianity appeared it was time for him to go.

But he dwelt in the memory of man and there continued his long life.

Therefore after his death there is more to be told of him: how he lived among the Cimbrians and followed them on their disastrous raid against Rome.

And still later he appears as Quetzalcoatl.

How?

In this way. Long before *Leif the Lucky* "discovered" America men of Northern origin had been there. Yes, and among them Gest. He sought the Island of the Dead in the West also, on one of his immensely long voyages, and came to a strange people, to whom he appeared no less strange; in the book of "Christopher Columbus" this myth will be told.

The last years of his life Norna Gest spent in Norway. There existence seemed to him younger. The fresh life of young herbs on the ancient black mountains appealed to his soul, it was as though his childhood was brought nearer to him in his extreme age.

He lived in his memories and with them he grew dim, sank into himself and was scarcely more conscious of his being than a tree in winter which bears scars where all its leaves have been. So distant was the summer, so distant the days of his youth.

His most delightful memories, belonging to the morning of his life when he and his companion, the first human couple, had shared a tree with the squirrel, were blended in his mind with the myths of other races, races which had wandered as far from their early home as he and preserved an early memory as clouded as his, the myth of Ygdrasil, the great world-tree, the origin of all life.

For memory is a tree, it grows in time and with time it becomes ever geater and richer. The older we are and the greater the expansion of our souls, the fuller will be the light which is reflected upon our beginning. Therefore our longing ever returns to what we have possessed in life without having soul enough to prize it, when we have grown sufficiently to possess it in the spirit; but then it has passed beyond our power of experience.

We learn from Norna Gest's Saga how he came to Olav Trygvason and was christened in his presence, shortly before his death. It gives one a thrill to see King Olav on this occasion, at a moment when he seems to stand still in his career, viewed from the past and by one who is to die before him; he was still like a glorious sun at noonday, and the Battle of Svolder far off; how far from us are the hero and Svolder now!

Norna Gest received baptism because King Olav counselled him thereto, and because he found that what the clerk who confessed him said about the future life seemed reasonable enough. Gest in the course of his long life had sought it upon earth, but from what he understood it was not to be sought so far away, it was close at hand, just over him, only death separated him from it. And indeed the time was not far off when the Kingdom of God was expected to come on the earth itself, the millennium was near, and then it was believed that the Kingdom would be established. Then all warfare and strife would be at an end, no more manslaughter, no pool of blood beneath the one while the other ran off with his arm-ring, no rapes of women, nor any hate, nor want and affliction for the less well-armed; all would be peace and righteousness.

To all this Gest nodded, nodded with his chin upon his

breast and dim, wise eyes; ay, was it not all he had hoped for? Easy was it to die, with the promise of so good a land, both above and below.

And when he had taken his candle out of the harp, where he kept it, and given it to the King that he might light it, he lay back and clasped his hands, as well as he could manage it according to the clerk's instruction, and prepared to depart.

Only a little stump of the candle was left, and it burned quickly. To those present in the hall it looked like an ordinary candle, nothing but a tiny drop of light in the great room, drowned in the glare of the fire which blazed upon the floor and filled the beams of the roof with shadows and smoke.

But when the wick sank and the candle was on the point of going out it struck them that the hall grew darker and colder, some began to shiver. Then Gest was cold and his hands numb. And when the candle went out he was dead.

They had noticed that the dying man's eyes were widened, as though he saw other worlds, mightier and more dazzling than the sun; the old man smiled, as one who meets his dear ones again. It was as though he was already in eternity, in the brief space his candle was burning out; many would fain have seen what Norna Gest saw.

A shudder fell upon all these sturdy young warriors when death approached Gest, a creeping at the roots of their hair; they were to have the same sensation once again, when they went overboard from the *Long Serpent* and the sea closed over their heads.

The King ordered wood to be thrown upon the fire, he had himself grown cold; the ashes were raked off between the logs, and in the light of clear flames and a shower of sparks the banquet was resumed.

XIII

FROM NORNA GEST'S LAYS

THE QUERN SONG

Maids at the quern
Their young strength straining;
The golden gift of the field
Gushes out glorious.

Sweet smells the malt
Like flowers of the summer,
Milling goes merrily
In a cloud of grain.

So do the sun, moon and stars
Grind out the gloom,
As meal from a rocking quern,
Worked by the warmth of woman.

Tell me not any
Can give nourishment
As the churning woman;
In sun's arts is she skilful.

I sang o'er the quern
To woman's honour
And felt me a captive
For ever of the fair one.

While yet is bread
The food of bairns,
I'll love the humble
Peasant mothers.

THE NORTHERN WOMAN

(*Fragment*)

In the morning of time,
When Man and Maid were born,
The world knew not death.
Then folly begat slaying.

Of wolf Man learned murder,
And a bloody bane had he.
But in her bower sat Maid
Giving bäirns the breast.

Among fragrant cows
Moved franklin's daughters,
Fair and mild were they,
With milky hands.

In rain-cooled forests
She grew erect.
Like rain and the dog-rose
Is the taste of her cheek.

Blue are her eyes
As limpid lakes,
Never found frankness
A fairer speech.

Nay, I swore in my soul,
When she turned them upon me,
Such blue simplicity
Never should suffer.

Rich is her hair
As fountains of light;
I sought to be snared
In thy braided tresses.

The wild foal's whinny
On springtime pastures
Recalls thy laughter;
Never was gladder mouth.

A maidenly joy
Was the Norns' gift to thee;
For this have I found—that beauty
Is ever akin to mirth.

As the growing wort
Discloses a wonder,
So flashes thy wit.
Whence hast thou it, Woman?

An ocean of kindness
Thy heart encloses!
All the world's warmth
Dwells in thee, darling.

Here I confess 'it—
Ne'er saw I a woman
But the hot blood mounted
To my lusting heart.

Yet was life too short,
Even with its nights added,
To learn to the full
The love of one only.

Thy fair arms held me
A prisoner for ever,
So lovely was thy being,
So lasting thy beauty.

In rain-cooled forests
I find thy soul anew;
In the dewy dog-rose,
There art thou, my darling.

Ah, in the hazel thicket
'Twas more than nuts we plucked;
Sweeter than leafy booths
Was the bower I found there.

Let me ever wander
In kindly woods.
Close thine arms about me,
Dewy-cool Denmark!

BOOK TWO
IN JUTLAND

DARKEST JUTLAND

UP through Jutland came a tall old man on foot, with his harp on his back and in long, loosehanging clothes, a staff in his hand as a third leg; he walked with long, slow strides and a great swing, like an elk, covering many miles between morning and evening; this was Norna Gest, the wandering scald, on his way from the South up into the parts of Jutland.

He held a mid-course through the land, following the high ground and the watershed, from an old predilection for a free view on every side; he took the roads when there were any and they suited him, but just as often he left them for paths and tracks he knew of and shared with the retiring creatures that used them, or went straight across country, through tangled forests and over heaths, the way the land pointed, in the northerly direction for which he was bound.

He had his own landmarks, on a great scale, the fjords of Jutland's east coast which cut into the land like so many deep pockets, one to the north of the other, from the foot of the peninsula facing the Baltic, through the Middelfart Sound with the coasts of Fyn opposite, to those which opened out towards the Cattegat, right up to the Limfjord. How many there were he did not count, but he knew them every one, they were like living beings to him, each with its mirror; they turned as he passed them like long gateways to the sea; and between the gaps lay the landscapes of East Jutland, a mighty undulation of hills and woods. Here the population was dense, with many wapentakes; the rich valleys showed at a distance their clearings, green and chequered on the floor of the dale, townlands with open home-fields and pastures running up the slopes and meadows beside the watercourses towards the fjord; all framed and protected by the wild, ancient forests with their hunting grounds, miles of swamps and commons lying outside as belts between the hundreds. Far away above the trees rose smoke from hidden dwellings, and in the fjords were craft among the bays and headlands, great masted vessels; beyond lay the sea-fog, the way out of the country. Here in the fjords and along the coast the population was still thickest, and here it was in communication with the outside world.

Few folk dwelt towards the centre of the country, where Norna Gest walked. Now and then the decorated gable-end of a newly built, freshly tarred house showed up in an opening of the forest, surrounded by newly cleared fields with the tree-stumps still standing and great stones scattered over the ground; the wooden bell of a cow moving about the yard was heard, a whiff of spicy smoke came from the settler's hearth, the bark of a dog, and Norna Gest made a wider circuit, he was not one to encroach upon other people's domains. He kept to the confines dividing inhabited districts and outlying settlers, on free ground and outside the law but with less chance of meeting people; though Norna Gest knew homesteads enough where he would be welcome, he kept to himself, he would not tarry, his way lay farther north this time.

A man could go through forest from one end of Jutland to the other and remain unseen the whole way if he wished, meeting no other creatures than deer or wild swine. Norna Gest had no need to hide but preferred to travel undisturbed; if he wanted to look about him he made for open country, and if now and then he came across herdsmen, hunters or other wayfarers, they usually knew him at once

and did not delay him, unless he chose to stop and talk;
they could see a long way off that it was Norna Gest.

Caution was the habit of wayfarers; if a man on coming
out of the forest became aware of the presence of an unknown in the open, it was entertaining to watch the way
their movements were influenced thereby. In a sidelong,
constrained fashion each held the other fast, as it were,
and tried to get away from him; a longsighted observer
could guess by their motions that the bow was being strung
and the quiver shifted to the front; sometimes they
vanished, crouching on the ground behind the shield, or
else there was nothing to be seen but bushes, until the two
seemed to grow out of the earth again, increasing the distance between them, with their backs to each other but
heads turned, until they were out of sight. For people
from different districts, separated by a fjord, a river or an
impassable swamp, had no business outside their own
territory and if they met on the dividing line it was not
as friends; on the contrary, they warned each other in
time, the border rangers kept an eye on each other, and
if a couple of men rose out of the brushwood on one side
of the river, another couple instantly appeared on the other
side; with drawn bows and brandishing of long spears
both sides struck fear into their neighbours and declared
their intentions—no ambush here, come forward with
bared chest if you have any message!

Jutland had many districts which thus blockaded each
other, as many as the fjords by which the people had
once come into the country, and on which they had grown
into several mutually independent tribes—others again on
the west coast side—with a prescriptive right to their
territory; a whole number of peoples with different names
for themselves and their neighbours, some forgotten later
or changed, others long remembered, not a few nameless
but by no means negligible if their frontiers were invaded.

These tribes were made up of small clans, originally scattered at great distances from each other and on a mutually hostile footing but derived from the same root. Their continually strained relations kept them in arms, they had no more dangerous adversaries than each other; but when circumstances stronger than the perpetual border skirmishes forced them together, they had no difficulty in uniting, and this fusion might lead to the sudden appearance of great hosts, which instead of holding each other in check were set in simultaneous motion beyond their borders against a common enemy, or perhaps clean out of the country to face new destinies, if their star so willed it. Many such composite hordes, unexpectedly appearing elsewhere in the light of a foreign tradition, had Jutland produced in prehistoric times, more than were remembered in Jutland itself, and many more she was yet to produce.

It was in the pause before Nature prepared one of these fusions of forces, while relations between the districts were strained to the utmost and the hundreds, nay, even the individual homesteads, were armed to the teeth in a state of equilibrium, that Norna Gest was on his way through Jutland to visit the Cimbrians, up in the out-of-the-way tracts on the Limfjord.

Everywhere along his track Norna Gest came upon traces of a state of war and picked up news here and there from some herdsmen or outlaw of cattle raids up country by men of the fjords, always a favourite way of rapidly increasing one's stock; of franklins who had burnt other franklins in their houses and had been burnt in their own in return; of levies and set battles with varying fortune; of sacrificial banquets out of the common, single combats much discussed, love affairs, scurrilous lays, everything that a district hums with when you come to close quarters, no matter how far out of the world it may seem. Norna Gest listened and added to his experience.

He liked to come to Jutland; here, the farther north he went, he still met with old times which were declining elsewhere, in the islands that were his home; in certain things he could feel transported right back to the first ages he had passed through with the early immigrants who settled in the country; here they still honoured the same things between heaven and earth that his origin had taught him to respect. Often he saw faces which seemed familiar to him among the hearty folk of the fjords, features that had been handed down from ancestors with whom he had walked upon earth in a morning of the ages of which no one retained the faintest idea.

It was Norna Gest's habit to visit Jutland in springtime, he came from the south where it had already burst out, and followed it, keeping pace with the birds of passage; he wished as it were, to see it arrive time after time, a show of permanence that delighted an aged wanderer. Besides, it was his secret joy to be himself received, through no merit of his own, as integral part of spring wherever he went. In Jutland they used to say that he and the stork came at the same time and were equally welcome; indeed, some were courteous enough to hint that it was through him and his powers spring came at all. In few parts did he meet with such happy faces as among the hard Cimbrians; here they knew how to value spring and held great festivities in honour of its return, the ancient grateful customs which Norna Gest loved; when he had long been dwelling with folk who waited on him with dressed food and closed beds he yearned for simple, coarse fare and nights under the open sky; thus it was that he chose to visit the Cimbrians in springtime.

Up in Mid-Jutland Norna Gest lost sight of the coasts and went over the broad inland hills which close in here, with the biggest timber of the peninsula, the great ridges clad in woods and heather with a ring of lakes at their feet. Here the land rides highest, and in the spaciousness

on every side one seems to feel the whole extent of Jutland, the foot of the peninsula on the south and the ragged
east coast, far away the backbone of the country towards
the North Sea, and behind receding horizons, like one ring
within another, North Jutland with a distant glimpse of an
arm of the Limfjord, and the country beyond that again,
with the neck of the peninsula, and farthest up the two seas
that break against The Skaw as against the spike of a
helmet.

Here the country already had a wilder look, with great
lonely, far-stretching woods in the hollows between the
heights, which gathered as though about a centre of gravity
that the whole country rested upon. From here the
lines ran out on every side; from sources rising in these
furrowed hills the brooks parted to form the great streams
of Mid-Jutland, some westward on their long winding way
to the North Sea, others through tortuous valleys, spreading
out league after league, to the broad east country and
out into the Cattegat; waste land much of it here, with the
population still collected down in the warmer valleys, and
the forest was tangled and wild; the deer were bigger here
than elsewhere and stood quiet when a wayfarer passed by,
many of the beasts had never seen a man before. The stag
showed his head with furry swelling burrs, the new growth
of antler which was coming on.

Signs of spring on every hand; the trees, dripping wet,
were swelling in the bark and stretched twigs and buds up
into the clean-washed air; there was a sparkling high and
low, the sun clear but not yet hot, like a sisterly light in
the sky, the daylight penetrating to the bottom of the
shadowless woods, the stems a gem-like green, a twittering
and calling of birds as in great empty chambers where they
were to move in, but soon there would be settling and
building. Away over the open plains hung the lark in a
dazzling noonday glory of sunlight.

And Norna Gest followed the lark into the open country,

continued northward over the heights, with broad horizons
lying beneath him, a sheet of water far away, fjord or lake,
clouds and sky in a mighty expanse above his head.

On the highest points of the long naked heather-clad
ridges he found the charred remains of bonfires, local
sanctuaries where the people of neighbouring hundreds
assembled on the high days of the year to kindle their fires
and perform their worship of the sun. The loneliness and
might of the high places appealed to a heritage in their
minds, the view threw open the traditions of the race, obscure to most of them, but Norna Gest, who acted as their
memory, knew what it meant: from here they saw the
way they had come into the country, which had been forgotten, it was a look into the past—the old tracks, the
rivers, the fjords, farthest out the sea, which perhaps the
inland dweller had never seen, but from which he had
come; what was swallowed up in the everyday life of the
valley became revealed as a great memorial up here in the
face of heaven. With this feeling they sacrificed to the sun,
made fire in its likeness and symbolically bound it to its
course. This was to be done on high places, for fire had
come from the mountain; even those who had never seen
a mountain and knew nothing of it performed the rite from
ancient and obscure but hallowed custom, a root in their
origin as men which was not to be pulled up. For the
solstices there were sacrifices, summer and winter; but
thanksgiving festivals were also held for the spring, the
reawakening of Nature, the bursting of the leaves and the
warm days; this was the gift of the sun, and as the sun
was beyond their reach they betook themselves to his kinsman, fire, with gifts and honours according to their means.
Soon the spring bonfires would blaze on the heights
throughout Jutland; this was what Norna Gest wanted to
witness, and this time among the Cimbrians, who laid
special stress on the spring festivals, perhaps because they
lived farther north and were poorer than the rest.

He took his time on the way up, paused when the spring paused, and started on again when it made a step forward; stayed for weeks in this place or that, in quiet corners of the forest or by a watercourse that tempted him to tarry.

At night he slept out. The air, so early in the year, was still wintry when the sun had gone down, and he sought shelter among rocks or in a thicket, with a big tree at his back and a fire burning in front of him; here he nodded the whole night long and passed from one doze into another, but heard every movement of bird or of footstep, far or near. The night was long.

But towards its end, in the hour before dawn when all living things fall into a trance, Nature's death-like truce, then Norna Gest too fell into a deep, heavy sleep, wrapt in skins to the chin and with his head bent low, like a sack beside the fire; and the flames died down, while rime covered the grass in the cold still dawn.

When he awoke he did not know at first where he was; he was stiff in the face with cold, chilled to his soul; only with difficulty, as though after a swoon, could he crawl out of his skins and stretch his limbs. It was like a dead man coming to life, a man without a face, inconceivably old; feebly the arms straightened themselves as though the joints belonged to a shadowy creature; he stirred up the ashes, plunged his lifeless hands into them and found warmth, an ember that was still alive, and he burned himself on it, gleefully, it went right into his veins; he laid on sticks, the smallest and thinnest he could find, as though he could lift no more, lay down and blew the fire with weak puffs that might have been his last, but the fire blazed up and soon he had high, clear flames. He rose, staggering, but recovered his strength, grew as the fire grew and got back his vital warmth.

Then he turned to the day and his vision came back: the dawn beleaguered all the sky, the sun was still below ground, but its outposts were advancing, crimson spears in the east. And lo! the forest came to life, the ancient oaks stepped forth from the dawning, created perfect from root to twig, marvellously full of being, the frosted slopes bent and received the light, the land threw open wide its gates, in a hushed and holy pause of frost the earth was reborn, while the horned moon sailed high and paled into the sky above the tree-tops.

A faint twittering of birds was heard, like a creaking in the trees, nothing more, and the sun rose, red and all-powerful. Norna Gest drew himself up before it, and his features became so clear and still; with a shake of the head he received the marvel, the old revelation.

In the morning hour the forest steamed as the rime passed from it, and Norna Gest saw how big, wet and tense the buds were; he recognized the spring in the volume of light, flocks of birds passed airily above his head, a distant, shivering music came as though from the clouds, the wild geese on their way north, and an irresistible impulse seized him to resume his wandering.

But first he went to the nearest water and uncoiled his fishing-line; turned over a stone, the roof of the worm's house, and found it there, just ready to be taken. He caught a meal of fish, with life must life be supported, and broke fast by the fire, chewing and looking before him with absent eyes, and many calm thoughts were his companions while he ate. Then he followed the sound of a spring and drank: strong springs here, they forced their way up from the greensward under the slopes in cold, clear, domed fountains, as though striving to reach a mouth; they tasted fresh of the earth's sweetness and quenched him to the very marrow. In drinking them he gained the freedom of the land, and they mirrored the sun; he drank in them the morning hour, the thaw and the air of spring, and in return he knelt and kissed them.

Then Norna Gest made ready to leave, shouldered his burdens and plucked up his staff, which he had planted by his resting-place; it had not taken root.

The beasts, who had risen in the valleys, heard some one clear his throat, a man, a strong hollow cough among the woods; an old solitary male striding along by himself; the echo resounded answering among the slopes, and the deer twitched their ears forward and twitched them back, and made off without more noise; no one could know what a man meant by clearing his throat so loudly. They went their way and Norna Gest his; rested and rejuvenated by the morning he strode northward with another day's travel before him. A lay of thankfulness took shape in his mind, after he had gone a little way and turned his back as though on a cast slough:

> Praised in my heart
> be the light of the world,
> the risen sun
> and the gift of sight!
> From sparks in the ashes
> the fire is rekindled.
> Ever o'erwhelms me
> the daily marvel.
>
> Where is refreshment
> like springs in the wild?
> Happy who laps from
> the veins of the land.
> Open heaven
> is hope's sure anchor.
> Homeless wanderer,
> worship the dust!

Now the country changed, becoming lower and spreading into wide expanses, plains and wastes with sparse vegetation, heaths so extensive that one forgot every other kind of country while crossing them, which took days; and then one was a lonely man, poor as the heather, closed in by

drear horizons, with no other company than the birds of
the heath, which ran in front and chirped in a queer distress, as though they did not know who they were and
were asking the stranger about it. One feared the face of
the sky and heard the throbbing of one's own blood in the
stillness; a chastening of the soul it was to cross the heath.

But even endlessness has an end, transient it is in reality;
though he had lost his way Norna Gest made for the north
in good heart; he had his landmarks on the left hand to
guide him in the direction he knew Vebjerg [1] to lie, and
the black horizons in front told him that now he was beginning to approach the Cimbrians' land.

All thoughts of the seas on both sides, the free coasts
of the peninsula, had now receded; this was an island tract,
as though no coasts existed, not even the Limfjord was yet
in sight. Otherwise the country was well enough watered
in itself, difficult of approach from the south when one was
on foot; the track led over swamps and streams running
from east to west; a long-legged man had trouble to ford
them even in the shallowest places, in their swollen springtime condition, and when across them he did not reach
dry ground, for floods and bogs barred the way for miles,
his feet sank in and he had to make long circuits.

Here was a great assemblage of birds, waders that had
just arrived, ducks in swift flocks, which filled the air,
alighted everywhere and tried the water, taking headers,
glad to find it open again after the winter ice. They gambolled on the surface as though caressing it, flung up the
precious element with snake-like neck and got drops on
their feathers; twisted round and wriggled their tails so
that the water powdered them with a fine rain and flashed
a rainbow over the spots on their wings, quacking loudly
all the while, and by the tone it could be heard that the

[1] Vebjerg—the Mount of Sacrifice. Now Viborg, where a Chris-
tian cathedral has taken the place of a sanctuary of the old religion.
—Tr.

drake was amorous, breeding-time was in the air. Away on lakes made unapproachable by banks of mud and quaking swamps white flocks of swans merged in the fiery reflection of the sunlight; the wind brought music from them, tones and light and distance blended together. Everywhere water, and the water was blue, the sky was blue, the air cold and clear, the meadows still bare, but catkins and shining white osier buds were on the bushes. The wanderer found the earliest birds' eggs lying before his foot in the marsh, the lapwing's exposed nest, and slipped a couple into his mouth, whole and with the shells on, full of their brooding warmth; thus he tasted the country's welcome.

The slightly higher land between the marshes was covered for miles with scrub and brushwood, osier bushes, tufts of grass and great stones, furrowed by sluggish watercourses and stagnant pools; it was a wild tract, a home for the wolf. That the country lay off the beaten track could be guessed by his showing himself in broad daylight, slinking from one thicket into another; a man might come face to face with him, but only for a moment; he dropped his eyes at once, shook his long jaws and sneezed when he had gone by—an unpleasant thing to exchange glances with a man, ugh, who wore a tanned wolfskin coat on his back! The thought of an old account crossed his mind, but he did not follow it up. The eagle was slow in leaving his tree, long after one had come within range: an innocent, undisturbed region, where the beasts kept their old habits, and Norna Gest did not hurry here, meeting many a creature that he seldom had the luck to see; it was clear that men did not often visit these wide border lands.

Spring tarried long in these parts, as though it could not get across. In the morning the bogs were frozen, the floods covered with thin ice, and the ducks sat on top of their element with their webbed feet on the cold floor. As the day went on the ice cracked under the sun and was slobbered up by blue waves in the fresh breeze; then it snowed, and the whole land lay as though smitten with snow for miles, when the shower had passed and the view cleared again, a relapse into winter. The noonday sun took away the snow, and once more the earth was black and new-born as far as the eye could reach; the withered grass was steaming, and the sky was like a bowl with immense abysses of cloud and shining peaks rising to the topmost roof of blue.

But by degrees the nights grew milder, the ditches brought forth toads that wallowed in water and sunshine, yellow flowers burst out, with their roots in the mud and their faces turned to the sun, all gold and growth.

And at last one day came the first pair of storks, gliding around each other up under the clouds, in great circles, like a solemn symbol of dedication over the land. Then Norna Gest travelled on.

The country now became more hilly again, with long, broad heights between the marshes, and traces of habitation began, pillars of smoke from clearings in the forest, and he prepared to meet the natives.

The heart of the Cimbrians' land was a highland, wide plains exposed to the wind, broken up on west and north, between the centre and the Limfjord, by many clefts and hollows, the beds of ancient fjords, now watercourses and marshes. Everywhere woods, but scattered and checked in their growth by the weather; bushy and impenetrable in the valleys, crouching and, as it were, thatched by the wind on the level ground. But in its highest parts the country was open, with a series of long, bare ridges running across the land from east to west which showed black outlines at a distance; covered with high-lying heaths; they stood out from the bushy country like bald pates, and along their crests long rows of burial mounds stood sharply against the sky, built in a yet older age by the forefathers of the Cimbrians, who had taken land here and bequeathed their taste for it, incomprehensible to others who had had the good fortune to occupy better regions, as a heritage to their descendants.

At a distance the first impression of life was the graves of the ancients. *Their* eyes had seen the long, strict lines in which the land was laid out, like a vast, black, storm-swept roof, these had been the frame of their existence, and the tearing winds that passed over the country were soul of their soul.

But if the heights and horizons were given over to de-parted generations, the living dwelt down in the valleys, in hereditary homesteads lying far apart, with extensive sur-roundings of wood and pasture; the wilds in the interior were for common use and were divided among the clans. The Cimbrians were great cattle-breeders, for half the year they moved about with their herds, and in winter they stayed at home on their farms, where they carried on agri-culture.

The first people Norna Gest met were two young men, whom he surprised by a beck where they were setting snares; one of them snatched up a spear to fling at the stranger, but dropped it in time when he saw it was Norna Gest.

They were a pair of very big fellows, immensely strong and active, free in their movements, showing that they had spent their whole lives out of doors in hunting and on horseback; they were weatherbeaten and perfectly blue, bilberry-blue, in the face, even their lips were blistered by wind and weather, their ears black and notched at the edge from old frostbites, with little eyes almost closed under a heavy growth of lashes, shunning the light behind their keen brows; their hair grew far down over the forehead and was tied together at the top, forming a long tail. They were lightly clad for hunting in leather breeches and jerkins; one of them had a freshly killed otter hanging at his belt.

Norna Gest's appearance seemed to cause them a certain excitement, which however did not find vent in words or work itself up into any play of the features; their thick lips were expressionless as before and their foreheads, puckered by nature, showed no fresh puckers; but they slung their shields on their backs again in silence, the defensive attitude was of course superfluous, and they looked at the scald and at his harp, exchanging a mutual glance, unnoticeable, but signifying fairly strong emotion: music and marvels came with Norna Gest, that was evident; for they had known him from their childhood, as far back as they could remember.

But then it turned out, by a wonderful piece of luck, that the scald was on his way to visit the man Tole, chief franklin in these parts. Did they know him? Both nodded at once, decidedly, and saw the whole thing, privately winking to each other. Then the elder went off and returned with a pair of shaggy horses that had been standing among the reeds; he looked at Norna Gest and at the horses, looked in the direction of Tole's homestead and wet his lips, but did not commit himself to words; though the offer was plain enough, it was the stranger's part and not his to make known his intentions. Norna Gest understood very well what was proposed: that he should mount and have company the rest of the way; and he gladly accepted. Without their having said so he concluded from the look of things that the two young hunters, obviously brothers, belonged to the very homestead he had enquired for; they might even be sons of Tole, though they were too polite to call any attention to themselves.

Before starting the elder of the brothers took his scrip from his horse, opened it and spread it out on the ground. It was a skin with holes round the edge through which ran a thong; the skin could be gathered up into a bag or laid completely open; it proved to contain curdled milk in clotted lumps; the man offered it with the idea that a traveller who perhaps came from afar might be hungry and in need of a bite before they reached home—all in a casual way and as a matter of course, one didn't want to lay any stress on one's power of doing a man a trifling service; anyhow, there was food. And Norna Gest, who understood the language of the country, took a handful of the curds. It tasted of smoke, from smoky houses, and like sweat, of cows, of women, of children, all creatures with a healthy skin; and an old man, who had walked alone for weeks, felt that now he was approaching human haunts again. The two men also helped themselves, after the old man had had what he wanted, but tried to conceal the movements of their lips, for their guest was so much their senior.

They washed it down with a draught of water from the beck. Norna Gest produced a big shell he used to drink out of, a coloured foreign conch, sky-blue with a rainbow sheen, flesh-coloured inside, which he had picked up once in the South; and the two young men were fascinated when they saw it, their eyes clung to the irresistible thing, without of course their showing the slightest curiosity; on the contrary, they screwed up their eyes and put on a hard look so as not to fall into temptation. Norna Gest did what he always did when any one marvelled at his shell, held it to his ear; and then he seemed to hear the beating of the waves on the far, far distant crater island in the Mediterranean, on whose shore he had found it; then he handed it to the men, and they put it to their ears in turn and listened; sat with frowning looks and absent eyes, shaking their heads; and they laughed inwardly, their gaze expanded, never had they heard anything so mysterious. Without their knowing it they sighed and their faces fell as though a sun had set, when Norna Gest took back the marvellous thing.

When Norna Gest was mounted the men joined him, one on each side, obviously regarding themselves as his escort; the little meal they had partaken of meant more than refreshment, it admitted the stranger to the country's protection.

The road to the homestead, a league or so, was covered in silence. The brothers took it in turn to ride, one running while the other had the horse. Uphill, when the strain on the horse's shoulders became too great, the rider would swing a leg over the neck of his mount, slip to the ground without halting and run by its side, with a hand in its mane.

And thus Norna Gest came riding in.

IN TOLE'S HOME

A T the top of one of the valleys which led into the country, towards the high land and the watershed, —a natural centre with streams communicating both northward and westward with the Limfjord—dwelt Tole. He was Thing-leader for the common people, and priest at the same time; a much venerated sanctuary stood on his land.

The homestead was more like a little town, consisting of many scattered dwelling-houses and outhouses along the foot of the slope and bordering on the marsh, most of them of earth. hollowed in the ground, others of wattle and daub, and a few more substantial buildings of timber. Round about were paddocks and cornfields, framed by the woods which filled the rest of the valley. Above were heaths and wastes.

Other homesteads of the same kind lay farther down the valley, hereditary properties whose occupants were more or less nearly related to one another and to Tole. Besides the master the whole family lived on the homestead, the sons and their offspring, the daughters and theirs, three generations at the same time; besides many other people who belonged to the place, the bondservants too, the thralls, if you counted them; altogether, with the domestic animals, an extensive settlement, to which were added outlying huts among the pastures, chiefly for use in summer, when the herds were not driven home.

To a man coming from uninhabited tracts the place was positively bustling; at any moment he saw people by the score and a busy traffic, deeply worn paths in the green-sward between the houses and countless tracks of men and beasts; a profusion of women and children, the houses were full of them and the wailing of infants came as though from the earth itself; the houses smoked, not only from the smoke-hole but through the roof of heather and from every pore, as though warmth and well-being were oozing out of them; often the house-door stood open with the smoke pouring up over the eaves; the season and the long days were beginning to make themselves felt, children sunned themselves outside the doors, shielding their eyes from the strong light. On the stones in front of the storehouses lay bonds-women bruising corn, on all fours with a promontory in the air, the attitude of grinding, and with their hair down over their eyes, blinded with toil; but a memory in their souls made even them seek the light and take their work out into the open air.

Sheep were shorn by a pool, a thing as regular and familiar at the season as the peculiar refraction of the light in the cold, clear ponds or as the appearance of the first short-stalked daisies in the meadow; it could be seen by the women shearers that spring had come, they sat with their kerchief pulled down as far as possible to screen their eyes from the sun. Cold for the sheep, which were first ducked in the pool with their feet tied together and afterwards released despoiled of their wool, disfigured and skinny, in the still biting air. Some of them already had lambs, which were staggering about on four unpractised pins, clumsy as footstools, and bleating with thin voices; ah, the young, tender year had come too early, but it had come.

From the smithy came the clang of the anvil, there too was strength and industry; a bellowing of cattle outdoors and in, the noise of dogs that seemed possessed, the tramping in and out of horsemen at a sharp trot on their fresh little horses, for which the riders were all too big; else-

where archery practice with a shield for target, the whirr
of the bowstring and the smack of the arrow when it hit;
a couple of lads wrestling in a field, with long, slow grips,
gasping, well-matched in strength, first one on top, then
the other; pig-killing, with the carcase hung up on a tree
and a woman on a ladder with her bare arms in the pig's
inside; everywhere life and activity, a whole little community, restless and agitated, but dependent, on old, fixed
custom, influenced and made yet more restless by the
season.

Out in the yard stood Tole, with both hands resting on
the handle of his ax, clad in furs down to his feet, view-
ing his cattle.

They had not yet been driven into the pastures, as there
was not enough for them to live on, but were allowed to
stretch their legs and get some fresh air outside their narrow stalls for a while every day. The cows, many of
them in calf, moved about licking the short grass; horsemen
and dogs kept together the herd, which took up some space,
a whole field of cattle to look at, brindled, black and white,
and dun, a mass of horns and blazed foreheads, a splendid
sight in the sunshine and a joy to listen to: cracking of
whips and shouting of men driving back stragglers, for
the sun had put heart into the cows and they wanted to go
their own way, attempting a gallop; the heifers were quite
out of control, feeling the call of the wild pastures; but
their hour of freedom had not yet struck. Tole had his
sun-marks; the shadows were still too long, and the woods
too backward. When everything tallied, when omens and
spring sacrifices had opened the year in regular fashion,
they would get out. It was high time, for this year there
was only just enough hay and fodder left to last out.

In a place by himself stood the bull, with a special
guard of honour of two men, who watched his movements at
a distance. But he was quite quiet; he stood in the sun-

shine, which made him sleepy, and enjoyed its far-away warmth, in noble animal calm, planted on all fours and dozing lightly.

He was a mighty beast, shaggy, with something in his build both of the aurochs and of the bison from which he was descended, with deep forequarters and enormous horns, doubly strengthened at the root like stakes going right through the head, only slightly bent upward and blunt at the ends; his way was not to pierce, he attacked as though with a pair of battering rams; no rapier play when *he* gored, everything was pulverized before there was time to make a hole!

Now, and as a general rule, he was docility itself, with slumbering forces; slowly he turned his huge angular head and made the sign of calm above it with his horns; he was heavy and drowsy about the eyes, all swollen and stupefied with latent vigour, curly-haired on the forehead with the whirling *star* in the middle, the mark of the bull with which he confronted his cows and which he turned towards his enemy. Hair and brows veiled the dark misty eyeballs, which gave no sign of intelligence but showed a white bloodshot ring when he turned them: power and rage ready to break out on occasion.

Ah, when he is wild! A terrible gallop dwells in his hindquarters and massive high shoulders, his forehead is bent forward from the thick, deep, fleshy neck and projects with its mass of bone and the roots of the horns, with these he charges, flying through the air with all his immense weight and impetus put into the blow; then a sweep of the horns, and what they have not destroyed he lays under him, with all his weight in the hoofs, each leg a battering-ram, and tramples it out of recognition; that is his way when he is mad.

But now the bull stands quietly reposing in his power, so still that the steam and vapour of his vital warmth, billowing from his shaggy flanks, rises straight up above him

like a column in the cold air.   Only now and then does he
make his voice heard as in a half-awakening, some foggy
bull's idea arising in his forehead; from deep down in the
belly of him comes a muffled bellowing, gloomy and subterranean, with a strange intensity; it sounds like a light
touch of a drum and vibrates in the air long after—what
then is he like when he rages and all his vital spirits roar
through his nostrils!

From time to time it is as though a dream of another
kind arises in his angular consciousness, buried beneath
horn and hair and bony structure; then he stretches his
neck and sniffs the breeze with wet and beady muzzle and
the white ring shows in his eyes; this is when a breath of
air from the cows reaches him.   But here again the year is
still asleep, the time has not yet come; the veil falls again
and he sinks back into himself, under the distant power
of the sunbeams.

As he stands thus he is the root symbol of the state of
nature from which he and those who have tamed him have
proceeded.   A long way they had travelled together, man
and the ox, and they were to be companions longer yet.
But the primitive state which the bull had inherited from
vanished ancestors who once inhabited these forests, was
not so very far away, and the savagery of the ancients, who
had seen the aurochs in these same valleys, might turn to
savagery again among their descendants, to whom they had
bequeathed the tame ox.

When the cattle had been driven back into the byres
Tole had all the horses collected; the men too, all his troop
of horsemen, could come and be reviewed at the same time.

And they came, sons and sons-in-laws, all the dreaded
clan of Tollings, tall upright fellows, and many of them;
how many sons Tole had nobody knew exactly, such things
were not counted or gone into very deeply, for decency's
sake, but there was a host of them and they struck awe

when assembled together in one spot, with almost the same
look, every one, like the formidable appearance of one and
the same man repeated again and again; all aggressive in
their bearing with their hair in a horsetail carried high
above the head, and all with Tole's features, Tole's red
face which reappeared in all his progeny, the daughters
too; but they were a pale pink, for they were less in the
open air; the sons were bright red, shading into blue, from
the wind of Jutland. Such were Tole's sons.

The sons-in-law showed more variety, from different
families in other valleys, but they were no starvelings
either; to be accepted as a son-in-law of Tole's meant fighting one's way through the sons first; it was only stout
adventurous gallants that won through to the girls, and
then came the question of pleasing *them*. So it was something of a sight and it made the earth shake when all the
Tollings trooped past at once.

If Tole gloated over his cattle with a broad, religious
joy of possession, which he concealed—since it is not wise
to boast of one's strength before the Powers to whom one
owes it all; they might change their minds, such things
have happened—it was impossible for him to restrain his
pride when the horses and the lads rode into the yard and
paraded before him. The horses were the apple of his eye,
he had bred them through many generations, from excellent mares and the choicest stallions; there was not a single
animal of his that he could not remember, all through his
long life; now they were as he wanted them, all pretty
much the same like his sons, derived from the stock which
was common to all the breeders in Jutland but yet with an
imperceptible strain which a judge's eye could detect: that's
one of Tole's, you might hear far and wide, when one of
the stud was seen.

They were small, short in the legs but with a big head
and fairly long in the back, shaggy, with a reddish hue, and
could easily stand being kept out in the winter; they had

big, spreading hoofs, so that they could carry a man on boggy ground without sinking in, were frugal and could be fed on straw alone with their big jaws, and were equally good for heavy draught work, for riding or driving. Tole himself had given up riding and always drove, but it was his delight to see the youngsters on horseback.

Every man was the friend of his charger and had trained it to tricks which they kept to themselves, only they two fully understood one another. The weight of the riders and the whole aptitude of the horses had resulted in their developing into trotters, and in this they were quick, sure and untiring; they broke into a gallop when the rider eased them of his weight and ran by their side with a hand in the horse's mane; by aiding each other in this way they got over any kind of ground and more quickly in the long run than much bigger coursers would have done it. Now off and now on the horse, that was the man's training, shooting in full career with arrow or lance; their stratagem was to hang on to the horse's side at a gallop so as to be covered by it, but with the shield protecting the horse's exposed flank; or to lie dead, both invisible on the ground, or again they stood upright on the horse's back at full gallop, stood on their heads even; all these tricks they were masters of, more or less, and Tole was full of glee while horses and riders disported themselves on the sward, and laughed his great laugh, ho, ho, ho, which told people at a distance that the master was enjoying himself, whenever one of the boys took the grass.

This was only a foretaste of what they were looking forward to before long, horse-races and stallion fights which would take place at the spring festival, with the horsemen in all their finery and fully armed; besides all the other attractions, the great bull chase, which was the men's keenest sport, for it meant risking life and limb; and then there would be the lur-blowers to put fire into horse and man; all this was in prospect and was drawing near.

The din and galloping in the yard brought the women out of their houses; they stood at a distance with pink faces, dazzled by sunshine and wonder: marvellous what daring fellows they were! They too promised themselves golden days to come; more than one girlish heart swelled at the thought of what *her* share would be when suns and Powers and swains and sorcery all joined forces and fell upon the female sex with a terrific rush. Oh, they felt so defenceless in their clothes and began to shiver; yes, it was really cold, they ought to go in, but all the same they stood there and could not take their girls' eyes off the men, who whirled about on their horses in perfect mastery, belonging more to the air than to the earth.

But far in the background dark heads appeared, half concealed by the outhouses, in the holes leading to the earth cellars they lived in—the thralls, who had nothing to look forward to, nothing to expect of the spring but the work it brought. The doings they witnessed in the yard did not belong to their world at all, it was the world of the free, a glorious world that seemed bound up with the sun and the air, they were the air and the daytime, the freemen, while the thralls crept upon the earth, with stooping back and bent knee, in a gait like a perpetual fall; and they were the night, it smouldered in their tarry eyes, they carried it with them in their black bushy hair. The newborn sun came on them like an itch and they wriggled in their coats of skin, without any thought of the great glow in the sky; their twilight souls gave birth to ideas only as worms are bred in muddy depths. The horsemen's performance set them staring. From the turbary in the bog black figures rose like turf of the turf and turned a listless gaze towards the homestead, where the young men were at play, their long hair like a halo of sunlight round their heads. Even the horses seemed ablaze with manes and tails; Tole's horses were all chestnuts, with a pink, human colour about the muzzle; one would think they were brothers to the men.   The whole place was like a wheel of light.

Up on the slopes was a man ploughing, with great trough-like wooden shoes on his feet and his head on his chest; he stopped his wooden plough for a moment and let the bullocks get their breath, while he looked through filmy eyes at what was going on in the yard without being able to make it out, for he was dull of apprehension, slobbered on his beard and stared: at their riding tricks again, were they? well, they'd break their necks at it one day or the other!   But *he* was going to get their fields ploughed. And he started his bullocks again and crawled along his clayey furrow.   A couple of short, broad creatures in skirts, girls from the byre, were spreading dung; they stood still betweenwhiles, steaming and looking towards the homestead through the trellis of their ragged hair.   They squinted up at the sun: would it be long to dinner-time?

The centre of observation, the one who attracted every eye was of course Tole, standing in a raised place, leaning on the handle of his ax and with his long thin white hair flowing out from his marten-skin cap.

He was an old man, thick-necked and stout, big-boned and heavy-limbed, with a slight tremble; the rims of his eyes turned out, red and watery, but there was power in his glance and it rested steadily on the person he was addressing.   A peculiar intensified power came into Tole's eyes when it was a woman they fixed upon, as though they exerted an influence from a distance, and the women became uneasy under the master's glance, friendly though it was.

Another reason for staring at the yard was the tall stranger who stood by Tole's side, in whose honour the feats of horsemanship had been performed, Norna Gest, who had arrived and was staying at the homestead.   Expectation was focussed upon him, it always meant something above the ordinary when he came.

Tole and the scald had much to talk about, they could be seen turning to each other and growing animated; Tole started back as though he would fall at something he heard, it must be great news; but not a soul could hear what they were talking about, the distance was too great for any one to catch a word of it. It was known from former years that the two were on very intimate terms, and things that had influenced the fate of many could be pointed out as the result of Norna Gest's visits to Tole. The very thralls looked at him, knowing that when it suited him he would visit them in their caves; things which even their owners did not know about them were known to him, he could share their world too. Those who had begun as captives and who had memories of another home found a release from their heaviness when they could confide in Norna Gest, it would be strange indeed if he had not been where they came from.

When the riding was over the two mighty ones were seen to make their way from the yard up the slope behind the homestead—hush! now they were going into the grove, the holy place, hu! to look at the stone of sacrifice, and conjure, and perhaps make magic broth, and meddle with the heavenly bodies!

It was broad daylight, one *dared* approach the grove, and a few daredevil boys followed in the wake of the two elders, the inquisitive train that is never noticed but sees everything.

And they saw them go through the fences into the little wood, which lay by itself like an island outside the forest, thick and closed round the edge by small trees and bushes, higher with big trees in the middle, where there was a source and a pond, the whole place unapproachably holy, to say nothing of the consecrated houses which stood on the open space and scattered among the trees; grim houses, the abode of the weird, and uncanniest of all the temple, the great timber house where was the holy of holies and the banquetting hall in which the men ate the offerings on the great high days of sacrifice. The trees, which were also uncanny, old, gnarled and with dead branches, were full of hanging skeletons, carcases of beasts, frontal bones and horns of slaughtered cattle, not a few men either, old stiff black corpses dried on to the bones; others had fallen and lay under the trees, there was a whole bone-yard in there. The ravens took wing as men entered the enclosure, big, lazy, bloated birds, almost tame; they settled on the trees again at once, with a knowing croak, obviously of recognition, when they saw who was coming.

The corpses and the smell were nothing to the boys, they were pretty well used to the sight of dead bodies and to all kinds of smells; it was the terror of the sanctuaries and their hidden contents that attracted them so irresistibly. They knew a little about them but not nearly enough, and they lay with their eyes glued to cracks in the wattle fence, trying to penetrate what was going on inside. So long as Tole and Norna Gest were walking about among the houses they could follow them; yes, there they were by the stone of sacrifice, and Tole laid his hand on it, whatever that might mean; but when they went into the houses the boys lost sight of them, could only guess and were in sore distress. But when at last they saw the two great initiates prepare to enter the temple, the holy of holies, the boys' hair stood on end and they took their eyes from the crack, looked out into the wide world as though to call it to witness, with round, terror-struck eyes and open mouth: now they were going right in to the god, ye gods! and would be blinded; for that was the only thing they knew about the Awful Thing in there, that you were struck blind if you looked at it. They could stand no more, creeping and crawling they worked themselves out of cover, away from the perilous region, until they were well out on the fields, then jumped to their feet and tore down to the house to announce to playmates and mothers that Grandfather and the tall old stranger had just gone right into the bogey place!

Tole and Norna Gest, however, felt no particular emotion as they entered the temple, ducking their heads in the doorway and taking a long step down, for the interior was half under ground and extended a long way, with no other opening for light but the door; a fire was burning on the floor, they passed from daylight into gloom, only half penetrated by the light of the fire; the corners and the background lay in shadow. An aged woman rose and came towards them; she was all bent forward, crippled with rheumatism, but brisk enough, chattering like a magpie with her toothless mouth; she had dirty red eyes and wrinkles full of soot, her tiny head perfectly bald and her claw black and scorched from tending the fire. It could never be allowed to go out, for it was the hearth of the whole country, on that account alone it was kept up all the year round and solemnly renewed at the sun festivals; the priestesses were responsible for it, besides their other sacred duties.

There were several of them, living close by in huts within the enclosure and relieving each other, and there were younger ones among them, even down to newly initiated little girls who were taught by the old ones and would learn all their arts by degrees, how to slay a victim and take omens from the entrails, how to make incantations and brew magic broth, and whatever other deeds of darkness a sibyl is expected to know. Once inside the fence there was no return; the women who were dedicated to the service of Heaven could not go back to life.

It happened sometime that the young initiates grew up into bonny lasses whose fame spread beyond the sanctuary, and then the young men had a taste of sorrow: in their

eyes much desirable intercourse, said to be reserved for
Heaven, regretably went begging. What the maidens
thought about it never came outside the enclosure, any more
than they did themselves. But however fair they may have
been in their youth, they all ended like the old priestesses,
if they lived long enough.

The priestesses were virgins; in some respects life and
death remained a closed world to them, in others a long life
gave them a grisly experience, they ceased to be human
without having even the simplicity of animals; of all creatures the priestesses were the most cruel.

Tole greeted the old woman who was on duty and went
about the sanctuary with Norna Gest, took the ring from
the sacred raised place in the background of the crypt;
the *ring*, of solid gold and so heavy that you could kill a
man with it; Tole laid it in Norna Gest's hand, no small
mark of confidence, for nobody but the priest himself was
allowed to take it, it was death at the stake simply to touch
it by accident, it pledged its victim to the fire. On holy
occasions it might be done, but then it involved heavy obligations; covenants made with an oath on the ring were
inviolable, and young couples were wedded by laying their
hands on it. For the ring was the sun, the golden circle,
by touching which one came under the ban of Heaven, but
also under its protection if one was true to one's oath.
Norna Gest weighed the ring in his hand, nodded and nodded again, and Tole nodded as he put it back in its place.

In front of the high place stood the huge sacrificial bowl,
of pure silver richly embossed with figures, the most intimate symbols of the Cimbrians buried as it were in hiero-
glyphics, only to be interpreted by the initiated; it was now
cleansed and bright, but on the great days of fate it reeked
with the blood of the victims, when priest and priestesses
performed the solemn rites that maintained the order of the
universe. Its mighty swelling form witnessed by its bulk

alone the powers that were set in motion when it was full of blood; at once clear and mysterious the figures stared out upon the gloomy crypt, the silver catching the red light of the fire.

But at the top of the high place there was as it were a house within the house with a door. Tole opened it and exposed the god.

There was a mewing by his side from the old priestess who was jealously following his movements and gave him angry looks. But he pushed her away with his elbow, put his hand into the shrine, the holy of holies, and took out the god.

He and Norna Gest put their heads together, did not say much but exchanged many wise nods and emphatic winks. Behind them the bent old crone shuffled about, making dull sounds of anxiety in her chest; she strewed something on the fire, as though to atone for what was taking place, and a spicy scent of gum filled the cave. One finger she put into the fire till it began to smell, then started cackling like a bird and smacked herself in the face; more than that could not be done.

But the two superinitiates were not doing anything to the god, only looking at it. It was a smallish god to look at, scarcely two spans high, a sort of embryo, made of wood roughly carved, not much more than a round billet with an indication of a head, no arms, but divided at its lower end by a slit, like the beginning of a pair of legs. The wood was black with age and saturated with grease; the mouth of the image, indicated by a slit across the head—nose and eyes were wanting—was newly smeared with butter. The god ate on the day of the summer solstice; then the rays of the sun fell into the temple through the doorway, right into the holy of holies and melted the butter on the god's mouth; that gave it food for the whole year. Ay, ay. It was she; Tole pointed a rude finger at the sex, saying nothing but giving a grunt. He turned her over; no art had been used on her back, she was not to be seen from behind. But all over its body, both in front and behind, the image was covered with holes, black and charred at the bottom, like those produced by drilling fire; and in fact the god was an old firestick, how old nobody could say, but at any rate as old as the Cimbrians themselves. It had *always,* from the very creation, been in their possession, and in more definite tradition it had been handed down from father to son in Tole's family; it was the most sacred thing in the country. Everybody knew that from the beginning of the world the lightning had dwelt in it, that was why it struck any one blind who looked at it. In the popular imagination all kinds of monstrous and supernatural ideas were formed about it.

Tole put the image back in the shrine and closed the door on it. Muttering to each other with many pertinent nods the two experts then betook themselves again to the daylight and left the fussy old priestess to smoke the place out after them; they still had the rest of the sacred gear to see and went into the house specially built for the *car,* the god's holy car which was used on behalf of the whole country on the most solemn occasions and which was a masterpiece, lavishly ornamented with costly mountings, a thing beyond all price. Tole's thoughts, however, were more concerned with the team; on certain occasions the car was drawn by heifers, on others by stallions, in both cases Tole took care that they were the best to be had. Whatever the team might be composed of, it almost gave the impression of being a kind of transformed human beings that drew the car in honour of the god; Tole bred his animals with a view to pink flesh tints; his own taste lay that way.

The car then was found to be in order and it was refreshing to see it again, many memories were connected with it, such as the rolling of time; but the car was ready

to roll once more, there would soon be use for it. Yes, so
long as it carried the Cimbrians' sacred traditions about
the country for the solace of the people, so long would they
and their cattle multiply and the produce of their fields be
assured.

Norna Gest was to be shown Tole's treasures, his store of
weapons and valuables; but first they made for the smithy,
and Tole was excited about something which they stopped
to discuss on the way.

It was a plan that had been matured between them years
before and which Tole was now carrying out; he was going to cast an image in the likeness of a bull. Norna Gest,
who had advised the smith about a silver bowl—a work inspired with secrets that only a travelled man had the key
to—had also promised his help in the matter of the bull.

The idea was that the ancient inviolable god which was
kept in the holy of holies should be enclosed in the
interior of the bull and thus be insured for ever against
being seen; its sanctity would then naturally pass to the
bull, and the image would take the place in the temple
now occupied by the god and would be borne on the car in
the sacred processions, a far more striking object to the eye
than the receptacle, insignificant in itself, in which the god
was now conveyed; this was the scheme the two wise old
men had hatched together, and now it was approaching
realization. For two years Tole had been collecting brass
for the image, including a number of old bronze swords,
greatly valued as heirlooms but surpassed as weapons by
the iron swords now used; they were to go into the making
of the bull, and thus their ancestors' most precious possessions would be applied to a holy purpose.

The work was now so far forward that the casting could
soon be taken in hand; it was the biggest piece of work that
had ever been undertaken in these parts and was much

talked about; its success was considered by no means certain. A pit and a furnace for the casting had been constructed on a hitherto unknown scale and many preparations had been made; a whole staff were employed on the work, among them many freemen, kinsmen of Tole, besides himself; the rest were trained thralls.

The smith, a good man, was Tole's friend and distant kinsman, a skilful armourer who also worked in precious metals; under his direction the image of the bull had been set up in clay. Then it was moulded in wax on the inner core, another coating of clay was to be applied outside, and then the whole thing would be fired and the wax melted out; finally the metal would be poured into the mould, an elaborate and doubtful operation which might come to grief on many a snag in its course.

The image was practically finished in its wax stage when Tole and Norna Gest came to see its progress. It was modelled in the round, not fully life-size but over half, and it looked remarkably lifelike in the hut where it stood, like a creature that had appeared there, clay and nothing else, but still alive.

The likeness of the bull had been astonishingly caught, it stood defiantly planted on its feet, rather squarely built, but so it should be, lifelike about the head, and Norna Gest saw at a glance that a hand unknown to him had been at work here, the smith had not made it alone; and involuntarily he looked about for its creator.

The smith, who saw the meaning of his glance, pointed with his thumb to one of the thralls in the background, and from further explanation it appeared that this man had disclosed special abilities while the work was in progress; he alone had carried out most of the final moulding in wax, which would be reproduced in the metal, assuming that first the firing and then the casting were successful. Yes, he was clever, could get it to look as it really looked; and if he was in doubt about the image he went straight and looked at the thing itself, took the bull by the horns so to speak; that was more than would have occurred to other people who thought they had seen enough to make an image out of their head.   Of course they had humoured the thrall in every way for the sake of the result, as soon as his gifts declared themselves; they had even brought the bull down to the hut so that he might look at it without leaving his work.   Evidently he was held in high esteem.

They called him "the Squirrel" for want of other name, not having been able to understand a word of his language or what he was called; now he was beginning to pick up a little human speech.   He had not been long in the smithy; Tole had bought him of a Baltic skipper at the fair on the Limfjord, and by all appearances he came from a distant country; he was dark-haired and well sunned, with a skin like gold, and must have passed through many hands before he came so far as this.   His name of "Squirrel" had been given him because he was small and agile, with big front teeth; he had gleaming eyes, looked like a handsome boy and in fact was not much more; quite young, but in spite of that he possessed this very valuable talent.   It was a lucky thing he had been sent to the smithy, for which at first glance he did not seem fitted; if he had been put to peat-digging, well, then he would no doubt have turned out uncommonly shapely peats, but it would have been a pity. As it was he gave satisfaction and was unreservedly appreciated.

The Squirrel smiled when he was noticed and talked about.   Nobody was readier to smile than he, with a bright, shining smile incomprehensible to the men about him, they could see no cause for his joy.   The women had noticed it; they sometimes passed by the smithy to see the young thrall smile through his soot.   He had curly hair which many a one might envy, and this too attracted the women's attention. Though small he was well built and there was charm in his gestures; without a doubt he was of gentle birth and through some misfortune had been sold as a slave, who could tell where? But perhaps Norna Gest was the very man to clear up the mystery.

Norna Gest took him in hand; to every one's surprise and deepest awe it appeared that the scald was able to address the foreigner in his own language, and they saw the thrall's eyes fill with tears.

It turned out that he was a Greek, a piece of information which did not convey much to some of those present; most of them only gathered with a shake of the head that it was a question of an immensely distant country, somewhere down in the Welsh parts [1] or perhaps even farther off, and they regarded the Squirrel with correspondingly vague feelings.

Tole vouchsafed him the full broadside of his attention for a moment, with head thrown back: so he was a Greek, was he?—whereupon he turned to some other subject.

But after that Norna Gest had several talks with the thrall and was able from his story to picture to himself a remarkable destiny, in which what seemed to be only the workings of chance were nevertheless fate. Five years before the thrall, whose real name was Cheiron, had been carried off by pirates from his home in the Greek archipelago, had been sold until by roundabout ways he reached the Black Sea, thence he passed from hand to hand along the trading routes of the Danube, still farther north and down other rivers, and it always seemed that there was no abiding place for him, whoever had bought him had sold him again, whether because he was too feeble or for some other reason. Finally his last sale had landed him in a place the situation of which he still could scarcely guess, though he believed that if he had his freedom he would be

[1] I. e. Italy.—Tr.

able to find the whole long way back, he had taken note of it. But now it looked as if he would stay here for good, since it had been discovered that he was of some use.

He did not complain of his lot; on the contrary, he was better off here than anywhere else he had been. His owners took no notice of him beyond his duties. With his fellow-thralls he did not get on so well since he had begun to be important; they dared not do him any injury, but secretly put filth into his food; at night he slept chained together with them in a sty, there was no help for that. But in the daytime he was happy; work, which to other thralls meant sighs and groans, was his delight. And now he was even gladdening his owners with it. Things could not have gone better with him. But . . .

Thus had fate dealt with a young Southerner, a friendly being, cut off entirely from his kin, who was not yet twenty. What things he had seen!

Every day Norna Gest went to the workshops to see how things were going, and he always found the Greek thrall cheerfully busy with his work on the image, to the obvious admiration of his master the smith, while others regarded him with lurking feelings of resentment. He was rather lame for a day or two, one of the thralls having chanced to drop a heavy pair of pincers on one of his feet, but even a limp became him.

Norna Gest was not the only one interested in the great bronze casting, every one who could or dared found an excuse to pass the smithy and see how it was getting on. Even the women, who were not supposed to know anything about smith's work and who as a rule tactfully avoided places where bulls or anything in the likeness of bulls attracted people—remarks unfit for their ears were liable to be heard in such places—even they could not keep away. But this was something quite out of the ordinary, which kept every one in suspense, and the women shared in the interest, strolling by in little groups, feeling strengthened by numbers after the way of women; but their courage was very half-hearted, they were really going somewhere else and just dawdled for a moment outside the door to have a peep at the men's dangerous arts. The Greek happened to be very busy, surveying his difficulties with a flashing eye, with all his fingers on his work; or perhaps his glance fell as though absently upon the crowd of girls, a glance deep as a well, impossible to plumb; or he limped over the floor with wonderful grace, or they just caught sight of his back and shoulders, which he carried in a way they had never seen in any other man.

Inge, Tole's young kinswoman, the daughter of one of his nephews and closely connected with his household, often found a pretext for visiting the smithy and came down there alone, to call the master or see if he was there, walked straight into the workshops with her fair head bare and stood there breathless an instant, looking about her—and then the Greek was always the quickest to give her an answer, he stepped forward and made an obeisance, his whole being in one long look, and said in his melodious foreign accent, No, the master was not there. Blushing like the wild rose Inge then went elsewhere to seek him, and they saw her vanish, erect and supple and rounded like a young shoot of the willow, with her heavy pale yellow plaits hanging down her back.

At evening too, now the evenings were so light, the Lady Inge went out without escort, not anywhere near the thralls' quarters, but an attentive observer would see a figure like a statue standing in the clear air in that direction, the Greek reposing apart after the day's work and gazing at the stars; not a sign, not the slightest connection between the two figures in the evening light, and more than the distance divided them, an absolutely impassable gulf lay between. But they happened to be there at the same time, and if one went in the other soon disappeared, like two stars which are placed far from each other in the sky but set together.

Norna Gest took note of things of this sort, but scarcely any one else; he had a sharp eye and nothing to occupy him but watching the growth of others' destiny. Ah, the others were too much taken up with their own affairs to have eyes for any but their own partner: everywhere in the twilight was a secret attraction, the young people would not sleep and stayed out till they could not see each other any more, could only glimpse a dewy face in the moonlight and feel the nearness of a marvel.

The moon, the spring moon was waxing. Far and wide from the marshes came a mating song in the coolness of the evening, frogs and all living things witnessing of the earth's increase. The lapwing cried in the darkness, the cry of a mother, the ever-wakeful, a soul in the vast wild chamber beneath the moon. From the woods came hollow sighs, ghostly sounds and echoes, the beasts were restless.

And an uproar was heard behind the closed doors of the cattle-sheds, restive cows hammering at their stalls, the milkmaid in tears, and much bellowing, deep and aggrieved; the cows were in an angry mood—now they *would* go out to grass, what was the Master waiting for?

All at once and from every side welled up forces which were not to be controlled.

Now the Greek would surely be quite beside himself with homesickness, and Norna Gest chatted with him to see how this might be; but the Greek was not exactly longing for his home any more, he said, and Norna Gest nodded. In his own mind he added the explanation of the young thrall staying so short a time in all the places he had been: the men must have quietly come to the conclusion that the best thing to do was to sell him again. Was he likely to be long here either?

But of the Lady Inge Norna Gest knew that, without her having an inkling of it, she had been chosen for the May

Bride of the year; it had been decided at a recent council at which he had been present. Every one was agreed that she was the fairest of all the girls of seventeen in the whole country on whom the choice could fall.

III

THE STRANGER MAID

THE trees were late in coming out that year, but at last they burst into leaf. The herald of spring came to Cimberland.

Much had been whispered about it beforehand. A surprise of course ought to come as a surprise, but you could not prevent at any rate those who were making all the preparations from knowing what would happen. Where the May Bride, the Stranger Maid, was coming from was known in this case among the Tollings. It had been so arranged that she should visit the other districts first, where nobody knew her, and come home to Tollingthorp last of all; there the May wedding was to be held, after the bridegroom had come to meet her.

On a certain day Inge vanished from her usual place; some asserted that they had seen her taken into the sanctuary, where she was to be made ready and adorned. A few of the irrepressibly curious who sacrificed their night's rest for the scent of a piece of news were able to relate that the sacred car with its escort had left there early one morning, long before sunrise, without attracting any notice, *that* of course was not to come until the procession began visiting the homesteads. Others had heard that horsemen, swains and bridesmaids from other parts of the country were to meet the bridal car at a certain spot in the forest, and when the procession was complete it would come forth in broad daylight and visit the haunts of men; a procession that made a show of coming from the forest, decked out in all the gifts of the woods, and was now to bring summer to every home.

Putting ourselves in the place of the people of some out-lying homestead where they had heard nothing but guessed what was coming, the spring procession had all the appearance of a revelation; they knew of course that it was mummery but had soul enough to take the visit seriously.

First of all they heard the music of lurs, as though there was war in the land; but this was not war, the notes were those of spring, easily recognized. In the morning, at sunrise, they might have heard distant lur notes brought on the wind from the forest, as though something was being born there, a sign for which all had longed; for now the cattle must be blessed or they would be too late, the woods were in leaf, it was full moon, all the signs agreed—so then summer *had* arrived!

Then old and young coming out, their souls already fired by the music, saw the approach of the May pageant, at a distance a bright green troop on horseback and on foot, surrounding something that looked like a swaying tree, a little wood in motion, when it came nearer a car bedecked and canopied with fresh green boughs.

The car moved slowly, decorously, drawn by a pair of heifers which were almost perfectly matched in their markings, white with a few splashes of dun, with white horns and hoofs like clouded amber, pale pink around the eyes and yellow downy udders; that they were Tole's cattle any child could see. They were very quiet and broken to driving, but still a girl walked by the head of each for the sake of security and spectacular effect. Beside the car walked all the bridesmaids with wreaths on their heads and green branches in their hands, and outside them was a guard of horsemen, young swains in their best finery but unarmed, bearing only white peeled hazel wands, the inviolable sign of peace, resting like lances on their thighs.

One thing was not mummery but solemn and awe-inspiring enough: the car bore the god, hidden from all eyes in the holy chest. No one had the slightest idea of its

nature or appearance, but all knew of its boundless power
both for good and evil. As the quintessence of all fertility
it was the real heart of the procession; the mere fact that
the car carried it over the land was enough to ensure the
crops. Its power was diffused over the whole pageant.

In the straw at the bottom of the car behind the sacred
object sat two sibyls, the oldest and most dignified to be
found, both bald as eggs, swathed in white pipe-clayed
cloaks which were tied under the chin, looking like two
bags of bones with a death's-head on top, nose and chin
meeting with age, shunning the light and annoyed by the
sunshine, being accustomed to live underground, but turning their beaks hither and thither, watchful as hawks.

But in front of them, high up on the car in a transparent
tent of foliage, sat the Stranger Maid, with flowing hair like
a mantle of light, still a child but full-grown in her loveliness, of a wonderful freshness, as though she had become a
woman that very morning: blushing, smiling, she was the
morning, the sunshine, the Spring in person!

She came from the wood, she was the wood, in her hand
she held a branch of fresh foliage, the unpretending symbol
of her power. But it was a magic wand; she held it out
towards the wood before her and it burst into light green
domes, new-born in the sunshine, like the wood she came
from; she stretched it out over the fields, and look, you
could see them grow green; she strewed wild flowers from
her car, and all the meadows were full of blossoms as far
as the eye could reach.

Those who had been blind to the springtime, to them she
gave sight. For she was the Stranger Maid who brought
new vision with her. And yet she was the soul of all
familiar things and gave to each its soul again. As she
was bright the sky was bright, the clear daylight was in her
eyes and the sun on her brow, cloudless was her soul. As
the blue of heaven merging into the blue fjords where rivers
run out, sky and sea and sunshine blended into one union,

so blue were her eyes, so open. She was warm as the breeze was warm, but with a cool breath from the forest, hot blood and sweet cool cheeks like wild roses still bedewed. She was laden with all the gifts of the land and gave them back with both hands, reanimated with her soul.

And the May song was sung:

> May, the mildest
> Maid, is coming!
> Crowned she goes
> to every home.
> > Bringing leaf
> > and bringing life,
> > to Man and Maid
> > so bountiful—
> > colt and cattle,
> > calf and kid,
> > fairest flowers
> > and children fair—
> > She, the fairest
> > young Midsummer!

> Bless our shores,
> ye southern breezes!
> Gentle Lady,
> bless our soil!
> > Bringing leaf
> > and bringing life,
> > to Man and Maid
> > so bountiful—
> > colt and cattle,
> > calf and kid,
> > fairest flowers
> > and children fair—
> > She, the fairest
> > young Midsummer!

> Light the bonfire,
> call the clansmen,
> show our Lady
> honor due!
> > Bringing leaf
> > and bringing life,

to Man and Maid
so bountiful—
colt and cattle,
calf and kid,
fairest flowers
and children fair—
She, the fairest
young Midsummer!

And while the May Bride stayed in her high seat on the car, the bridesmaids went into the homestead waving fertility to everything and everybody; they entered the houses, touching beds and benches with their wands, the stables, blessing the cattle; they blessed the whole place, even the old grandfather lying wrapt in his skins, never to rise again, saw a vision approach and strike his bedclothes with fresh leaves, a message from the woods which made him speechless, staring with wide-open eyes.

But the people of the place crowded about the wonderful car, which shone with its newly polished bronze mountings as though made all of gold, and tried to touch it for luck. the wheels, the symbols of the sun, the tail of the car, the innocent heifers, if possible the Bride herself, or but the fringe of her garment; they kissed their fingers to her that she might give them a flower or even a single leaf which they might keep to bring luck to the house.

But nobody ventured to touch the holy coffer, they knelt before it at a respectful distance and made a sign on their foreheads with clay; if any one came too near, the two old birds on guard at the back of the car shrieked and opened a toothless chasm in their faces; terrible boys who *could* not behave themselves got a stroke on the neck from the white wands of the escort.

Then the trumpeters blew their lurs again and took their places at the head of the procession as it passed on to the next farm. But it had not gone far before it became quite superfluous to visit them all; the people came of themselves, pouring from every side to meet the Spring pageant.

The sound of lurs was heard far and wide: first came people running at full speed, then men on horseback galloping from place to place, with the earth flying from their horses' hoofs as they thundered over the heath-mould, shouting and making signals to each other at a distance . . . before midday the whole of Cimberland knew that the May Bride had come that morning, and people from the valleys began to flock up towards the high central land, the heaths, the wastes and the forests, where they knew the procession would pass.

Before evening they were all home again bringing a green bough fresh from the May Bride's hand, hallowed by her touch; the messengers' lips crusted with their exertions, their eyes ringed round with sweat, their lungs at the last gasp, but they triumphed, holding the green bough high in the air; and before the sun went down every single home in Cimberland and all its fields were blessed. The cattle had now to be passed through the fire, then they could be let out and the open air life would begin. Not a soul thought of living indoors any more.

In the evening bonfires were lighted on all the beacon hills, as though all the hearths of the country had been moved out into the open. Everywhere people trooped up to the long heath-covered ridges, which gave a free view over the country so that they could see each other's fires, row upon row of fires all round the horizon as far as one could see; and they knew every place, knew whose fire each one was, some blazing up fiercely, others only a distant dying spark in the glimmering moonlit night. All the clans and families of Cimberland were in communication through the fires on the heights; it was as though they could read each other's thoughts from place to place.

And everywhere the same picture, if you approached the bonfire, the height and a ring around it illuminated by the great blaze which burned straight up in the still air, sending up a pillar of smoke; shadows like the cogs of a wheel

THE STRANGER MAID CAME, HOLDING THE UNPRETENDING
SYMBOL OF HER POWER

thrown outward from the top of the hill, with the fire like a hub in the middle; and the wheel turned, for the shadows were those of men going hand in hand about the fire, the sun dance, the symbol of the year and its course, the joyful return.

Now all fires were put out in every house in the country, the old, used-up winter fire, and new fire was kindled on the heights from the friction of wood brought from the temple and consecrated there. But in the sanctuary it was known that tonight Tole the priest would renew the sacred temple fire on behalf of the whole country, and tonight and the following nights great sacrifices would seal the covenant. Brands from the new fire were carried to every home to light the hearth again, the cattle were blessed by being driven through the smoke of a fire in the open, and then the summer had begun.

Nobody went to bed that night, they were all up and out of doors, at the bonfires and on the heights, to see the sun rise and rejoice over it. With the deepest interest they observed and recognized the fires all round the country; such and such a one was burning low, another burned brightly, and they thought of the farm and its owner, took omens and sent each other all good wishes.

Tonight too they felt a certain connection with strangers, in foreign parts, they could see the fires beyond the borders of the country, right over on the other side of the fjord both on the west and on the north; there too they kept the festival, the rude men of Salling, the savages of Thy, ignorant they were in many ways and needed a drubbing on occasion, yet they scarcely deserved to lose their sight like the mole, since they still acknowledged the sun and honoured it with new fire when it was new. Far to the southward they could see great fires and guessed them to be in the neighbourhood of Vebjerg; of course there would be a big festival at the temple there, though this was not a gathering of the whole country. At still greater festivals, with intervals of years, they assembled there for sacrifices, Cimbrians, Aaboers, and Harders, a levy of the whole of Jutland; but the Spring celebration was the affair of each district.   Hereabouts it was Tollingthorp that took the lead.

And there a mighty fire was seen; but it looked as if there were two!   People shook their heads and could not understand it; they knew the position of the bonfire on the slopes above the homestead, and that they could recognize, but there was another burning below, apparently in the homestead itself, and it was even bigger—the place could not be on fire?

No, the place was not on fire, though it looked very much like it: the hut which contained the great image of the bull was burning.   But this was no accident.   The clay mould was ready and the firing was to be attempted; they had then decided to sacrifice the hut to avoid moving the image; they had filled it with firewood and turves and set fire to the hut at the same time as the Spring bonfire was kindled; this had been thought out beforehand as auguring a fortunate result.

One thing promised good luck, a fateful coincidence: on that very day the bull himself, who had served as model for the image, had been sacrificed.

It had to be.   The bull was the chiefest and most honourable offering with which the sacrifices were inaugurated, as the being who was accounted nearest to the supreme deity, in an obscure sense almost the god himself, a mystery associated with sun and moon, secrets of which only a few initiates had the key; but for laymen it was enough that the bull was sacrificed, it was to be given to the fire and its horns hung on the sacred ash in the sanctuary.   There could be no greater mark of distinction.   The bull had had his time, younger bulls were to take his place and to fight their way in the course of the summer to the leadership of the herd.   It was as though the old year was sacrificed for the benefit of the new, the accomplishment of the very order of the universe.

The sacrifice was carried out with special rites, an entertainment with sacred significance: the death of the bull was the culmination of a hunt by the young men of the district.

On the same day as the Spring pageant left the woods and revealed itself to the inhabitants young men from all parts of the country assembled on horseback at the home of the Tollings, all those who desired to take part in the chasing of the bull and believed themselves equal to the encounter.

They were the doughtiest lads of the neighbouring hundreds, horsemen and runners if any there were, experts in the art of slaughter, great rough, reckless fellows, who spent their whole lives in hunting, manly exercises and sporting contests; in everything they were pretty equally balanced, and here was a chance of proving which of them was the smartest. It was a game where they risked their skins; so much the better.

A hot-headed crowd while they were waiting to start, all on choice prancing horses with fire in their nostrils, and each with a leash of hounds, which all flew furiously at each other's throats until the chase should give them other work to do. The hunters were armed with swords only, for the fight would be at close quarters; all carried their heads thrown back intrepidly, rolling their hazy blue eyes, with their hair tied together on the top of the head and waving in a tail. There was not a young warrior in all these parts who did not wear his hair thus, it was the latest fashion and the idea was based on utility: as each one hoped to get a handy grip of his foe's hair when he was severing his head from his body, so he would oblige *him* with something to take hold of—when and where he wished! As they curbed their unmanageable horses the lads' patience, of which they had but little, ebbed, their eyes were wild, their foreheads frowning: when was it coming off? If they were not given something to contend for, a death to face, a life to take, why, it wouldn't be many minutes before they began to devour each other!

But their quarry had been prepared. At last Tole came out, clad in the sacrificial robe he would wear all day, with his sacred staff in his hand, and announced to the crowd that the bull they were demanding had already been let loose early in the morning in the wastes; *where*, it was their affair to find out. Tole hoped the bull would be properly mad when they came across him—good morning!

The men flung their horses around, all of them together, and the sudden tramp of many horses sounded like a landslide, a drumming on the turf as the united band dashed across the yard and out of the homestead, all their straight backs swinging up and down, all their tails of hair waving, a rain of earth and pebbles flying from their horses' hoofs. On reaching the fields the band divided and scattered in every direction, seeking cover, each with his own plan, not to be spied on by the rest; in a moment they were all swallowed up by thicket, wood, heath or bog, and only the distant baying of hounds was heard from every point of the compass.

Some, the more methodical, cast about for the trail, taking their time; others made at once for the highest ground to get a view; a number trusted to instinct and galloped straight ahead, one way or another, only at full speed; it was by no means all who could be in at the finish.

The bull had gone far, several leagues to the eastward towards the moorland, and was found on a wooded slope surrounded by a ring of hounds, whose terrific howls proclaimed the place. The horseman who had been first on the scene was found by the next who rode up following the sound; he lay dead together with his horse, mashed into a confused heap on the ground, with a huge rent in his body as though the whole bull had gone right through him. More hounds came up, with a baying that smote the sky, more and more of the hunters; those who had not heard the din scented where the bull was found, by tracking instinct, dots seen in the landscape, twitching of the limbs, anyhow they were there, a score or more of horsemen who were fortunate enough to be on that side of the country; so they shared in the chase and were in at the death.

But first the bull was to be driven back all the way home, a stiff piece of work but not to be avoided; the slaughter had to take place in the neighbourhood of the sanctuary, and it was to be *seen*, witnesses and spectators were waiting for it.

It was late in the day when they reached home with their quarry, after a breakneck ride and many feats, pursuing the bull and letting him pursue them, in the right direction, loss of horses and hounds and several men badly hurt. The bull was visibly fainter, could not be expected to be at the top of his fury all the time, only now and then he turned on the dogs, and you could see him shooting white jets from his nostrils, challenging them; a hound or two would fly into the air from his horns, but he could never get at the whole pack. He seemed to know the last part of the way and to want to get home, went of his own accord, and they let him recover his strength, so that the game might be more equal when it came to the last round.

He was brought to bay in the paddock between the homestead and the sanctuary, and hundreds of people had collected to see the tussle, the greatest of their public amusements, not one of the elder men but had taken part in bull hunts in his young days, and all the younger ones were in a state of excitement, eager to learn against the day when their turn would come. In an age which none of those present had known but of which they had traditions, it was the wild aurochs, now extinct in the country, that was hunted; this trial of manhood was an ancient and holy institution, an inherited passion in the blood of every man.

The struggle was short but fierce and bloody; for the last time the bull was incited to a full display of rage; the men attacked from every side without thought of life or limb, and in this merciless charge the beast went down. To look at it was a whirlwind of men and horses with the bull in the middle, scooping up black streams of earth with his forefeet, his muzzle to the ground, roaring with all the force of his lungs, a sound not unlike the bursting of ice in winter, and lashing his tail; the hunters could be seen flying in the air above him with legs and arms free, leaping in the nick of time before the attacking horns, horses crumpled up on the ground in front of the bull, trampled down; fresh attacks by the men, leaping over the raging beast, a creaking of hoofs and joints, horses rearing straight up in air as though they would jump to heaven— and then an instant when the whole immense uproar subsided all at once . . . a silence in which was heard a long *Oh* from the women, who had witnessed the wild scene from a distance, sheltered behind the men: the bull had received his death-blow.

No more than *one* wound must be found on the slain victim, and that had been dealt.

The men all aimed at the chest with their sharp two-edged swords as the shortest way to the heart; the plan was to ride up as close as was safe, then throw one's self off one's horse and receive the bull's charge; if there was no chance of a thrust, take a leap lengthways over the beast and land behind it, a dangerous jump with a drawn sword in the hand, as a rule they rolled over many times on the ground after it, but that they thought nothing of, up again and another try!

But the man who had dealt the lucky stroke had discovered entirely new tactics. They saw him jump, but not in front of the bull; it was a running leap from the side, such as the men practised when jumping on their horses in full career, and he landed with perfect sureness *astride the bull*. In breathless suspense the spectators watched him ride a short distance as in a swing, the bull now on

his forelegs and now on his hindlegs, shaking himself in
the wildest frenzy; but the man kept his seat, and they saw
him aim his blade, throw himself forward and put his
whole weight on it, and the beast sank on its knees under
him. It was all over. From above he had pierced right
through the lung to the heart. Immense relief of the spectators, which found vent in shouts, hurrahs, transports of
joy: a fairer sacrifice could not have been accomplished.

The priestesses with kilted skirts ran with buckets of the
warm blood across the fields to the sacred grove and poured
it into the sacrificial bowl in the temple; it covered the
bull's image at the bottom of the bowl, where the hunt was
pictured, both its course and its finish: the stricken bull
lying down, surrounded by dogs, and the hunter in a flying
leap above it with a drawn sword in his hand. It was as
though the image appealed to be hidden; when a sea of
blood swam above it its summons had not been in vain.

But the hunter who had achieved the victory was led in
triumph with his horse; the others who had taken part in
the hunt surrounded him and formed his escort; he was
their chief, all loved him for his supreme achievement,
their joy on his account knew no bounds.

And now he was to be escorted to his wedding! For
he who laid the bull low was by that very deed chosen as
the May Bridegroom, to be wedded to the May Bride before the bonfires were kindled.

Ah, yes, the prize of victory was such that every single
young swain in the country had dreams of it that put him
in a fever, and one would have thought they would *all* be
present at the bull hunt. The number of those who came,
however, was not so overwhelmingly great: as many as had
seen Inge had also seen the Tolling bull! And those who
did not show themselves might hope to remain in their ob-
scurity.

But the competitors were the flower of the first families
of Cimberland, the hardiest and most dreaded of all the

dare-devil youths in the land. And he who proved himself Number One among them all was the most reckless, he
had the most splendid top-knot of straw-coloured hair, the
lightest, fiercest and haziest eyes, an eagle tattooed on each
cheek and a serpent—the lightning—on his forehead. He
was so young that his beard was as yet scarcely a down of
bog-cotton on his lip. Boierik was his name.

If the May Bride had driven out with heifers at a most
orderly walk, so that even a child could keep up, she was
brought home at the fastest gallop a pair of horses, white
stallions, could flash out of the ground, the bridesmen in a
ring round the car with their green boughs flying like ban-
ners in the air, Boierik seated nobly beside the Bride in
the high seat, and two old sibyls nodding and smacking
their gums behind with their sacred charge.

Both it and they came near being shaken out of the
straw, for the driving was so reckless, road or no road,
scrub or bog, that at times the car flew through the air
with not more than one wheel or none at all touching the
ground; and it is certain that if they had driven slower
they *would* have been upset, but at the pace the car was
going it could not overbalance. It was the kind of driving that meant life or death, wedding or childbirth; there
was laughter in the banqueting hall when the young people
arrived and they saw what haste they had made.

Thus the Stranger Maid came back and made her final
entry at her own home, and it really seemed as if her
familiars scarcely knew her, they thought she had grown
in the course of that one day, taller, more beautiful, with
bluer eyes, as though the sky and the sounds she had seen
lay in them, with the wonderful first freshness of the woods
over all her being. And yet, the shadows were long when
she came home, the day was sinking, and was there not
something like a shadow on the May Bride's brow? She
might well be tired after such a day. All were agreed that

no better matched bridal couple than Boierik and Inge had been seen in any year.

The May Bride was led by her maidens to the women's quarters to rest and be prepared for her wedding.

But the car with its sacred burden and the two sibyls drove back into the sanctuary. Here the holy coffer was put in its place in the temple, with the door of its shrine open, so that the god might enjoy the smell of the bull's blood in the great bowl. The heart was roasting at the sacred fire before the high place, filling the whole temple with sweet fumes, and the two sibyls cackled with delight at being home again, sheltered underground from the hated daylight. Much labour awaited them during the coming night and day, sacrificial duties, and they began to make themselves ready, pipe-claying not only their clothes but their faces and scalps, sharpening knives against one another, old slaughtering knives, pliable in the back, that had been ground so often that there was only a thin strip of blade left, regular women's knives, but they could depend upon them for their work. And their gums were on the go; ugh, they had been listening to the song of birds the whole long disgusting day; this song, *hwee, hwee,* the song of knife against knife, that was better.

Meanwhile the bridegroom was received by Tole and conducted into the men's circle, for the first time in his life, with a certain ostentation on Tole's part, while Boierik took pains to conceal his feelings, as though it were an everyday affair; but something in his walk betrayed him, the honour was too great. Happy friends followed him in the background and saw the great old franklins, chiefs of neighbouring clans, offer him their hands.

They had arrived in the course of the afternoon to be Tole's guests at the sacrificial feast. If the bridal pair had driven smartly there were some of the visitors who had not spared their horses either; those who were going the

same way had raced each other so that the stones flew;
some of their cars were muddy to the hubs, they seemed
to have driven over peat-bogs and everything, a few up-
sets there had been too. Now they were out in the yard
in the evening twilight, looking over each other's teams.
Every one of them had a matchless pair of horses, trotters
that could not be beaten if you searched the world over,
the owner offered to bet any odds, and the teams should
be tried against one another in the morning! All kinds
and all colours were there, it was not everybody who swore
by Tole's brood mare with the maidenly hue; there were
brown horses of every shade, down to raven black; there
were roans and mouse-coloured nags, but otherwise all
were pretty much alike in their build, long-haired, with
bony heads and spreading hoofs, made to swim with, the
Jutland ideal and the first point looked for in any horse
one saw.

And Boierik took his part in the horse talk, as his
friends in the background could see, he was not at a loss
among all these knowing ones; they saw him lay his hand
on an animal's flank, feel its leg lightly down to the
pastern and give his opinion, and the wise old franklins
nodded in a ring round him, yes, yes, that's so; the friends
in the background laughed aloud in their excitement and
gratitude at the solemn way Boierik behaved, with impenetrable features, going straight to the heart of the matter
when he spoke. He was so obviously at home in the men's
circle, without any effort, but at the same time as though he
had taken twenty years at a single leap.

IV

THE WEDDING

THERE were no heroics about Boierik when he afterwards accompanied the elder men to the sanctuary to take part in the sacrificial repast, where the bull was to be served up: with toes turned in and swinging stride he marched with the others, whose precedence was part of the nature of things.

And here his friends lost sight of him, within the sanctuary they could not follow him. Perhaps he missed *them* a little in his great new dignity; now they would be amusing themselves with bathing in the stream and other pastimes that belonged to spring, before the bonfires were lighted.

Washing and purification were part of the inauguration of the new season, for it was impossible to pass into springtime unpurged of the winter; when smoking out the old season it was fitting to scrub one's old self and put on a new one. The houses were aired; they were lined with soot from the winter and not fit to be seen in the strong light which now poured in through the doors; people had been living and breathing in an atmosphere of lamp-black for the last few months without noticing it and the daylight exposed this horrible state of things. The old bed-straw was carried out and burnt, with all its mice's nests and fungus; some made straw men of it and burned winter in effigy, replacing it by fresh grass. But few of them hoped to sleep indoors again for the next half year.

Men and women visited the bath-house and had themselves steamed, well and long. And after the bath they put on entirely new clothes, linen and light frieze; their winter skins were put away if they were fit to wear again, otherwise offered to the fire, and a fine blaze they made, smoking and crackling; what is nastier than an old cast slough?

The young unmarried people preferred the stream to the bath-house, boys and girls together, a whole swarm of them down in the meadows below the homestead, in full view of all; you could tell the boys from the girls at a distance, the latter were pinker and more compact in figure, with excrescences before and behind, they kept to the ground when running, as though they couldn't take their feet from it; the boys were up in the air, and they were bony and dead white, with a mother-of-pearl tint of muscles and joints under their thin skin. The water was evidently cold and the air coolish, they raced for their lives to reach their clothes, shirts and linen smocks fluttered over their heads and were pulled down over wet bodies.

Home they came fresh and carefree, blue about the lips, in new clothes from head to foot, dressed for the feast and ready for the evening ceremony. In getting into their clothes they had the unconscious feeling of having shed a state of nature and put on a better man, washed and renewed, in this as in other ways keeping pace with the year and its resurrection.

The supper was a festival one, and now Mother and her fleshpots came into their own; the band of young people mingled with women and children from the homes around, who were taking their meal in the open air for the first time of the year, at open smoking fireplaces on the grass, crowding round the cauldrons with wooden spoons in readiness. Holiday fare it was: barley groats boiled in sweet milk, dried mutton-ham and smoked pork, cheese as much as they wanted; bread only for favourites, for Mother was sparing of her loaf, there was not much of last year's corn left and the new harvest was a long way off. On the other hand mast-bread was passed round freely, but at the mention of it the young people politely said, thank you, they *had* finished. Their meal was only a hurried affair, the whole band wanted to be up on the heath as quickly as possible, the heights and the night were calling. Thirst was quenched, a big wooden bowl of whey went round, without further ceremony than that the bowl was of maple with handles carved in the form of horses' heads, and that one or other of the young fellows cleverly managed to drink just after some particular girl. What feeling she put into it as she handed him the drink!

Dusk fell, their souls felt the power of the long evening twilight, they sought each other with wider eyes. Up rose the moon.

But at sunset a shower had veiled the blue sky, before it turned red, and a few cold drops had fallen, still with the bitterness of winter, but no more came. The women who were dressing the Bride remarked at the same time that she wept and was distressed; they read in it an omen of abundant rain in the coming season.

Up in the sanctuary meanwhile the men were assembled in the banqueting hall, as the guests of the god, in whose honour they partook of the repast; for though the Bull was an offering to the fire, it was to be eaten in order that the sacrifice might be consummated and all might share in the sanctification.

Not every one could explain wherein this consisted, it was the secret of Tole and the holy women. But that the Bull and the Sun and the Moon had something to do with each other, were to a certain extent one and the same Power, was comprehensible even to a layman. The Bull was absorbed into the Sun when it was sacrificed, and that renewed the year, so much at any rate one could understand. Therefore in eating of it one of course shared in its resurrection. Anyhow it was Tole who had the responsi-

bility of maintaining the Sun and the year, and they could
trust to him. He and the sibyls had searched the bull's
heart and reins and drawn omens from them for the year,
uncommonly good, it was said; so there was nothing more
to be done but to see how the beef tasted.

All the partakers had spots and splashes of blood on
their faces, which were left to dry and might not be wiped
off; it was the blood of the Bull wherewith the oldest and
most reverend of the sibyls had besprinkled the congrega-
tion; by this act they had been washed of the old year and
their old selves in the blood of the Bull and were made
partakers in the Sun and its renewal; all felt like new men.

Reddest of all was Boierik, splashed to the elbows and
with a mask of clotted blood over his face; he had received
a jet of blood as he plunged his sword into the bull, a
sanctification which ought to be of some use. The greater
part of the bull's strength had passed into him, whether
the others liked it or not. Ah, he was a lucky man, all
privileges had fallen to him in one day. Outside the
temple door the bull's pizzle was now hanging to dry; he
had a right to it for a riding-whip and sign of authority;
oh yes, he was in luck!

The hall in which they sat was a low room, half under
ground, with walls of earth and stone and roofed with timber; an open fire burned on the floor—the god himself,
present in a tamed, domestic form. Round about the fire
sat the men as the god's immediate guests and took their
meal; the tender beef went down without much previous
preparation, each man did his own cooking and could
roast it to please himself, holding it in the fire on the end
of a stick or contenting himself with rubbing it a little in
the glowing embers. Horns went round, but the drink was
neither ale nor mead at this time of the year, everything
of that sort had been drunk up at Yule; they had spring
water, the best thirst-quencher after meat, as the wolf
knows, and it was not any ordinary water, it came from

the spring in the sacred grove and had powers which there was no fathoming. True, it kept them sober; but with sunshine and summer coming on nobody needs a spur to his vital spirits.

And sober things were discussed, sowing time, border questions, strained relations with neighbouring tribes, all which things, however, would not be taken seriously in hand until the day when the Thing was called together on the Thing mound. Horses were talked about again, a subject not to be avoided, and they had a taste of those which had lost their lives on the bull's horns, bits of kidney and tongue; the regular sacrifice where horseflesh was the chief dish came later. Hunting was discussed: not many deer nowadays, compared with what every one could remember; on the other hand wild boars were too plentiful, they rooted up the cornfields and ought to be hunted more often. The wolf had been fierce this winter, in one place it had killed eleven sheep, *in* the pen; such and such a man had lost his grandmother one winter evening on her way from one house to the other and had had only half of her to burn, a shameful business. The ice had taken some people this year; the fjord opened its mouth in broad daylight and swallowed four men spearing eels, and that in spite of its having been given a thrall at the proper time. Oh, ay.

The death of the bull was gone over again, with kindly glances at Boierik, who sat feeling hot and swollen about the head, snuffling violently and with eyes quite drowned in moisture from the strangeness of finding himself in a room; his nose ran and he felt as if he had had a blow on the head when he came under a roof, it was much tougher work for him to sit at table than to jump sixteen times over the bull; but he stood it manfully, did not move a muscle of his face when assailed by praises and modestly changed the subject when they grew too strong. His behaviour greatly pleased the elders, who had been quietly trying him.

But the culminating point of the feast came when Norna Gest was asked to touch the harp and perhaps reveal some of his treasures of song or story; they knew that he came from afar this year, from travels beyond all known bounds, so far as to baffle the imagination of most of those present. With repletion came a desire for spiritual expansion. They had eaten the second course, soup with the meat boiled in it; after that black puddings, with smuggled bits of pork in them, not belonging to the bull (swine had their turn at other solemn festivals), and finally came the dainties and sweet things, bread, of which there was no lack in this company, long slices like the soles of one's foot, cut from the broad loaf and spread with butter; with this they drank a native wine made from cranberries and whortleberries, sweetened with honey and spiced with bog myrtle; oh yes, they knew how to live.

And now they were disposed for fable and approached Norna Gest with respectful questions, seeking knowledge. One wanted to know if he had seen the World's Pillars, and whether one could be sure that they would hold, so much depended on them; another asked if it was really true that there were animals as big as peat stacks with their nose hanging down between their tusks and provided with a sort of hand at the end. Just imagine, taking hold of things with your nose! They were said to be quite invulnerable, covered with iron all over the body and with plates of it on their heads, born in armour. Well, one was told all sorts of things, and of course there were pictures on the sacrificial bowl which everybody could see, not only of the snouted beast but of many other supernatural creatures. One wasn't altogether ignorant either, and even if there were no such wonders here at home, the pictures of them proved at any rate that one knew the gods and recognized their omnipotence in the diversity of created forms. Truly there were more marvels under the sun and more Powers than any one had an idea of. And that had been in the smith's mind, when he and his mates in all reverence had made the great silver bowl, the work of many years, to the glory of Heaven and all the gods. In it were honoured all the gods they had heard of, with their attributes: the god of Valland,[1] who had hart's horns on his head, the ring of oaths in one hand and a serpent with a ram's head, the lightning-stroke, in the other; he ruled the thunder in Valland and was a god worthy of fear. Besides him there were many others, some of the female sex, every Power under the sun to whom they owed deference and sacrifice; therefore they were all symbolically present on the sacrificial bowl to be remembered every time blood flowed into it. Ay, was it not a strange world—you even heard talk of invisible gods now, and they were said to be the most powerful of all; but they could be left to such folks as believed in them, here they preferred to keep to those they could see, Sun and Moon, oh yes, that was there way.

At the time the smith was fashioning the bowl and ornamenting it with all kinds of symbols and animals it was known that he had questioned none other than Norna Gest, who had been to the world's end, and been instructed by him—of course, here was a witness who had seen the things with his own eyes. How did these wonders look in reality? The griffin now, did that fly about everywhere, like eagles or cranes here, or was it a rare bird? Did it fly with a car up in the sky and help to draw the sun? Then it would have to be fireproof—but of course there were other creatures that were that, the dragon both ate and vomited fire, as every one knew. Did it dazzle you much to see a griffin? As to horses, no doubt they were very different in other lands, they had winged horses for use in the air and horses with finned tails that swam in the sea. How did one manage to ride on whales in Serkland?[2] There was no denying that the means of getting about had

[1] Gaul.—Tr.
[2] Syria.—Tr.

reached a high development in the South, in this the Welsh were ahead of the Northern farmer, sure enough. But weren't they unsafe countries to live in, didn't you have to fight monsters and defend yourself all the time? The wild beasts—there were some of them that had curved swords or sickles on all four feet and mowed everything down with them, regularly cropped their way through every living thing. And the women in the South were said to be so beautiful that you were quite bewitched and crippled if you looked at them. Were there really females with a score of breasts? All these things and more they wanted to know.

Boierik joined in, modestly as became the youngest, but clearly, straight to the point, and the old men nodded, yes, he would turn out well. It was a technical point; young as he was Boierik was collecting military knowledge and wished to hear something about the castles in the South, both in Valland and elsewhere. About Valland he was fairly well informed and always made a point of interrogating the merchants and travellers who came into the fjord to trade. But Norna Gest no doubt would have special information. What they understood here by a castle was one of the long earthern ramparts which they threw up on high ground or deep in the forest, and to which they withdrew with their cattle in time of trouble; but he had heard that in the South there were fortresses entirely of stone, each stone cut into a square, with chambers high up, one above the other, and constructed on such a scale that a whole population could live inside. How then did you take them? They said that you could sling stones, so big that one man could not lift them, to a distance of more than three or four bowshots; how much truth was there in all this? And what about their arms generally?

Norna Gest looked at each man who questioned him, Boierik too, as though storing their enquiries in his

memory, but he did not answer at once, nor was his answer a direct one. He, the scald and story-teller, was the
most silent of men. What he knew or had seen he kept
to himself, until it turned to images; the clearest speech,
he knew, was but an image. What he gave them should
have form, terseness, his language should be coloured by
the world and by his being. He began to think.

He placed the harp between his knees and began to play,
a simple twanging of its few strings, with no great display of skill, more tones than melody; but at once it had
a strange effect, in this murky house half under ground,
upon his wild audience. It seized upon their features, as
though in distress they looked towards the harper and
turned cold, what was it? A faint and distant world
streamed from his strings, difficult to catch, and it possessed their hearts, they became so heavy, with burning
eyes.

And while he thus held them spellbound the old man was
meditating, with his chin sunk on his breast and with no
light in his eyes; long he meditated, as one who was far,
far away. At last he rose and recited a lay, only one,
obscure and, as it seemed, of deep symbolic meaning. He
stood at his full height and recited, after the manner of
a scald, slowly, in a full and penetrating voice:

> A stronghold stands
> in southern clime,
> its walls a hundred leagues;
> countless its roofs
> of icy peaks
> that strive toward the stars.

> Upon that roof
> ranges the goat,
> and over it the eagle.
> The dizzy eaves
> drip into dales,
> whence run the mighty rivers.

Dismal pine-trees,
sadly sighing,
close its northern portal.
Southward opening,
sunny gateways
show their azure arches.

Two worlds confront
the castle walls:
misty and murk the one side.
Brightness and blue
in sky and shore,
these are the other's portion.

Lonely the white bear
floats on his iceberg,
sniffing the waves for seal.
Limber the reindeer
runs in the ghost-light,
fleet-footed captive of cold.

Elsewhere the elephant
trumpets in plenty,
tramping beneath the palms.
Sun-hued lion
leaves to the vulture
bones of a naked black.

He who has built
so firm a fortress,
he willed that 'it should stand.
Eternally,
unshakeably,
to sever North and South.

May be the marmot
chooses the midway,
building his house between;
seeks not the South,
nor haunts the North;
better a boundless view.

Creep over, ant,
and mole, crawl under!
Fly over, fowls of the air:

none may o'erthrow
so old a bulwark.
Still firm that wall shall stand.

Man of the North,
be hope thy nurture!
Better is soul than sunshine.
What will the sons
of Nile in the North?
No rover gathers riches.

The dun hyena,
nor dog nor lion,
laughs ever at the luckless.
Full oft I found
noble the native,
and poor the newcome stranger.

Wisdom it 'is
that sundered worlds
seek not their place to change.
Respect a rampart
of ancient rearing:
still firm the wall shall stand!

Norna Gest ceased, and there was silence. All had a
deferential sense of having received instruction, and each
one seemed to find a hint of an answer to his own questions. In particular the lay had much to tell of animals
they had never heard of before. Undoubtedly it was a
good lay, and the feast was much honoured thereby.
Boierik flushed; he could see before him the castle he had
asked about, towering to the sky with its ice-blue walls!
So faithful was his memory that it retained the once-heard
lay and it came back to him word for word, years later,
when its meaning became clear to him.

The thralls who had been in attendance now brought
water for the guests to wash their hands, and the feast
was at an end. As they held the basins the thralls stole
glances at the heap of bones in the corner: it looked like
a lavish heap; that was their portion.

Yes, behind the outhouses and middens, in the thralls' quarters, preparations were going on for another festival supper. They were to have bone broth and were strengthening it with toads and other creeping things from the marsh which they could manage to catch; the black cauldron was stirred with a great shin-bone, as the mouths of all watered in expectation. Here too a lay accompanied the feast; when the pot boiled over and hissed in the fire they put their heads together and sang right down in their stomachs this ventriloquial song:

> Hubble bubble
> Pooh!
> Sweet smells our broth!
> But bones and fat,
> They'll breed you bantlings!
> Gorge yourselves,
> Swill it down,
> Fill your guts!
> Hubble bubble.
> Brew a broth for your masters,
> Scorch 'em and scald 'em,
> We'll rifle the robbers!
> Hubble bubble.
> Pooh!

They were in high spirits, those who were cooking the supper, for on them the lot had not fallen that morning, *they* were not to be sacrificed. That was the fate of twelve others of their band, seven of whom were now sitting apart in the condemned cage, where they had been left to their meditations the whole day long; they were not to be sacrificed till midnight. The other five had got it over; they were the ones who were taken out to wash the sacred car when it returned to the sanctuary; they had to follow it up to the grove, and you could hear their shrieks a mile away, no doubt when they were washing the god, which it was supposed they would have to do, and that of course would blind them and scorch them. They did not shriek long. The last that was heard of them was a loud roar of hydrophobia; no doubt they ended by being drowned in the pond. Quite different was the fate of those who were boiling broth. Without the least effort on their part they had had a lucky day.

Among the seven victims who were still awaiting their fate was one from the smithy, the man they called the Squirrel. He danced no more. That toady! Now he could see the result of making his mark! He'd tried to rub shoulders with the masters, and now he'd get rubbed the wrong way. Doubled up with delight, lusting with malice, they gave the pot a good stir at the thought.

But the Greek sat behind the bars, keeping quiet the whole day. The other six had begun by howling, had then subsided into lethargy and were now pretty nearly out of their wits. But the Greek was at work; yes, to the no small surprise of the Tollings who happened to pass the cage they found him occupied; he had got some clay and spent the whole day modelling a figure. And they simply could not take their eyes off what he was doing; it was extraordinary, a woman to the life, not full size of course, but otherwise exactly as if you saw a girl, with nothing on, perfectly lovely, they had never seen anything like it or imagined that such a thing could be.

Not a few of the Tollings thought it rather hard luck on the Greek, no small loss either, a useful man like that; but what was there to be said, they had themselves seen Tole throw the wands, split sticks of which the bark side meant freedom, the white side death; he had flung them up to heaven and it was heaven's decision when they came down; who could change it? Others expressed no opinion and maybe had harsh looks for the handsome Greek, when they noticed in the course of the day that the women walked by the cage just as they had been in the habit of passing the smithy. However that might be, he was now handed over to the priestesses.

By evening the Greek had finished his image, and they saw him smile as he gazed at it. Then a thing happened which saddened the onlookers; he destroyed the figure, hastily kneading it together in his hands and throwing the lump of clay to the ground. But many who had seen the image never forgot it, it remained alive in their memories as long as they lived.

The rest of the time the Greek sat idle, silent, and very, very sorry for himself; yes, there was no concealing it. He sat looking through the bars and could see the meadows and the stream; he stretched his neck when the young people were bathing.

Sunset turned the meadows green as fire; a mist rose from the stream.

He watched the shower as it came and went. And he looked upon it all as one who saw it for the last time.

From the sanctuary came a sound of lurs, shrill and harsh, the signal for the evening festival.

All fires were extinguished, all arms, everything of iron hidden away. God's gifts were to be received again as new, that men might value them rightly. The only light that burned above the earth was the moon; deepening in colour its full orb climbed in the sky.

The homestead lay in stillness, all whose legs could carry them were ready to move up to the heath; but first the fire was to be born. This most momentous and holy act was taking place within the sanctuary; not a sound came from thence, enclosed in its gloom the grove was like an island of darkness among the fields, and all eyes were turned towards it.

Some there were who knew, what they were not supposed to know, that as one part of the secret deeds of darkness now going forward in the grove the old priestesses would ride on sticks round the newly kindled fire as soon as the first spark was seen; a strange and revolting ride, what-

ever its meaning might have been, whether it was to show
that they fetched the fire, had been away and come home
again, or was a magic circle which they drew about the
fire; many insisted that certain smoky and ardent Powers
of a dangerous kind were conjured up by the ceremony.
Many sinister acts were performed. But the birth of the
fire announced itself to outsiders by being seen at a distance, when the hag's dance was over, and by the blaring
of lurs. That was what they were waiting for.

Then the lurs brayed, tu, tu, tu, tu, a triumphant flourish,
tu-h, long notes of deliverance, and they saw the fire among
the trees, more fire, flickering up all at once, many torches;
the procession left the grove with Tole at its head, all
bearing torches, turned off towards the heath, and all
the people joined it, lighting their torches from the others,
a whole migration of torch-bearers from the houses up to
the heath.

Behind Tole came the bridal couple, Boierik and Inge,
festively adorned, now wedded, since they had joined hands
upon the ring.

At the highest spot of the heath the bonfire was lighted,
a regular timber stack, and a minute after it had blazed
up, all the fires began to show for miles around, as far as
the eye could reach.

The newly married pair were then sent away, in a covered
cart like those used in the fields in summer, with a tent
and all the gear required for living out of doors. Many
hundreds of the same kind would leave the homesteads on
the morrow and take to the pastures with the cattle, the
beginning of the free summer life; the young couple were
the first, they were to initiate the move. It was their first
journey together; to begin with they could drive where
they pleased and spend the night in any part of the woods.

The young people accompanied the cart for some distance, in happy envy. Lucky couple! In the morning
they would return to the homestead to be honoured and

placed at the high table at a banquet, and would receive
gifts, and look beautiful and mysterious, and be admitted
to all the privileges of the elders, lucky people! Shouts
of joy followed them as they disappeared in the moonshine
which blended with the beginning of the night-long twilight, and many a merry cry from swains who ran by the
side of the cart and permitted themselves some liberty of
speech; but it drove all the faster and they were left behind with their good advice and rank laughter. Thus the
bridal pair went off.

Oh! The half-grown girls sighed and groaned and
stamped their feet; when *would* they come to that, when
would they be grown up!

While the dance was in full swing round the bonfire
Tole betook himself to his father's grave-mound, alone, as
was his custom.

In his absence the dance assumed a less sacred character,
the solemn circling degenerated somewhat in the direction
of a hop, and a game was started which was the privilege
of the young and to their minds the most attractive part
of the feast—the races between boys and girls.

It began almost of itself, through some young couple
breaking out of the ranks on a secret instigation, hidden
threads that pass between the young and bind them two and
two together; for it was usually the fact that the pair who
broke out and took to flight as though in sudden disagreement had agreed upon it beforehand or had just discovered
that they were of one mind; for many of them a connection
that lasted for life would begin in this game of catch.
However that might be, the girl took to flight, and the man
after her. As a rule she was soon caught and brought
back to the ranks, happy to be overpowered; sweet was the
flight, but sweeter to be fetched back with gentle com-
pulsion.

Yet the girl did not always allow herself to be caught

as a matter of course. Though she ran as though glued to
the ground, like the hedgehog, her sticks kept going under
her all the time, and she could not get tired, had incredible
tricks of twisting and turning and slipping from her pur-
suer at the last moment, so that it might take all the wind
of a hardy, vaulting young hunter to overtake her.

The game spread from the height far over the heath and
away to the woods, and sometimes a couple would disappear from view among bushes and undergrowth in the
distant twilight. If the man then caught the girl he was
liable to be heated and take hold of her roughly, but if
she asked it she was given quarter; the game was not to
have a painful ending, it was not for that these big, boisterous youths had their strength, and they could not associate
love with injury. Any dog can pull down a weaker opponent. They would be friends first. Hand in hand the
reconciled pair came back to their companions.

This racing, though not many knew it, was no doubt
originally a symbol, obscurely connected with the movements of the heavenly bodies, the sun and moon pursuing
one another. A dangerous third element comes in, in the
form of a rival who tries to separate the two racers and
to force himself in between them to the detriment of one;
this leads to a doubly exciting chase, but in the end the
right ones come together and the order of the universe is
re-established.

Occasionally the game takes a violent turn, through some
outstanding quarrel among three which here comes to a
head. There are two men in pursuit and the girl runs
for her life, in earnest as it seems; she is hampered by
her skirt and you can see her unfasten it as she runs, stand
still a second and let it fall; she jumps out of it in her
shift and flies on; that too is in the way, and she pulls it
up to her waist, running on with her dazzling bare legs,
and if her pursuers were not leaping high before they do
so now. The girl disappears into the wood, with a good

start, for in the middle distance the men are seen to rush at one another suddenly and roll over on the ground. After a short, sharp wrestling-bout one of them is left lying there, to get up presently and hobble away. But the other is up again and on the track of the fugitive into the wood; and that pair is seen no more. Their companions comfort themselves with the thought that if the man hasn't caught the girl he is hunting her still!

With dancing and chasing and all kinds of games the hours went by till past midnight; the fires all round were burning low and sunrise was not far off.

About midnight the lurs were heard sounding from the neighbourhood of the temple, long discordant notes, intentionally false, which seemed to rasp against each other, death-notes, and they knew what was happening: now they were being dispatched, the seven wretches who had been chosen to satisfy the harsh gods; the fire craved life in return for giving its warmth and holding back lightning and destruction, the sun and stars demanded an offering for maintaining the course of the year. But nobody liked the business, except perhaps the priestesses. Any who had ever seen it—the priestesses by the stone of sacrifice with sleeves rolled up over their shrunken, wiry forearms, the grove lit up by torches, with skeletons and corpses hanging about on the trees like walls of horror, the moon above —he would see it all again and shudder; any one who had been near and *heard* it—ugh! But the young people did not give much thought to the sacrifice, it was a ceremony of the elders, a manifestation of stony-hearted necessity, the order of the universe and that kind of thing, it did not weigh on their shoulders yet!

By degrees as the night wore on the groups round the fire dissolved, some would see the sun rise and dance before it in the wood, others stayed; one group had a fancy for the fjord, which glistened a couple of leagues away in the hazy moonshine and slumbering half-light of the night;

they felt a longing for salt water and a briny smell and would bathe at sunrise; others stretched themselves behind the bushes and would doze an hour or so; the groups went their several ways, to reassemble after sunrise for driving out the cattle, whose summer life was also to begin.

The fires died out; only smoke was to be seen far away on many heights; the dawn asserted itself and the country recovered its distances. The moon paled and faded out in the sky.

Over the moorland rose the lark, that herald of the birth of light, infinitely small as he sang in the sky, with the immense wide plains beneath him.

But the forest is closed within its leaves, with all its curtains drawn, a stagnant air as of a bedchamber, heavy with fragrance. Light begins to break through the leafy roof, golden green, and now the birds awaken. One after another they chirp, hidden beneath the foliage, from a thousand nests, a tiny, sleepy note full of the warmth of brooding; soon it is taken up and swells into a vast united many-voiced chorus through the woods.

And the sun rises, as a deep glow on the edge of the wood, rays of fire shooting up between the trunks, a dazzling world of light that merges trees and a whole quarter of the heavens in a ring of fire in which the sun moves, climbing free of the forest; like a ship of fire it casts off from the earth and sails into the open blue. Light and dew and morning stillness over all creation!

Misty forms rise from the grass, twirl as though picking up a trailing garment, and disappear. Spirits drift as borne upon a gust towards the trees of the forest and are merged in them, become one with the fresh light-green foliage; they are the souls of the trees returning home with the daylight.

But they leave a trace behind them even at high noon, a mysterious nakedness in the woods; the trees seem bewitched, with swelling, rounded limbs, forked limbs, like creatures standing on their heads with legs in air; forked trees everywhere, with scars like mouths in their bark, and their foliage trembles as long hanging hair, blue eyes open, the sky opens among the leaves, the forest is as though wrapt in the silent presence of woman.

And deep in the wooded dales the cuckoo, that mischievous wag, sounds his note that echoes between the slopes, with a flighty laughter to follow, ha, ga, ga, ga! Nothing that he does not know, and never will he keep silence!

V

CIMBERLAND'S BULL

AN hour or two after sunrise those who were up on the high ground could trace, if their ears were fine enough, a change in the tone of the whole country: the song of birds, the wind in the reeds and a chance human voice were not the only prevailing sounds, but from every quarter came the lowing of cattle, far and near, an impetuous, oft-repeated bellowing from the valleys below, and in the distance a sort of tissue of subtle, high-pitched sound which blended with the horizon and the sunshine. All over the land the cattle were being driven into the fields and greeted the pastures with the roar of enthusiasm that was their own.

And they came in sight; just below the Tolling cattle moved in a great straggling herd up to the wastes, with horsemen and dogs swarming in a ring outside them; farther off were motley cattle from other homesteads, all the fens dotted and dun-coloured with cattle; such would be the appearance of the country for the coming months. Behind the herds covered carts were seen crawling, bringing the tents and household goods, last of all whole loads of leather bags that would be returned in the course of the summer full of cheese.

But back to Tollingthorp came in the course of the day all the men who could be spared from the herds, from the whole country; now was the real beginning of the feast.

From early morning interest was centred on the smithy, where all preparations were being made for the final casting of the bull.

The firing of the mould had been successful—so far as could be judged. The outer crust was burnt red and crisp, here and there it had run, the heat had been as much as it could bear; what the core was like was not easy to say, but it did not rattle about inside; every trace of wax had naturally evaporated. Now they would chance it and make the casting, however it might turn out; and so impatient was the smith that he had already begun to heat the furnace the evening before and had kept the fire going all night. The metal lay like a flowing, crackling lake of fire in the white-hot furnace; the mould had been lowered into the pit, all was ready, with eyes weary with watching and sore from the fire and scorched fingers every one was waiting for a sign from Tole.

At the last moment Tole threw something into the furnace, no one knew what, and a green, immensely hot flame rose from the fiery lake in its interior. Then the smith with his own hands hammered away the fireproof stone from the outlet of the furnace, and the metal ran in a smooth bubbling stream into the mould, until it was full and the metal spurted over the side, spitting and flaming; quickly the smith plunged a spade into the stream and turned it off by another channel into a hole where the superfluous metal cooled and solidified.

The suspense was extreme while waiting for the bronze to harden and cool sufficiently to be approached; the smith stood by with furrowed face and deep-sunk eyes, worn out by weeks of doubting.

With tackles and winches the mould was hoisted up and brought into position above the pit, the smith seized a heavy wooden mallet and attacked it: even if he was knocking away the ground under his own feet, he went at it! The clay crust split and rang, he had aimed his blow at the bull's forehead, down rained the sherds and the bull's head was revealed as if by magic, newly cast and reflecting all the colours of fire, perfect and whole, even to the tips of the horns! But the smith hammered on, as though in anger, along the flanks, down the back, the hindquarters, the legs, and the chips hailed down like a vestment falling off: everywhere the image came out, whole and complete in the casting from head to foot!

Then the smith smiled, through soot and sweat and cinders, wrinkles and beard the smith smiled with all his white teeth like a child. Tole raised his broad hand high over his shoulder and brought it down in the smith's: Well done and thanks!

And the enthusiasm was general, for it was the finest sight that could be seen, the bull risen again, alive in the flashing, iridescent metal, like a bull of gold and sunshine; yesterday mortal and gone the way of all bulls; today re-born for eternity!

And that it was an event for the whole country was clear to all, a new sacred sign of union had here been created, an image which would gather all to worship. Ah, a fate-ful figure it would prove!

The smith walked round the image, a mirror of joy, bright and new-made like itself; it was still too hot to touch but he looked at it here, stooped down to examine it there, and nodded: the casting had come out in the small-est details, every trace on the surface of the wax was shown in the metal, even to the prints of fingers; yes, it was true, a finger-print, the finest possible thing was made imperishable.

And the smith shook his head, a shadow passed over his face: what a pity the Greek could not see it! For properly speaking the whole thing was his work: the mould, the figure of the bull was his. The casting and all its troubles, the responsibility and hard work had been borne by others, but the spirit was his. Yes, that the smith would say.

Artists are touchy people, who either complain when others, as they allege, steal their ideas, or else energetically refuse rewards in favour of a superior; degrees of merit too rare and personal for the attention of the ordinary man. Here, of course, between a freeman and a thrall, no comparison was possible. The Greek—he would be well on his way to the South by now, and they would like to know how he would chisel his way through the forests all alone. . . .

What was that? Not everybody was so well informed. The Greek, the "Squirrel," hadn't he been slaughtered with the other six last night?

Well no, it seemed he'd got away. He was missing in the cage when the others were fetched, however he had managed to get out, and it had been no use setting the dogs on his trail, he was too far off, a start of several hours; naturally a horse was missing too. So they had pulled a substitute out of the turf huts, of somewhere about the same size, and sacrificed him instead.

That was all that was known, and it was all forgotten before many days were past. But in certain circles, women's circles, there was a buzz of rumours which had a longer life. No complete story was ever pieced together, some knew one thing, others said it was all wrong, as true as they were alive and standing there; so what was the truth?

That it was Norna Gest who had set the captive free and let him run seemed to be a fixed point that nobody could get away from; it had happened at dusk when every one was up at the bonfire, and had not been discovered till several hours later. But what could have been the scald's motive? Here it was that one particular woman with a shrill voice and not very pleasant-looking eyes declared roundly that it was Inge, the young newly wedded wife, that had been behind the scald, for the two had been seen together up on the heath and Inge had had her arms on the old man's neck and had certainly whispered something to him, and she had been weeping and quite beside herself!

Some boys had seen this, but the woman who told the story hoped it would never come to the ears of Boierik. . . .

Nor did it, for the things which the women discussed at great length among themselves and which were meat and drink to them, never went any further; the men had a thousand other things to think about. And besides, it is said that men's senses are too coarse to catch the higher and finer tones, such as the chirping of grasshoppers.

In any case the wedding feast went off without the slightest discord. The young couple received costly gifts, especially the bride, clasps and stuffs and dresses to the value of many score of cattle, for their families on both sides were among the first in the land; it was not often that a Spring Bridal occurred so near the top.

From Norna Gest she received a gift on which many cast envious eyes, in spite of its being the smallest of all her gifts, but it was a gem from the South, to be worn on the neck, possessing undoubtedly the greatest powers for bringing luck. The old heads of families took it between their big fingers like an insect, held it at arm's length before them, without being able to make out quite what it was. But it was really an insect, very like a beetle, of highly polished black stone, with a hole through it for the string; on the flat under-surface a tiny picture was engraved, almost invisible, the head of a woman. Probably it was a very powerful divinity under whose protection the wearer of this jewel would come. It did not escape the notice of some that the young wife showed signs of emotion on receiving the gift.

Inge now sat among the women and wore her hair gathered up and hidden under the little married woman's cap, it would never again flow freely, and its light was quenched; to make up for it she had a heavy band of gold on her head.

The banquet took place in the open air, and this time the women took part in it; they had driven in from all parts of the country, stout mothers of families hung round with amber beads, with their children and grandchildren; great family gatherings there were, cooking and eating their food in the open under the great trees round the homestead; provisions had been brought and everything necessary for camping out. For that matter the feast might have lasted all the summer; they carried everything with them wherever they went, and the summer life was as a feast in itself.

But this was a special opportunity of meeting and seeing one another. Families were introduced, the offspring of the years exhibited, proud mothers pushed their children into the foreground and held them there with a hard grip until they had been admired, for the children did not like coming forward.

The matrons put Inge through her paces and talked to her about washing, and Inge came off in housemotherly fashion, answering with all she knew about washing. In brewing she also passed, came fairly well through a long examination in weaving, but with the bright tears twinkling on her eyelashes, the matrons were so strict. Well, well, they would let her go, and the women rolled off somewhere else to hold another matron's council there and dazzle one another with amber beads as big as fists and rattle them and turn the broad side of their arm-rings outward and smile sweetly to one another, showing a lot of teeth.

The young people took stock of each other in their own way, with the unavoidable glance young people have, the unconscious power of the first impression—a pair of seven-year-olds looking at each other! Ah, many were the looks that their souls recorded on *that* fine May Day.

If the wedding was an event on account of the two great families, the best known in the country, which thereby united their branches, it gained in importance from the consecration of the great image of the Bull, which took place at the same time and provided a background; in the popular chronology the year was afterwards known as that in which Boierik and Inge were married and Cimberland's Bull taken into the sanctuary.

It happened the same day. The image was actually finished, only the supports which had separated the nucleus from the outer crust had to be removed, otherwise the figure was whole, cast in one piece with its pedestal, faultless in every way and imperishable.

With particular joy and awe Tole gazed at the Bull's forehead; here, just where the "star" should be, the sacred symbol of rotation had been inserted, looking like a glittering little golden sun in the freshly cast metal. Some years before the smith had punched out the same sign on the Bull's forehead in the figure at the base of the great silver bowl, by order of Tole, and it was seen at the end of the pole of the sacred car; it was the symbol of coming to life, which connected the innermost centre of life with the secret of the fire's conception and the course of the heavenly bodies.

Tole ordained that the laying of hands upon the Bull's forehead and the ancient symbol should be decisive for every Cimbrian; no man *could* be unfaithful to the obligations and destiny thus assumed.

The sacred car was brought and the image set up in it, with great solemnity and in the presence of the chiefs of all the clans in the country. The effect of it was excellent when standing in the car, as though cast in one piece with it; thus it would be driven in future round the hundreds at the great festivals; and every one could see that in this Tole had added both to the sacred import and to the splendour of the country's worship, when the holiest of all symbols, whose nature was only known to the priest and the priestesses, was enclosed within the image, as was intended. That the image exercised immediate power could already be seen: the women and the common folk, whose presence in the direct vicinity of the car was of course not permitted, spontaneously made signs of submission at a distance, putting earth on their foreheads, when they saw the gleaming Bull being driven up to the sacred grove to the music of lurs.

The transference of the holy of holies took place at midnight, only Tole and the priestesses attending to the important and uncanny ceremonies connected therewith.

Here a conflict arose; the ancient sibyls were not pleased with Tole's new dispositions and would not have the god moved from his house to the belly of a bull, they raised a disturbance like a lot of cats, and Tole was obliged to use a stick on them before he could carry out his purpose. It came to a positively scandalous scene when Tole wanted to take the fire god out and put it in the hollow prepared in the Bull, closing with a door; the priestesses held on to the god and Tole had to wrest it from them and hit them over the fingers and on the skull with it; and that hurt, for it was a hard god, but it made them give in.

Fortunately this scene remained one of the inner secrets which never came outside the temple; only Norna Gest, who was present as Tole's confidential friend, had any inkling of it; and perhaps the old ravens of the grove who were so tame that they wriggled their way right into the houses and said How d'ye do and blinked the whites of their eyes.

They were having a good time, all day long and for half the light night they could be heard chattering in the trees and presumably exchanging observations about the new fruits the trees were bearing for them: such and such a one was good, but the one over there was superlatively excellent; thus it was once more proved that many a man's merits are not fully manifested until he is dead.

Other great flocks of birds came and hovered in swarms circling like great wheels above the grove, crows, jackdaws, even eagles; but they had not been invited and were chased away with loud croaks and screams by the ravens, the right-

ful owners; great battles were fought in the air and the
feathers flew above the sacred grove.

The Spring Wedding and the consecration of the Bull
God were celebrated during the following days with great
driving matches, horse-races, tournaments and ball games.

But first the spring sowing was consecrated, a holy act
accomplished on behalf of the whole country by Tole, who
sowed the spring seed in a field, alone in the presence of
earth and sun; thus the covenant was observed, and the rest
could be left to the thralls. The sowing fell late this year,
as Tole had not been able to get the solar signs to agree
before.

In the driving races a franklin from the west came off
victorious with a pair of mares that were not much to look
at but good goers; the distances were greater where he came
from and the nags of those parts simply had to stretch their
legs. In the riding races a certain thin, vicious animal was
successful, as was expected. Of course it was the quality
of the animals that was here decided; of the riders neither
the strongest nor the nimblest could count on winning, but
the lightest, and of these again the most expert.

The interest and excitement were extraordinary; women
were admitted to this sport and brightened the green turf
with their spick and span-new spring dresses, heavy-footed,
each with a perceptible weight of jewelry about her, silver
chains, clasps, amber, bronze and gold, all the family treasures.

The dress was the same for all, though with very slight
differences which showed from what part of the country
they came. Their clothing was composed of two pieces,
smock and skirt. Foot-gear, none. The foot trod the
ground with delight in the direct contact with earth and the
free passage of air about the legs under the skirt; the woo-
ing of spring was felt to the waist. Over the smock a

sleeveless bodice was worn, in bright colours and very varied patterns; it was here that the taste of each separate district showed itself, and critical were the glances bestowed upon anything new and seen for the first time, without the slightest notice of the wearer; the dress was examined with a pursing of the mouth: no, that was really too much; and a note was made to copy it.   Finally a cloak, worn either over the shoulders and fastened with a splendid brooch, or over the arm, completed the costume.   No display of furs, squirrel or marten, could be made, it was too warm for that. Herbs were carried in the hand, the head was bare, the matrons wearing thin grey pigtails under their circlets of gold.

The men's passion for gambling was aroused and many bets were made, the horses that competed changed hands again and again, and sometimes more went with them; bargaining flourished and few came home with the same team which they had set out; a love of bartering and change had seized on the franklins, who coveted their neighbour's jade as violently as they suddenly despised their own precious colt.   But however much the nags changed hands, they remained in the clans.

In the evening there was great feasting, men and women affectionately together, sitting in each other's laps and sipping lovingly at the same bowl, offering their sweethearts nuts from lip to lip.

Somehow or other, though the feast began with spring water, it ended with old ale, first a single keg, discovered in the straw of one of the carts, then another, several more, as though the kegs were breeding; and as the night wore on there were sounds of exuberant song from the yard and the surrounding groves where the leather tents were pitched, a joyous howling and roaring as of many wild beasts, screams of delight and loud cacklings, songs of praise and warm bursts of laughter, a general uproar of satisfaction.

Nobody slept, the night was too good for that; on the

other hand there was much scurrying of bare legs among
the tents and flapping of flying smocks, as when birds are
on the move, cuckoo-cries and hide-and-seek, a carefree
rapture through the long, blessed night, with a blush in the
northern sky and the meadows full of elves. The moon
sailed high, pale with watching; only with sunrise and the
song of birds did the tents fall silent little by little.

All in the most profound peace and harmony. Only a
single unpleasant incident happened: a couple of young
fellows who flew at each other over a girl, one much bigger
and stronger than the other, so it was rather unfair when
he doubled up his opponent and made fun of him into the
bargain. All weapons had been laid aside; the smaller
man dashed at his conqueror and killed him with a nail;
instantly he was seized—dastard's deed! no fair fight! no
challenge made! The men dragged him to a tree, and with
a voluptuous feeling the sinner went to his punishment,
conscious of his shame but not regretting it; to die would
be a relief! But he shed salt tears and held his breath
when the noose was round his neck, not from fear but in
order to die more quickly, so unbearable was the thought
that, though he had spoilt the other man's prospects—in a
cowardly way, yes, but still the swine was dead—he would
not after all get the girl he had set his heart on! The two
fighting-cocks were burnt together and their ashes deposited
in the same grave, with razor and tatooing-needle; it was
to be hoped they would get on better hereafter, beyond the
fire.

On the second day the feast took on a more scattered character. The women did their cooking on the turf between
the tents, all the country's families like one great family,
smoke and the smell of food wherever you went, and everywhere the gossip of women, more and more intimate as
they got into each other's confidence. Ah yes, all their
troubles and trials, but a good deal of merriment besides;

they laughed and laughed, with tight-shut lips and inward
chuckling, their stomachs dancing, over some of the things
they heard—*men!*

Meanwhile these same men were up on the heath, holding
the Thing; they could be seen sitting the best part of the day
within the circle of white wands, discussing serious matters,
and the ears of the neighbouring peoples would no doubt
be tingling; perhaps it was historic decisions that were being made, plans for invading the land of the Aaboers and
laying it waste, or a raid into Salling with burning of
houses and lifting of cattle; they were said to have good
steers in that part.   Everyday conditions had returned to
the extent that the men were armed again, which made a
certain difference in their bearing; every man saw the long
spear in his neighbour's hand, and joking seemed to have
been dropped.   Show rides in full armour, with the animal-
crested helmet, formed part of the day's amusements.   It
seemed as though there was a longing for a taste of warfare
and manslaughter after so much softness.

Afterwards some went hunting, spearing the wild boar in
the marshes, with much merriment, or followed the deer on
horseback halfway across the country with hounds and
hallooing; while mummeries and masked dances by torch-
light were prepared in the deepest secrecy for the evening.

Others betook themselves to the river, where a fair was
being held; several traders had come sailing up as far as
their light craft could go and had spread out their wares in
tents upon the meadows; the women especially went that
way.   Betrothed couples who had met during the nights of
the festival, two hearts with one beat, came hand in hand
to tie the knot for ever with clasps and chains and pend-
ants, the handsomest the trader might have to show.

It turned their heads, like the revelation of the starry sky,
to look into the booths and the opened chests of wares that
had travelled a thousand miles, from the shores of the sunrise, through all the kingdoms of the world, till they had

finally arrived at the very head of a narrow river to dazzle the eyes of the fresh-faced countrymen: burnished bronze mirrors from the south, the finest glass beads, golden trinkets of incredibly delicate filigree work, stuffs with woven figures of birds, so fine that you could not see the threads, clinging to the finger-tips like cob-webs; pins, the costliest pins, and finger-rings whose stones had magic powers over the soul.

Bartering was brisk and long, the buyers with flushed cheeks, unable to resist their desires, bidding too much simply to satisfy them quickly; the trader impenetrable, with dark eyes in which nothing was to be read. When the fair was over the foreign merchants took a whole fleet of prams down the river, laden to the water's edge with the wares received in barter, furs, hides and wool, which were now to travel southward the way all the finery had come.

With the third and fourth days the Spring festival ebbed out. One covered cart after another was loaded with tents and cooking-pots, youngsters and puppies, the bullocks were put in and it rocked out of the yard towards that part of the country where the owner's herds were to be found.

Norna Gest wandered off one day; they saw his back disappearing to the southward, his long staff measuring the ground as he walked. Then all knew that the holiday was at an end.

VI

VEDIS

THE summer passed, in self-forgetfulness, like all summers. The birds hatched the spring's eggs into young, the calves became heifers, the lambs grew big and fat, boisterous from a whole summer's sporting and galloping about.

Summer narrows the mental vision; men live in the moment, with the animals that know nothing of time. All through the long summer the families moved from place to place in the moors together with their herds, staying a while now here, now there, in tents or huts but mostly under the open sky, and often for weeks they had nothing but sour milk, even hunting did not tempt them; and for the rest they lived on the wind, on song, light nights and each other's company, few thoughts and much fellowship. The heat of midsummer was exhausting, they sought shade and dozed among green leaves. The sheep hid their heads under each other's bodies in search of coolness.

The bees swarmed, it was their hour of being, you could see how they were born of the sun, great hot hosts of them came out of the sun's fire in the dazzling noonday sky and flung themselves down to find a hollow tree to live in; and men noticed where they settled so as to take their honey from them in the autumn.

And as the honey stored up sun, fragrance and summer, they entered upon autumn with a reserve of warmth in the blood, sunburnt and saturated with light. The long dark months that followed took away the sunburn and transformed the red blood into memories and visions. Then it

228

snowed for the first time, and to many it was as though summer had never been. Winter, ay, that is our life, it blots out all summers.

But in autumn the spring lived again with its fruit. The brief infatuation, the blossoming, life's fleeting touch, all soul and perfume, this now begins to grow and gather weight; the sun's smile over the corn is forgotten, but the grain is there.

In the depth of winter's most hopeless night hope was reborn: Inge, the May Bride, gave birth to her firstborn, a spring of the springtime, a star in the midwinter night. The new life appeared and grew together with the solstice.

It was a girl; the young father's first glance was not for the child but for its mother, when the women called him in; had it been a boy it was usually the other way about. She was given to the mother and was called Vedis. Her destiny was fixed at birth, she was devoted to Heaven and was to be a vestal and a sibyl; as soon as she was five winters old she would be given to the priestesses to be educated in her duties.

But so long as her mother could keep her, she was her joy. She who herself had so lately been a child continued her childhood in her daughter; it might almost be said that she played with her firstborn like a doll.

She was fair like both her parents, the lightest creature that had ever been seen, a doubled fairness, with eyes like the milky blue sky of early spring, and a skin so white that it suggested snow and moonlight, almost greenish in the shadows, like the white shoots that grow in caves and never see the sun. But as she was fair and pure so was she cheerful, healthy and round, a rarely happy child, bubbling over with joy as soon as she could distinguish one thing from another.

Life began for her like a great darkness from which the world emerged, a world within a world. They were two in it, when her first memories began, one smaller than herself, but it was a boy, a little fat thing that tottered about and copied all she did, was silent and sleepy, but wanted everything he saw. To those two life appeared as a series of important discoveries, every day some new wonder or other revealed itself to them. Even while they had scarcely been outside the narrow room in which they were born the world came to them, in fragmentary fashion but so that they could never afterwards forget it.

*The winters were long, it seemed to be always winter and the memory of any other state of things was lost; they were indoors for all eternity, on the floor between their little bed and their stool; the grown-ups towered in a world above them, to which they looked up with head bent back. Above them was the roof with its beams and hanging shapes of soot, a primeval world that had always existed; and at the top of all was the smoke-hole, a glimmering well leading to outer space, always coloured by the smoke of the fire, but at night when the room was cold showing clear right up to the stars, which swam a little in the warm breath that rose through the hole. They were always the same stars, although they were so many; they only saw them now and then when they woke at night and were alone with the immense darkness, and it seemed as if the cold that fell upon their faces came from them. Then when they cried they heard their mother's voice close by in the darkness and felt her hand on the bed until they fell asleep again.

Wonderful messages came from the world outside. In the doorway, where was the threshold which might not be passed, strangely disguised forms appeared, wrapt to the nose in cloths, and brought in peats and heather, letting in icy air with them, so that the floor was cold for a long time. And the heather seemed to be wrapt round with cold, it held snow and the bundles were frozen together, with little icicles that quickly thawed and wetted the fingers and tasted freshly of earth.

What a scent the heather had, as soon as it came into the

warmth! A strong, violent scent, like the emanation of a
being, the heather's being; it filled the room and penetrated
into every corner, spicy, sweet and astringent, a smell that
got into the nose, into the throat, into the forehead; and as
it smelled, so it tasted, hot and bitter, cooled by ice-water,
like a hot world that had concealed and concentrated itself
in the tiny green needles of the heather.

The children made their first and greatest discoveries in
the bundles of heather by the sloppy door, they pulled out
the prettiest plants from them and busied themselves all
day long with evergreen whortleberry, whose small hollowed leaves tasted so strong; with twigs of bearberry,
which looked almost the same but greyer, with berries most
attractively red but a disappointment to the tooth, only pulp
with no taste—they spat them out again and wiped their
tongue on their sleeve; bog myrtle, with lovely little cones,
not fit to eat, sharp as certain insects they had chanced to
get into their mouths, but valuable things to collect and
keep; crowberries, of which the grown-ups cleverly made
brooms to sweep the floor, but they were the best of all,
they might have blackberries on them, even in winter
time, they were dark-red and watery inside, had felt the
frost, tasted of rain with a sluggish sweetness and a bitter
bracing aftertaste from the little pips in the fruit. Moss
they picked out of the heather and long, branching green
stalks of club-moss; a dreadful bug they came upon which
made their fingers smell; the heather revealed a whole
world to the two children of winter.

Even stronger was the scent of the heather's soul when it
came into the fire; then it crackled and sweated white smoke
and gave out a burnt, hot breath; the twigs popped and
sputtered before they burst into flame, shrank up as they
burned and shrivelled into little worms of fire that had a
charred smell and fell into ashes.

The fire was a world in itself, glowing and unapproachable. It was only to be looked at from a distance—you're

not to play with *that*, their mother warned them—and the little ones stood away from it and watched the heather burn, felt the radiant heat on their faces and were lighted up by the fire, with serious, puzzled looks, such as the fire always holds with its enchantment. In its hot places they thought they could see into infinite abysses of fire, the infinity of light.

Between these two abysses, the sky above the smoke-hole and the fire, the little ones lived, these were their Up and Down. In space they were cramped, but they lived in presentiments; the house-door shut out the world, and through its cracks the fine drift-snow found its way, an icy cold powder shaped into little tongues by the draught. The timber of the walls had cracks in it, deep black mysterious slits, through which cold came; these were the children's caves, in which they hid their fir-cones, pebbles and other treasures.

Glum was the name of the little brother with whom Vedis shared the world; his tongue soon found its freedom and a little language of their own sprang up between the two.

Later on a new voice was heard in the room, a being for the present invisible, but seemingly a powerful being, for it upset the peace of the whole world; the two were banished from the room and from Mother in charge of other, unknown grown-ups; their existence was thrown into confusion and was never the same again.

No, only once again did they see the room where their world had begun, and then it was completely cleared, the beds and everything taken away, leaving nothing but the four bare timber walls; the fire on the floor was extinguished and a thick carpet of juniper twigs laid in its place. And in the middle of the empty room lay Mother, a long white form with only the face to be seen, and it was whiter than the white snow.

Some one joined their hands and led them to the bier, and

then they saw that Mothers' cheeks were frozen, there were flowers of ice on them and on her forehead, fine stars and spraying fronds, as when the water freezes at night. The room was colder than the coldest night, everywhere the walls were glistening with rime and threads of ice, water that had trickled down over the timber and frozen.

The dead woman was so young, they had given her a wreath of the evergreen whortleberry leaves on her head. And in her hands they had placed the orchis, not its stalk and leaves, which were not to be found now, but the roots, which they had dug up under the snow; two roots, one black, the other white: the old year and the new, death and resurrection.

Daylight fell upon the bier through the smoke-hole, which was no longer discoloured nor disturbed, the air above it was quite clear and still, with a light as of ice from heaven, the bitter, blinding frost-glare outside.

And then, another day, the two little ones were led outside, where they had to be carried, and shown a mighty fire blazing with white flames in the wintry sunshine, a little way off in the midst of the snow. Many grown-up people were passing round it to the sound of lurs and throwing clothes and other things into the fire. And when Mother never showed herself again and they asked for her, they were told that she had gone to the home of the Sun.

BOOK THREE
THE RAID

THE FLOODS

AGAIN Vedis's world widened, there were now three of them in it, a new little fat brother who tottered about and took Glum's things and had to have them wrested out of his hands by the offended Glum; his name was Ingvar and for a time he only expressed himself in shrieks, but afterwards he mastered their language and the three got on well together, so long as Vedis maintained peace and no disturbing interference on the part of the grown-ups took place.

They were now in another house, in the not very sympathetic charge of women who chased them away from the fire and from the door, but had no compensation to offer for all the things they prohibited. The three then shut themselves up in their own world, which nobody took from them, since nobody had any inkling of it.

But, alas, they were parted; the day arrived when Vedis was taken from her brothers and led away to her duties, at the age of five. She was brought before a number of hunchbacked old women who smelt of mice and had bristly hair on their chins, they felt her over, without a smile, and turned her round between their bony fists, croaking to each other the while. Then she was placed under the care of one of the younger sibyls and had to begin looking on when the fire was tended, but was still too young to take a turn herself. She was led into the holy of holies, and there she saw the bronze Bull, big and shining like a creature of light, and she was taught to make the sign of submission with her forehead to the ground.

On the whole she was well treated; they put her to sleep in a house with two young girls who were also to be sibyls and who received her kindly; they played together on the sly and knew a way of laughing heartily without a sound being heard. Their house was round, made of wattlework plastered with clay, and at the top was a smoke-hole, through which Vedis could see the same stars as she knew from the house she came from, soon to be forgotten.

If she woke at night she thought of her mother, whom she no longer remembered except as she had seen her for the last time, the long white form under the light from the smoke-hole. And then she was always reminded of the glittering cold motes in the air, like the finest powdered ice, which descended into the room from the smoke-hole, stars that sank down and were so cold and rested upon Mother's frozen face. But when she awoke and was afraid in her loneliness she felt at her neck where she had a chain that could not be taken off, with a holy protecting object on it, a little black beetle; this her mother had given her, kissing it again and again on her breast, as though to kiss it fast there; little as she was she understood that it was her protector.

But Glum and Ingvar were always in her thoughts and for the first few weeks she was dumb with grief at being taken away from them. And afterwards, when she had to live without them, the loss was enshrined within her heart in a grave of pain; never, never did she cease to regret them.

Later on she saw them now and then, when she was occasionally allowed to leave the sanctuary; but they had quickly grown into boys and their feelings for Sister were different from those she had for them. They soon became aware that they were sons of Boierik and aspired with all their might to the world of men, began to talk horses even before they could pronounce their words properly and were always in the open air near the young men. Nor were

they themselves unnoticed, their father made them their
first toy bows with his own hands; the popularity of the
two lads reached even Tole himself and the old man was
often seen leading his great-niece's sons by the hand; of
all the innumerable offshoots of his family who swarmed
about the place he seemed to be specially fond of these
two.

But although her brothers were always there, Vedis
could only half approach them. Her father she seldom
saw, his eyes were always kind when he looked at her, but
it was only a flying glance as he went by on horseback;
more than that he never gave any one. So Vedis's eyes
followed her father and brothers as a greatness she loved
but which always escaped her; the sense of her loss buried
itself more deeply in her soul, the loss of a world which
vanished in a world. Never, never would she cease to
regret.

Within the fence surrounding the sanctuary Vedis had a
secret hiding-place to which she could steal unseen and
spy out through the bushes towards the homestead and the
world of men. She watched the wonderful young braves
tearing over the ground, now on their horse and now off,
flying in the air, now with their arms on the horse's neck,
now with a hand in its mane, inseparable, a galloping
friendship; she heard a shower of stones from the impetuous hoofs, and she loved them, loved them, horses and
men, the terrible, magnificent, rough and nimble heroes!

None of them knew that a watcher sat within the sanctuary yearning for those who durst not approach it; the
inviolable one who dreamed of great transgressors, in un-
selfish worship, soulful and fervid, all emotion and nothing else, as only a child's heart with a budding woman
within can love.

She became a woman, grew and was grown-up, and alas,
her heart grew with her; with love and anguish she looked
upon the warriors from *her* world, the world of the vestals,

the lifelong virgins; and heard the clamour of their iron accoutrements and grating shields, when the horsemen rode past and the fierce fellows all jingled together, with a wave swinging over them of heads and shoulders going up and down, the splendid, splendid butchers!

But then it was no longer from the sanctuary that she watched them, but always from the travelling waggon, always on the road towards new lands, new worlds, with the homeland almost forgotten as the years passed since they all broke up and migrated and existence became quite, quite changed.

Yes, the Cimbrians had left their country. It had come about through great disasters, threatening all with destruction and drowning; flocking together of people in one place as though all the men and women alive sought each other's company, a crowd that hid the green grass from view, of wrathful men and silent women; and so they had left.

Their misfortunes went as far back as Vedis could remember, they were a part of her life, she had never known anything else. As early as the year of her birth the waters were high in· all Cimberland, and over the whole of Jutland, as they learned; the thaw was followed by floods that put all the meadows and lowlands under water, the fjords rose above their banks, the rivers swelled and were stemmed so that they filled the valleys far up the country, the broad ancient valleys through which the waters of the Ice Age had once found an outlet, they were now full again.

In summer the waters subsided, but every autumn opened with storms and rain, the sea rose and made itself felt far up the fjords like a strong, violent pulse, and outside it was black, with high, steep waves; the frost bound the water like an armour upon the land, snow piled itself above, and in the spring when the ice was gone and the lowlands

dried at last, the floods had left seaweed high up on the
fields, the ground was white with salt, and that year no
corn was sown.

For five years in succession the floods returned and rose
higher from year to year. Nobody could doubt that the
sea aimed at the conquest of the land and every year sent
down new waves so as finally to be strong enough to lay
it low.

Every attempt was made to propitiate the humid Powers
by sacrifices, direct appeals; cattle were driven in hosts
into the sea, and the poor horned beasts floated back on to
the land with bellies distended and hoofs in the air; the
sea would not accept the peace offering.

The whole country was summoned to meet at the Vebjerg, in the midst of Jutland, Harders and Aaboers from
the south, even the men of Salling and Thy were there, all
ancient quarrels set aside for the time, for the floods threatened the whole of Jutland; and when all the country's
leaders and chiefs of clans were assembled a high Thing
was solemnly proclaimed and the sea was arraigned before
it.

Yes, all the great franklins in their united wisdom dug
up ancient prescriptive rights and asserted the claims of
justice: the land was theirs, thus far and no farther; they
denounced the conduct of the sea as robbery and aggres-
sion! And the sea actually accepted the summons, made
its appearance in the country that same year with heaving
black waters and spewed up a whale which rotted and
stank in the fields the whole summer, not so far from the
Vebjerg itself but that it could be seen from there. The
sea had declined to be governed by the judgment of the
assembled franklins: to remain outside their coasts.
Powerless their court and sentence!

Some of the younger men, who found the ways of legal
chicanery too slow, formed themselves into a mixed body

from many districts, with Boierik, as was to be expected, at their head, and made an armed attack on the sea, rode in full harness and in serried ranks eastward to the Cattegat and challenged the blue sea, pressed on and pierced it with their spears; as far as the outer shoals they carried their charge, scoffing the waves; but then they had to turn again, the sea only yawned and made the warriors wet; their campaign was a failure.

The same year Boierik disappeared together with a troop of Cimbrians of the same spirit as himself, southward, it was said; and, flood or no flood, his absence was felt almost as a welcome change of weather in his usual haunts, the thralls hugged themselves, got the wounds of his whip healed and scratched their backs as far as they could reach, with sounds that were something like song; among the freemen too many a young fellow held up his crest and took up more room in the landscape. But good manners returned and the thralls dropped their singing when Boierik came back a few months later.

Secret meetings and discussions followed; it leaked out that Boierik had been far down in the South, all the way to Valland, to spy out the lands, and was now for leaving the country in a body and seeking fresh pastures where pastures were to be had. He was keener than ever and appeared in a foreign helmet which was closed all round, nothing but iron to be seen, and he never took it off, as far as he was concerned a state of war had begun and would last for ever; if the country turned beggarly then out of it!

Finally came the last grievous year, when both seas attacked the land at the same time, fjords and rivers swollen, rain as from opened sluices, foaming lakes rushing in from every quarter; then they thought their doom was near.

It was springtime after the thaw and the previous year had ended with high water and the valleys filled to the brim, masses of snow on the high ground which melted and added to the flood, rain in torrents, and a north-westerly gale which brought in the North Sea on the back of the land and packed the Cattegat with spring tides that flooded all the fjords of the east coast.

This drove the inhabitants of Cimberland out of the valleys and up to the high ground with their cattle, horses and poultry, all that they could save; but much was lost, including many hundred human lives. Houses and dwellings were flooded, the earth huts filled and were washed out, the timber houses floated away, and that was the last sight the fugitives saw, house and home floating down the fjord and out to sea, while they themselves with children in their arms and their shivering, bellowing cattle in front sought safety in the interior, wading in mud and sodden turf, battered with rain and blasts, in half darkness at high noon: would they live through the day?

Waggons and possessions were saved, life was saved, and then they formed camp up on the moors as they were used to do in summer; but alas, it was not summer, and it looked as though it would never be summer again.

Here on the heaths and in the wind-scourged woods the clans and families met from every quarter of Cimberland, all who bore the name of Cimbrian, the whole people in their thousands, an immense concourse of victims, a meeting as in the face of death. As one great family they had once entered the country and had spread and increased in the good days; now that disaster was upon them they assembled again and their numbers were great, immensely great; was this the end, or was it a new beginning?

Origin and destruction had met, even the dumb beasts felt that and it overcame lesser fears; stags could be seen amongst the cattle, they were banished from the dales; wolves and wild boars made for the dry land, shook themselves and looked with the eyes of sinners upon all these men, who on their side were too miserable to do anything to the wet creatures of sorrow. Even the horses did not snort and lose their wits as usual when the scent of wolves reached their nostrils; they stooped in herds with head down and tail in the air, the wet forelock hanging over the eye, coughing in their throats with jaw awry and teeth bared, throwing their dejected heads backward, quite old all of them with rain and adversity, rumbling in their empty bellies but with no appetite for the withered winter grass that was stuck to the ground with rain; they lowered their muzzles and sniffed at it, but brought them up again and sighed, in the way of horses, very composedly, and scraped the ground with numbed feet as though to find some other destiny.

Here then were men and beasts driven together as on an island, with floods and waters on every hand, exposed to cold downpours and hail-showers, the earth wet, the heather wet, the woods another bath of rain if they sought shelter there, their waggons and skins wet, the fire smouldering in musty leather tents with wood too wet to burn, everything red with rust, even the swords in their sheaths, straps and clothes swollen with water, men's skins blotched and benumbed, their backs wet, their brows full of raindrops—and no one knew how long.

The storm increased, blasts of rain came on in hosts like one wet wall behind another over the wild country, pressing down the woods, low and bent already, raising a cold fog of lashed and vapourized drops from the heather, creasing the surface of pools and floods, as though all the water would forcibly tear itself free and go the way the wind went. It blew so that big strong men leaned forward on the wind beyond their balance, to keep their feet; with hand to mouth they shouted to each other to be heard; it made every man feel alone with his thoughts and the cold roots of his hair.

Terrible tidings arrived, messengers who returned half senseless and blinded by riding in rain and against the wind; the men drove them in under a bluff, behind big stones, where there was shelter so that they could be heard, and the ring closed about them to keep the news from going further, but a rumour of it reached the crowd and madness was stamped on the women's faces: the North Sea had come a league into the land!

From people who came from Salling, where they had it from Mors, news just arrived from Thy, it had been heard that the sea was riding in upon the neck of Jutland with waves that stood on each other's shoulders; the sea was raging madly, perfectly white with flying foam and scum, the waves chewed up great rocks, sand-dunes and corn-fields disappeared, the sea came round behind, broke through and surrounded whole districts, islands lay out in the surging deep, remains of the mainland that had gone bit by bit into the billows!

From the fjords on the east news came that almost every tract was gone already, and from far to the south vague rumours found their way that the sea was swallowing the root of Jutland, many leagues of land and thousands of human beings had gone beneath the waves.

Then there was weeping in the Cimbrians' camp, the women sat over their children and wailed, put their wet plaits of hair to their eyes and wept into them, making them wetter still: Alas, their poor country! Far and near was the sound of sniffing and suppressed sighs, the weeping of the women which blended like another stray gust with the gale and the rain and made the men turn pale.

Three days the storm lasted, and for all that time semi-darkness brooded over the homeless, with rain, hail and snow succeeding each other; short commons prevailed in waggons and tents, bread was unknown, milk scarce at this time of the year, the herds were thinned, to slaughter meant making one's self poorer. If the danger of drowning should pass the spectre of famine arose behind it.

The Elders waited and waited, letting the storm pass over their heads, there was nothing else to be done. But the young men took it in a strange way, with mad passion; it seemed as though the storm fired them with new, inconceivable joys, they rode out at night into the tempest, galloping and roaring with the mighty Breather; shaking their heads the Elders saw that if the rude, dark Lord of the Storm continued to rage the young men would end by making friends with him. And indeed that actually happened.

Boierik was out in the tempest, and his following grew greater and greater; assemblies to which half Cimberland flocked, with Boierik's rusty helmet always towering in the middle, and from it came speeches that swept with the force of the storm; men armed themselves noisily, revolt was in the air, and great decisions.

And the decision came the first time the sun appeared. It was a mighty moment. One forenoon it was, and the sun was only out a short time, the clouds opened in wings of fire from heaven to earth with an immense hole between, full of a welter of light, blue abysses and in the midst the sun, with the clearness of spring but cold; it sent a passing smile over the country, swift as the wind light and shadow hurried across the woods like a ray of hope. And then an extraordinary thing happened: *it hailed in sunshine*, from the height of that vast fiery door, which was black as pitch on one side and white as fire on the other, a hail-shower came down to earth like thousands of fiery arrows; *the rainbow stretched in glowing colours across the chasm of the sky, and right through it flashed the lightning!* A thunderclap was heard in storm and iight; then the hail-shower shut out the sun again, and in the whirling gloom every man bowed his head, trembling at the revelation of Heaven.

But in the moment when the sun was out, the lot was cast which decided the fate of the Cimbrians.

Boierik cast it, and he was terrible to behold as he did it, fierce on behalf of all his people, in a ferment of fate-fulness. He flung the cleft ash-stick towards heaven more in sign of challenge than as a devout appeal for a decision affecting himself and his followers. The stick did not go very high; the wind took it and twirled it round several times before it fell some way off; twelve men, the witnesses, approached and picked it up, brought it back to the Thing and gave their testimony: the white, split side was upper-most. That meant leaving the country.

Swords flew from their scabbards in the hailstorm and thundered upon shields; a loud war-cry sounded in unison: Accept the omen! The act took place on a mound with all legal forms, a duly constituted Thing and all the neces-sary sacrifices; they had only waited to see the sun's face before casting the lot; now it had been done.

But the court was entirely self-established; the young men with Boierik at their head had simply taken matters into their own hands without consulting the Elders; they had been their own Thing, and now the step was taken there was no going back, they had challenged a decision from Heaven and intended to stand by it.

Before this nobody but Tole could take omens, but he had not been asked. Nor had he made any objection; when he heard what the young men had done and all that depended on it, he simply shook his head or nodded; but nowadays Tole was always nodding and shaking his head.

It was never said in so many words, nor was there any need to say it, but everybody knew that in recent years Tole's rule had not maintained any favourable relations with the Powers, whether it was that his sacrifices had not been acceptable or, still more unfortunate, that he had

mistaken the Powers to whom he ought to have applied.
Many dark hints were dropped that the old man had made
too much of the Sun, with poor return, seeing that it became clearer year by year that storm and cloud were more
powerful. It would surely have been wiser to have some
thoughts for the Blusterer as well, perhaps even more
than the others, considering the power unmistakably exercised in heaven and in the life of men by tempest and
night.

Boierik's idea in casting the lot was that the Sun should
see it, but it was the wind that turned the lot and he
accepted the result as far as he was concerned more as a
pact with the Speedy One than with the Sun. The
younger men had no fear of associating with the Powers
of Darkness when the old sources of Light failed them.
Waiting for things to grow . . . if they would grow no
more the only thing was to get up and follow the way of
the wind!

A new era announced itself in this abandonment of an
ancient pact, the transition from direct confidence in the
endurance of Light to a worship of the dangerous Powers
connected with doubt. But even if they were to be called
confederates of the Enemy of Light, they would make trial
of the God of Storm and see how far *his* power extended;
so thought the young in their harshness. No abiding place
for them either! War for war's sake! New gods! In
this turning of the soul away from their father's relations
of gratitude to Heaven lay the germ of the later conception
of the weather and war god's restless being.

And what objection could be made when the young men
openly professed the worship of the Light's antagonist?
A flight, Tole considered it; they would have been more
courageous to stay, to accept their lot as their fathers had
accepted it, so he might have spoken to Boierik and his
men; but Tole held his peace. For causes he could not

understand the Sun had failed him, he was no longer a man whose words claimed attention.

So the Cimbrians set out. Almost the whole people followed Boierik.

Scarcely was their decision made when the storm subsided, as though it had its will. It fell dead calm, and the morning after the Cimbrians had committed themselves to the migration they were aware, as they stood on the high ground, of a mighty, inexplicable, seemingly subterranean thunder, they hardly knew whether it was as a sound or a shaking that went through the very foundations of the country. It came in long-drawn beats like the distant breath of an immense being embracing the earth; and at last they grasped that it was the North Sea, many, many leagues away, which few of them had seen and which had never before made its surf heard so far inland; they could plainly hear each separate wave as it thundered upon the shore.

In the clear cold air they saw the valleys below full of water, the country seemed surrounded by water, black and still after the storm, with all things doubled in the mirror of its surface, floating trees with their roots in the air, drowned cattle, wooden houses tilted by the current with their floor-timbers uppermost. The quiet morning was like a weary pause in the tempest, the sky was threatening and leaden, holding the world in a narrow compass; before noon snow was falling. And it should have been spring . . .

Nobody would stay any longer, the hair of the strongest stood on end when they felt the earth rumbling beneath the attacks of the distant ocean which they could not see. They turned to put their waggons in order, or to build new ones. A month later the country was emptied.

Tole stayed behind. He would not leave the neighbourhood of his father's grave-mound. But he voluntarily

gave over his authority and all the signs of it to Boierik
before they parted.

The sacred car with the image of the Bull and the ring
of covenant were to be taken on the march; they were sacred things inseparable from the Cimbrians as a people;
where they went their sacred things should go. In this
Boierik agreed with him; whatever heavenly Power they
placed their trust in, the Bull should always be the expression of the Cimbrians' inmost nature and of their earthly
fortunes.

And when in the course of the spring the ground became
passable and the expedition started—an endless line of waggons on the way south—a shining speck of gold could be
seen miles off at its head: this was the Bull set up in the
open on the sacred car and led before the emigrants. It
was accompanied by priestesses and sibyls with all their
secret arts for maintaining the sacred fire.

The country was not entirely depopulated; besides Tole
many of the other old heads of families, men and women,
stayed in their homesteads, with a few cows and horses, the
remains of the great herds that were driven away with the
expedition. Some odds and ends of the thralls were also
left behind, such as had been overlooked underground or
in the turbaries, where they escaped notice on account of
their colour. Tole kept a stallion and a couple of mares;
though he had not long to live he could not bear that the
marking whereby every one could tell his horses should die
out in the country. He had asked to be allowed to keep the
youngest of Boierik's sons, Ingvar, who was still only a
child, so that the privileges of the clan might one day pass
to him, and his request had been granted.

From what was thus left behind new possessors of the
soil were to grow up. The manhood was gone, the effete
and the budding were left.

Empty and unused the temple outlived Tole, the sacred

grove uncared for and overgrown. No perpetual fire burned there any longer, only the night brooded there at night-time, and there was a rustling as of a thousand spirits in the high, creaking trees, wind and weather had resumed their sway, the elements had returned untamed.

In a mud hut on the site of his home, which the flood had destroyed, shivering by a big fire, Norna Gest found the old chief, one spring when the scald's steps brought him back to the land of the Cimbrians. The nation itself he had met far down in Europe and could give Tole all the information he desired about them; the two old men put their heads together and exchanged wise words as they had so often done before, but Tole's was a broken wisdom, the wondering of a lonely, melancholy old man over all that had forsaken him.

A last sacrificial act Tole had performed in silence, as Norna Gest learned, shortly after the expedition set out; he had taken the great silver bowl, which had been left behind, into the moors, broken it in pieces, that it might never again be used by men, and had left it in the open, in a certain waste place, feared and avoided by the common people from time immemorial, a damp marshy hole buried in a gloomy, unwholesome thicket full of hedgehogs and weasels, the home of shrikes and hawks, forbidding in its loneliness.

An old heap of bones on the ground showed that this had once been a place of sacrifice, at a time when their ancestors had only vague notions of divinity and worshipped cruelty in this wild and remote spot. Here children had been given to the grim spirits.

Nowhere else were so many adders seen; on sunny days the grass round the swamp seemed alive with them, whole bunches and knots of them lived in the earth; at a distance you could hear their hissing and scaly gliding through bushes and heather—not a place to come near. All the

more important had the men of old thought it to maintain
a good footing with the reptiles.   They had gone so far as
forcing young girls to go naked into this pen of serpents,
which they surrounded with dogs, until a scream from within convinced them that the victim had been bitten.

Tole remembered that his grandfather had sacrificed in
this weird spot, secretly, as though ashamed of it, but firm
as a rock in his belief in its necessity, shaking his head
over the young men of his day who thought otherwise, as—
ay, just as Tole shook his head over the young men of his
time.

Sacrificing to the adders, there was no sense in that, even
though the men of old were right in looking upon them as
in some supernatural way an embodiment of the lightning.
But Tole had never been able to interpret such things otherwise than as symbols.   Certain people kept snakes in their
houses, under their beds even, and fed them in the hope that
they would keep off lightning-strokes, and there could be no
harm in that; but if an enlightened man wanted to be on
good terms with the Thunderer he went to the fountain-
head, the Powers in heaven itself, with his head erect, not
staring in the dust.   But nevertheless the silver bowl
should stay there, as long as it lasted, abandoned to whatever horror there was left in the place, even if the local
gods had had their time.   This was a fit place for it, since
it too was out of use, belonged to the past.

It had been seen that the Power in heaven to whom so
much had been sacrificed in the sacred bowl had not accepted the offerings.   Had there been no strength in them,
or had the Powers proved powerless?   The images on the
bowl, which represented the trust and the fear of the Cimbrians, were they but images?

Was anything more?

As nothing was certain Tole had committed the things
and their images to each other, in the face of Heaven.   It

was for Heaven to regard the wreckage it had wrought and
to preserve it or let it perish as Heaven pleased.

Yes, Norna Gest had met the Cimbrians and it was a
consolation to Tole to hear that they fared well, so far as
Norna Gest could gives news of them.

He had come across them down in the south of the
Frisians' land; they formed camps of their waggons for
safety's sake, though they had fairly empty tracts on all
sides, forest and moor, much that they were accustomed to
at home, only farther to the south. Their herds could
range undisturbed, though of course a guard of horsemen
had to be always in the field to keep off the nearest strangers, who were not very friendly disposed; but that they
were also used to at home. The country was not suited for
agriculture, so the talk was of breaking up and moving on
with all speed. Probably they were already much farther
south.

They had suffered no misfortune or perceptible loss of
life; on the contrary, they were much more numerous than
when they set out. On its way through Jutland the expedition had absorbed a multitude of the various tribes who
had also suffered from the inundations and preferred to
emigrate; they had had to lay their hands on the Bull's
forehead and swear obedience to Boierik; and Tole nodded,
shutting his eyes, when he heard it; that pleased him, it
was right and proper. Trouble they had met with, of
course; not every tribe was content with their bringing a
whole country's cattle to graze off their land, even if they
kept to the common lands in the middle of the country, they
grazed there themselves; but Boierik had used force where
leave was not given and had thrashed the men sent to order
him away. Not without the noise and tumult of arms had
they come out of the peninsula; the border folk had sent
the arrow round to call every man to arms; a battle and a

rapidly concluded peace were the result, and when Boierik marched on he had incorporated a number of them in his army, by their own consent, the rest he packed off home. One of the hostile leaders, who had shown himself particularly stubborn and who fell into Boierik's hands, was harnessed with other bullocks to a waggon when the march was resumed. . . .

Ho, ho, ho! Then Tole roared, with something of his old horse-laugh in his voice. Was that true? Ho, ho!

He wanted to hear all details of the action, his face clouded on hearing of the enemy's impudence, scowled when Boierik prepared to meet and chastise them, and glowed, with a young look on his big, pale features, when the braggarts were sent about their business and their leader put in harness. Oh yes, now he knew his lads!

How were they getting on in other ways, what about the women, how did they take the change? How did they get through the winters? Could they manage altogether without corn? If they had no chance of sowing any of their own, there must be other people's fields here and there? The horses, were they looked after and not shamefully overridden on the long marches? And the *Bull*—did it hold its own under a foreign sky, did it inspire respect wherever it went?

Strange, strange, they had hardly cast and consecrated the great image before it became a sign which united all the men in longing to leave the country! Assuredly that had not been Tole's thought in setting up the Bull; on the contrary, he had hoped it would bind its worshippers for ever to the place where it stood. But he was glad they had wanted to take it with them, since they had to go; he was glad of that, yes he was.

And Tole was lost in thought. As he listened to news of his sons and his clan and all the other countrymen whose chief he had been, it seemed that they and all the old, happy state of things were still present to him. But soon reality asserted itself again; they were all gone, for him existence had gone to pieces. He pondered, could not yet grasp it.

He raised his head and turned a candid look on Norna Gest, in dismay . . . what could it mean? That it should happen to him: the whole, whole country gone, leaving him utterly alone with his thoughts! His youth, his years, his whole life gone at a stroke!

Gently Norna Gest reminded him that such things had happened before. Fathers and sons! Even a whole race turning its back at once on its traditions and its land had been seen before. It might happen at such long intervals that neither the emigrants nor they that stayed behind preserved any memory of it. But *he* had once before seen the population break up and pour out of Jutland, the same line of waggons, as though foreboding another migration, or the next as a ghost of the old. The waggons were rougher in former times, the wheels scarcely round, but they too covered the ground; their axes were of stone, but they cleared a place for them. Now the old forgotten march of their ancestors was repeating itself—and it would repeat itself again more than once in the future!

Did he mean that? Tole dropped his voice deferentially and thought over it, shaking his head feebly; did he really mean that! Those were omniscient words. But for his own part the pain remained the same. He placed his two big useless hands in one another and pondered, rocking to and fro, and his eyes grew dim. At last he looked up again, in another train of thought, with features in which tears were working:

Then Echo is dead.

Norna Gest was silent, with a questioning, wondering look.

Yes, Echo was dead, Tole explained in grief and fear.

He never heard voices now either on the slopes or in the woods. Nothing answered him any more. The spirits of the land were dead.

That was the last time Norna Gest saw Tole. He left Jutland on a sea voyage and was away a long time.

NEW VISION

ONCE more he exchanged the staff for the oar and made ready a craft on the shore of the Limfjord, thence made his way to the Baltic and lost himself on its rivers, moving southward towards the countries of the Mediterranean.

When the rivers became mountain streams he landed and hid himself in the depths of old pine forests he knew, in the mountains where the sources of the great rivers of Europe lay not far from each other; wrapped himself in perfect solitude and became like the ancient pines, like the deepest shadow beneath them among the granite boulders, like Time, which announces itself in the falling pine-needles or the long dark sighing of the trees.

Legends went abroad among the mountains of a great forest spirit some thought they had seen, woodcutters and herdsmen; and it was long ere they recovered of the sight, though the spirit had no air of wishing them ill.

A lonely old wanderer was set upon by robbers in a desert place in the mountains, they threw a spear through him, but in that instant he was not there, it was a cloud that lashed them about the ears with hailstones; and when it cleared they saw the wanderer step out of a shred of cloud farther off and continue his way: with fierce howls the robbers were turned into a pack of wolves and tore each other to pieces. That was Norna Gest.

But when the legends had formed and remained behind, *he* was gone, had hollowed out a boat of a pine-tree by the

Danube's source and committed himself to the stream, appeared as an old fisherman, with nothing odd about him, floating in a trough that would carry a thin man but no more; like many another old angler who has had enough of society and keeps to the water, because its disposition is retiring and the fish are taciturn.

So he fished his way down the stream, drank the good water of the river and hauled up his food from its depths, river fish, sheat-fish, whose swollen spiky faces he had seen before. The river was rapid and bustling to begin with; afterwards it took to itself tributaries and became broad, entered the low country and spread itself, comfortably and strong, with much running hither and thither, exactly like a man; Gest became one with it, while vessels from countries far apart sailed up and down it and life approached its banks; animals coming to lap their morning drink at sunrise, when the moon's watch was relieved; women at their eternal washing, who knelt to the river here as elsewhere and dipped their arms in the stream. . . .

And who were those he saw jogging down to the watering-places on brisk little nags, long-legged riders out of all proportion to their horses, with crests of fair hair waving from their heads; who were they but the Cimbrians, astray in the wide world!

There they were, living on the south bank of the river, which they had crossed not long before, slowly drawing to the southward, not much faster than their herds could graze their way.

They were now a vast swarm, doubled many times over since they left their home; they filled whole countries as they passed, spread beyond the range of vision when they were divided into many small camps with their cattle, the smoke of their hearths rising far and wide with miles between, like a whole settled country, which the next day might have vanished beyond the horizon; and like a town of many, many thousand inhabitants when they were in hostile parts and collected behind their waggons and entrenchments. Thus it was that Norna Gest found them, in an attitude of expectation, while the country in front was being reconnoitred; prepared for peace or war with the next nation they intended to pass through or round.

The Cimbrians were no longer alone in their raid, they were accompanied by other young nations from the North who were also looking for new homes and made common cause with them, on equal terms, but each forming a troop by itself. For that matter they might all have been brothers, since they were all big, fair fellows, distinguishable from each other by a slightly different fashion of wearing the hair and other small matters; a difference of dialect no greater than that they understood each other quite well; their ideas were the same, their prospects the same, the world was open to them and in one respect they were united —in the intention to conquer it as soon as possible.

A strange, overpowering town it was to come into; for Norna Gest was recognized at once and joyfully admitted. But the way to Boierik's presence had more stages than before; it meant passing from the hands of one high commander to another's—ranks had come about of themselves —and in the centre of the circle being brought before Boierik, who sat on a raised chair in a decorated tent, in armour except for his helmet. With closed lips, cold and weary, he received the stranger, but smiled like a boy when he saw who it was, the sun of remembrance rising between the two; he was still himself, but the intervening years had drawn lines in his young face like a map of all the countries he had already forced his way through.

News was exchanged, greetings from Tole given; but Boierik was absent-minded and broke in with cross-questions, wanting information about other things which he

thought the travelled scald would be able to give him; it
was easy to hear that his plans could never for a moment
be driven from his head. Had Norna Gest been in Rome?
Not lately, but earlier . . . and Boierik questioned him
about its situation, defence, the course of the Tiber, the
heights round about, the nature of the surrounding country
—things which the much-seeing Gest had to admit he had
not noticed exactly, but it appeared nevertheless that in a
roundabout way Boierik gained information from his an-
swers.

He had learnt an astonishing amount in these years of exile, knew as much as Norna Gest about the countries of the
South, in some respects more, but extracted from it all a
special dry score of knowledge which he kept within himself
without disclosing its purpose. He expressed no wonder
at all the new worlds that had opened before him, he had
simply absorbed them and at the same time had become
another man. But when the conversation offered no further
advantage and he accompanied Norna Gest to the tent-door,
he smiled again, with a glance of the rare sun of Cimberland, and the old man left him with the feeling that a
wild young soul had vanished and given place to a
maturity which, come what might, pursued uncommon
ends.

The other young men of the camp had not changed in so
striking a way. Their eyes indeed showed that they had
seen a good deal of the world. The old, becoming respect
which had distinguished them at home was a thing they no
longer had time for; they laughed on every occasion, were
quick to fly into a passion, their features had grown harder,
they made a noise in the camp like a pack of hounds. But
they were splendid to look at, hardened by wind and
weather, the acme of manly strength, bursting with reckless
courage. The many thousands of them gathered in one
place made the strongest impression, a mighty natural

force, as yet uncertain of its object, but terrible if it should
be aimed in one direction.

It did not escape observation that the ancient, highly
developed nations to the south of the Alps, whom they were
approaching but had not yet seen, had already set their
mark on their behaviour, without their knowing it; the influence had encountered them on the way and could be seen
in the clothes and trinkets they wore, plundered from people they had come in contact with; the influence had even
wormed its way into their language with a few Latin words
which they already used as their own without troubling
where they had them from.

Everything they had heard about the Romans occupied
them and was their constant topic of conversation; lately
they had seen the first watermills and were much intrigued
by them; a smart invention that, it made you laugh but was
worth copying, getting a wheel to go round and round and
do the work without your having to move a muscle. But
what had the river to say to it? It was pretty cool treatment of the river spirit to harness him to a mill like that.
It would mean plenty of sacrifices, one would think.
Treadmills they had also heard about, but not yet seen;
another Roman idea, wheels that they filled with slaves,
making them climb up and up the whole time, driving the
wheel round; enough to kill you with laughter, one of the
best things ever heard! Ah, no doubt they'd see some fine
things when they got right down and had a talk with the
Romans, who had taught people all these tricks.

As might be expected, it was in their dress that the wom-
en showed signs of the change. They had collected colours
wherever they went, giving the camp a motley look. It was
noticeable that the distance between them and the men was
less pronounced, the women had a freer look and took part
in the talk; their travels and what they had accomplished on
the route had evidently added to their prestige; but they

were not merry.   Of children there were countless hordes,
noisy as birds; what with them and the cattle and all, the
camp was one great roar.

Of unalloyed beauty was the impression made by the
young girls, those who were still children when the raid
began and who had become women on the march, had
grown up walking, so to speak, with new souls, new eyes,
a generation cast in the same mould, all of them upright,
strong, sunburnt maids, hosts of them, all light-hearted and
gentle, robust young women, the good spirits of the camp;
a more vigorous breed of girls had never been seen, so
many and so much alike, collected in one place.

The incessant rough attentions of the young men swathed
the girls in an atmosphere of desire, as they were swathed
in sun and wind, the whole day long.   With a cow on one
side and the big, sure hands of a deceitful swain on the
other, a woman was always hard pressed.   A great deal
of equivocal laughter and play, suppressed giggling, hide-
and-seek and mock wrestling took place between the sexes;
there was no thought but of love.   But shy feelings lay beneath the surface, bashfulness wearing a coarse mask, and
no two lovers were united in earnest unless they felt a secret
sweetness in the blood, and a deep, kind warming of soul to
soul.   Ah, the young couple's subtlest art was to adopt the
naughty tone in fashion among the youthful crowd, while
concealing the deep emotion and craving for compassion
which united them for ever.   Not before they wished it,
but early, the young women became mothers.

But however free and powerful were the manifestations
and achievements of love, however sensitive and beautiful
it might be at heart, its inmost yearnings remained unsat-
isfied.   A desire that was all soul, longing personified as
woman, sought an object in vain, and Norna Gest had not
lived long in the camp before he discovered the quarter to
which the worship of the young men was directed.   For it

was worship, and it was centred, unuttered but with the strength of a natural force, upon a single woman, still scarce a woman, half a child—the vestal Vedis.

If the relations between the sexes within the camp were a continual state of siege in which the finest expansion of the soul was lost, this higher feeling was focussed in a blameless devotion to her, an enthusiasm which all shared and all held holy. She had become a young maiden on the march, not yet grown up but on the border between child and woman, a tall and lovely girl, a revelation as it were of all the strong young girls of the camp in one person, but more graceful, delicate and fair than all of them together.

In the middle of the camp, surrounded by an additional rampart of waggons, a great and roomy leather pavilion was raised, besides the tent of the leader Boierik; in it stood the sacred car when not on the march, and here burned the ancestral fire, which might never go out. In tents around lived the sibyls and their assistants, women young and old dedicated to the fire, and youngest among them Vedis.

By birth alone she was the highest, as the daughter of Boierik himself, but that was not the chief cause of her renown; she was the most beautiful creature that had ever been seen among the Cimbrian nation, the flower of their dreams, the perfect realization of all they loved piece-meal in many others lavished upon a single woman, the finest picture of the race in one person.

With all their force and all their wiles the men secretly sought to be entrusted with some trifling message to headquarters, merely in the hope of seeing her, of catching a glimpse of her fair form with her hair flowing down her back, either among the tents or by the fire in the holy of holies, where she sat among old cinder-smeared sibyls, like Beauty herself caught and caged among vultures, a sight never to be forgotten.

The luck of perhaps being seen by her was the men's

happiness; she smiled, a wonderful smile, at once like a child, a maiden and a mother; she smiled on all the men, and her face shone upon a sinner, no one had seen so bright a face as hers; hardened warriors were melted and came back with its reflection, as though they had seen a marvel; the others knew what they had seen and envied them, but were not spiteful; a heart that is touched is not to be meddled with, and they were all affected in the same way. More than the sanctuary itself, in whose precincts she moved, was she worshipped and loved.

When the host was on the march the sacred car was uncovered and driven at its head surrounded by horsemen, and then the sacred bronze Bull was exposed to all eyes, green rusted with the weather now, with head and horns turned in the direction of the march, the solar sign on its forehead facing the sun, towards uncertain landmarks: mountains ahead, with horns raised to the sky, but the Bull bent his forehead to the new horizon, horn against horn, and every man was staunch in the trust that he would open a path. Charge, thrust and raise a dust in the world, they would be with him!

Scouts and scattered troops looked from afar for the familiar sign at the head of the column, the Bull's horns like a sickle turned against the world; but more often their eyes sought a possible glimpse of the fair girl's head on the car, which would catch the sun and shine to a great distance, itself a little sun on earth.

If the Bull led them into all the kingdoms of the world, then they were leading her! She was the luck of the raid. They felt that what her eyes rested on came out in a richer, fairer, sweeter light. She was a living treasure the host carried with it, a precious centre about which all gathered. Their hearts beat faster and they gripped their lances with a firmer hold when they marched with her; they rode up closer to the car and jostled each other, a wall of horseman about the car and her.

With buried passion they regarded her, who was inviolable and to remain so; never would a man's eyes rest on her otherwise than as a child and a virgin; as such she shone upon their path, and a host armed to the teeth surrounded her.

Even the inarticulate thralls in charge of the bullocks and waggons kept their eyes on a bright head in front of the column, a ray therefrom penetrated even their darkness, but she was a creature not of their world; unearthly they thought her, a spirit of Heaven's grace, and they threw themselves beneath the wheels, let themselves be crushed to death, if the idea entered their thick skulls that they might thereby serve her.

From afar the warriors saw their fairy driving on, like a little fire in the daylight which they knew to be she, in the midst of a strange world; and they loved the countries they passed through, stock and stone, rivers and foreign skies, because she was in the midst of them. So mightily did a maiden shine upon the host that everything their eyes rested upon was made beautiful in her name.

Up and down went Norna Gest, not losing sight of the Cimbrians; of so strange a destiny as that he foresaw awaiting them he would fain be a witness.

It would scarcely be their fate to find land somewhere and settle down on it, as was the intention with which they had set out and of which they still talked; but they were already a changed people. The plough had not yet found soil, would it ever find it? What they had gone through on the way had made them more warriors than husbandmen, they were now rather an army than a nation.

This could be seen in the horses; they were fresher than ever, but ungroomed, trained to the utmost as war-horses, but no longer showing crests and plated manes as in the days when their masters were at home and had nothing to do; the raid had taught them to dispense with the unnecessary, to use up a horse for what there was in him.

The cattle could not be dispensed with, it was what the people lived on, their whole fortune, but the tending of the beasts was left entirely to women and children and the household servants; the men's old delight in their cattle seemed to find expression exclusively in the bronze Bull, the symbol carried at the head of the column; as for the rest, they thought only of their warlike equipment. They had good arms, fashioned in a rough and ready way with an eye to use alone; great single-edged swords that looked like scythes, and indeed came in as such now and then, in another man's fields; but it was for a different harvest they were meant.

The past years had been one long campaign, ever since they fought their way through kinsfolk and out of Jutland, extricated themselves from many fierce tribes in the densely wooded inland tracts, covered their rear with the rivers and had trouble in crossing them, with many sacrifices, now to the rivers, now to the woods; then war with formidable antagonists still farther inland, conciliation with some, others taken into their company, but nowhere an abiding place, wherever they came the land was occupied or unsuitable; they were many, no small country was required to contain them and provide pasture and arable land sufficient to secure their future.

Hitherto the peoples with whom they had come into collision had been of a Northern type like themselves, with characteristics of their own but not very different in nature, nor in hardiness; the Cimbrians had doubtless looked on them as foreigners, since the distant kinship did not happen to strike their eye. But very soon they were to meet people who were foreign in earnest, an entirely opposite world.

They entered the countries between the Danube and the Eastern Alps. Norna Gest followed them as far as their first collision with the Romans, the battle of Noreia, a name till then unknown but destined to ring, as all the names of places and peoples involved in the Raid would ring. It echoed through the world. And a more stirring sound was to follow.

The external destiny of the Cimbrians, when from an obscure past they entered the light of annals, is a theme which extends from that time to all times, the ghost-world of history; henceforth it is this we follow in following them.

Great was the derision of the Cimbrians when for the first time they made the chance acquaintance of writing. They were shown a couple of scribes who performed great exploits, so it was said, by sitting and scratching with a bodkin on a coated tablet, the trail of a worm in wax; no, now they must really be excused, and they went into fits of laughter, killing funny it was, this galloping of lice; what was the idea?—to see who pricked best, who could fill up his tablet first? Could you bet on it? The clowns did not know what ignorance was, for runes were still unknown to the North, the wizardry of writing had not yet occurred to them. But it was by this scratching that their posthumous fame would be kept alive.

The tablet hangs on the wall of History, with all the Cimbrians' exploits, not omitting their fall. But the new vision of their blue eyes looked upon a world which was on the verge of growing old, and never more could it remain the same.

To rehearse the chronicle in brief: the power of Rome had shot a tentacle up to the north of the Eastern Alps, the province of Noricum, and to this the Cimbrians came, after having been a good way down the Balkan peninsula, which had returned them—a foolish people down there and thick as fleas, no chance of getting through; the Cimbrians then turned about and went northward again to knock at the door of the Norici, a prosperous mountain people, whose villages they emptied of corn and other movable goods. Up came the Romans and pronounced an inter-dict, under their proconsul Gnæus Papirius Carbo: palaver of the leaders, bringing face to face for the first time men of widely different horizons and degrees of culture; the Romans condescending, the savages innocent,—without the slightest ill intention had happened to remove property which they could not possibly know to be owned by the Romans . . . as a matter of fact they were bound for Valland and had taken the wrong turning among the three big promontories in which they knew Europe ended on the south, had struck the easternmost, but if they were given guides they would quickly disappear. Guides they were given for Gaul, and Gnæus Papirius Carbo smartly took advantage of their innocence to entice them into a dan-gerous mountain region, where he then fell upon them unawares with his legions. Unexpected result: Gnæus Papirius Carbo and his army cut to pieces.

At Noreia the Cimbrians learned some of their first Latin. The highly developed military organization of the Romans, which they had heard so much of and honestly feared, had failed before them at the first shock.

If Boierik's plans aimed at an immediate advance on Rome, the way was now open across the passes of the Alps. But it rested with the first collision for the present, whether Boierik's plans were not yet mature or the omens were against following up the victory; in any case the Cim-brians actually drew off to the westward along the north-ern edge of the Alps in the direction of Gaul.

The Romans had also extended their experience. Wise men in Rome took advantage of the barbarians' absence to make preparations for the event of their return.

But when Norna Gest had seen the result of Noreia and guessed that nothing very important would happen for the time being, he parted for a while from the Cimbrians and went south as they went west.

For his own part Gest had a journey in mind which he had begun before but not yet brought to an end, the weightiest of all his journeys—to the Land of the Dead.

He had looked for it, we know, in all the islands that lay towards the sun, in the Mediterranean and in the East, in vain, as is related in his book; now he intended to go farther south, through Africa; he would try the Nile.

He had been up it before but had had misgivings about penetrating farther than to the boundaries of Egypt; now a hope urged him to try again, farther south this time if possible; so far as the river went he must be able to sail. When one considered it, where did the Nile come from? Nobody knew, therefore nobody could know what a voyage up the whole length of its course would lead to, before it was tried.

So he made for the Mediterranean, rowed round its coasts, a grey old fisherman of whom nobody took notice, many coasts, and came to the Nile, smelt once more its muddy smell of bodily warmth, as of infants in swaddling-clothes, the smell of life's beginning, dung and vinegar, the salve of Mother Earth; here began the warmth, at whose source, which none had seen, the ancient life-giving river was born—where?

With the sun always facing him Gest rowed through Egypt, past temple-cities and pyramids, the fabulous works of the ancients which reduce a man to silence and take away his cheerfulness: the efforts of generations, so great a bulwark against time and so long ago ready! But *one* step towards heaven, and that already in ruins!

From the desert a face, the ruin of a face, looks out upon the desert, so great that it seems a part of the earth, the land itself stretching its neck to look; and indeed so it is, a piece of living rock shaped by the hand of man,

like a lion below, drifted over and buried in sand; above,
a head with the features of an Egyptian: the emblem of
a riddle, but no other riddle than that the symbols which
gave rise to so imperishable a work are forgotten.

Norna Gest rowed past, and it was as though the head
first turned its full face towards him, then its low profile.
Slowly he left Egypt behind him, took all the windings
of the Nile, going almost north again for a long while, then
south once more, through Nubia, with the crocodile and
hippopotamus for company, flocks of screeching birds over
his head and familiar notes among them now and then,
the birds of passage from the North making for the South
with him. They called up meaningless memories of a
coolness which was now so far away, in these burning lands
where sunshine lay upon the boat like a bonfire close at
hand and the surface of the water flashed lazy lightnings
in his eyes. Gest clothed himself in grass and green leaves,
rowed, rowed, and the heat increased; in the fierce light of
the sun on the river, framed in primeval forest on both
sides, he and his boat disappeared.

Seven years later he came back, still alone; for he had
not found the Land of the Dead nor the dead he looked
for, the ever-dead; ah no, their abode was not in that
quarter either.

He had gone deep into the continent, into immense hot
countries, the home of beasts; in flocks they moved beside
each other, zebra, lion and giraffe, as in the morning of
creation, but not for friendship's sake, only because they
were many, the lot of earth. The lion struck down a beast
when he was thirsty, he was the murderer; afterwards the
vultures invited themselves and plucked at the carrion,
and last came the hyena in the foul darkness of night and
cleaned up the bones: the partition of the ruminant! The
elephant tramped down to the drinking-places, pumped his
trunk full and blew it into his mouth, flapping his big
muddy ears with pleasure and squirting water over his

back. Out on the farthest branches over the river came the apes, hanging out of dark chambers under the leaves, and showed their teeth, dazzled by the light into an ugly grin. Man could be seen, in the depths of the steaming swamps of the forest where it was always dark like a sombre underworld, skinny and shy, stark-naked snivelling dwarfs like children out of their wits, a vermin that haunted the accursed woods.

But at last Gest had gone so far that he had the sun behind him; and then he saw his voyage was in vain and turned back.

Back he came down the Nile, with the stream now, but poorer by a hope; the man of the desert showed him his profile when he came in sight again, then his full face, then the opposite profile; to swing past him was like swinging round Time.

Up on the skirts of the desert Gest found caves with ancient hearths, once inhabited—who could tell by whom? —and deserted again; here he took up his abode and digested his journey, training himself to entertain no more desires.

But when he had been absorbed long enough and penetrated with calm, had brought Time to rest in himself, he felt a new craving to mirror himself in the perishable and to share time with the living. Refreshing were the nights of Egypt, the stars lavishly great and brilliant, as though all suns, but for whom was this peacock's tail in heaven displayed?

Hardened and disappointed Gest felt that a man is alone, even with a god's glory over his head, when he is alone.

For domestic animals and for company he had procured himself poultry, but when the cock embittered his hours with its crowing, he wrung its neck. The wretched bird mounted his meagre scrap-heap and filled the world with crowing, flapped his wings as though it was he who waved permission to the dawn each morning: now it might begin down in the valley of the Nile and Numidia and Mauritania; one would think a cockadoodle had produced the world, could anybody stand it?

After that Gest had peace, a perfectly dead stillness in heaven and earth, stars and sand staring at each other like corpses. Then Gest retired within himself and put his thought into words:

> Hate-filled I fed on
> the heart of the cock.
> Now is the dawn like death
> without his crowing.

> Much may a man
> achieve with a knife:
> yet never raised he
> life in a worm.

> Ill has befallen
> the feathered one's foe.
> Who cares not for cackling
> were best in his coffin!

Gest then turned his back on the desert and rowed with all his might towards the thronged and motley cities of Egypt, the great towns of the Mediterranean, Alexandria, and from there, when the season was calm, he set out direct for Rome.

III

THE BULL AND THE SHE-WOLF

UP the Tiber he rowed one morning and saw at a great distance the wide-spread cloud of smoke and dust which hung over Rome, clinging to the land; white pinnacles and columns towered above it like the mirage of a marble city, but it was real, the high-placed temples of the Capitol, and the flaming things that caught the light and floated like golden eyes in the haze were gilded statues crowning terraces and pediments. The voice of the city was heard, a distant surf-like sound, as of a sea within the land.

The river traffic already proclaimed the great city; the winding course was covered with ships, outward-bound and up-stream, heavy-laden cargo-boats and transports from every corner of the Mediterranean, fleets bringing tribute to Rome from subject countries, great corn-boats from Africa and Sicily, Greek ships, ships all the way from Asia with sacks piled high above their bulwarks, fruit-boats like floating cornucopias, long barges from Egypt laden with onions—who could eat all those onions!—salt-ships, oil-ships, cattle-ships, wool-ships with bulky cargo—all for the insatiable city yonder.

And down from it in the opposite direction came Rome's galleys bound for the provinces, fitted out for war; long, black hulls with castles fore and aft, ballistas and cata-pults on the superstructure, the ram frothing the yellow water at the stem like the trident of a sea-giant; sweeping down the stream with all the force of their oars, the helms-man and a helmeted commander on the poop, the clash of cymbals, a ringing word of command and a quicker beat running along the two and three banks of oars which all swung at the same time and caught the water at the same time like gigantic fins; Rome's eagles and ensigns raised over file upon file of colonial troops: it was the power of Rome and the obedience of the tributary countries that met here at the entrance to the capital of the world!

For a man floating low in the water in a canoe it was not so easy to keep clear of all these high bluff bows; Norna Gest and others with him cautiously gave way and made for the bank, where it was shallow. But in another respect he could feel easy, for he remained unnoticed; among so many vessels great and small he disappeared completely like a magnitude invisible to the eye.

Unseen as though wrapt in a cloak of invisibility, Gest rowed into Rome, and entirely unnoticed he came alongside under the bridge by the island outside the walls, where so many other fishermen had their quarters; made fast to an old ring in the quay-side, where he had tied up before, and made ready in all modesty to become a nameless Roman among Romans.

He did not abandon his boat; he slept in it at night and awoke when the rumble of waggons and many feet passing above his head announced that early market-carts and traders were coming into town; in the evening he fell asleep with the secure feeling of having the bridge above him for a roof, no small convenience to a man accustomed to sleep under the open sky. The place was of bad repute, the Tiber fisherman being notorious for not taking more account of life than of the fish he caught; even thieves and murderers preferred to give it a wide berth rather than get a knife in the gizzard; one could therefore find perfect peace there, when once adopted into the circle of the simple fishermen.

The street-sellers filled Rome's mornings with their me-

lodious cries, a sunrise chorus which embraced the whole
city and which many a Roman never heard except in his
sleep; by the time citizens were up the costermonger had
long ago passed through the street and bargained with
the kitchen slaves and brought in fresh things for the first
meal; other kinds came by and sang their song, until in
the course of the day the chorus was swallowed up in the
general uproar. There was the poultry man who went up
street and down street with his bunch of hens quietly tied
together by the feet with their heads hanging down, alive,
for they had to last until they were sold; the fruit-seller
who bawled in the narrow slums, with pigs in the gutter
and stuffy air that you could cut with a knife, between
houses of eight or ten stories; the snail-woman with her
basket and her song, constantly interrupted while she
picked a snail out of its shell with a hairpin and fortified
herself on her round; and others of all sorts, indistinguish-
able from the sunny streets of Rome, with their small-
wares and their cries of self-preservation, which had turned
to song.

And Gest mingled among them, a man with a sturgeon
who was seen and not seen about the city; he did not
call his fish, it spoke for him, and sometimes it was
bought of him, but just as often he came home with his
fish dried and curled up by the day's sunshine.

Or he was a porter, took a cord over his shoulder and
placed himself by the riverside among the other porters,
was then one of them and went up and down the city on
all kinds of errands, in and out of all sorts of houses.

Between whiles he was a harper in some place of resort,
outside the circus or the theatre, by the look of him some
Thracian or Scythian vagabond; few took any notice of
him, there were so many foreigners in Rome; but he saw
the world. Often he would have a sesterce put into his
hand by a high-born matron, stola-clad and with hair
freshly oiled. large, fine, plum-coloured eyes; and he did

not forget it of her that they had been bedewed for him, if only for an instant.

Gest would sit the whole day long in the Forum in the sunshine, only a greybeard and a bundle of rags among the beggars and idlers who drank up the sunshine from Rome's paving-stones as with suckers; and his eyes were busy, without moving he observed the world, for here it was collected, Europe, Asia and Africa, all complexions, all languages, all kinds of eyes, and just as many souls, widely different; the old and new races of the Mediter-ranean countries were here in an epitome, irreconcilable contradictions, but agreed in meeting at Rome, the refuge of the world.

In the sun-haze, the perpetual summer, above the Forum at the top of the steps leading to the Capitol gleamed a metallic green-rusted form which every one knew and understood: the She-Wolf with the founders of Rome under her paps, guarding the city and showing her teeth at its enemies. Under this symbol they all loved to live, from the beggar to the corpulent senator swinging across the Forum in his letter on the way to the Curia; the slaves groaning under the weight of him had other dangerous desires but not that of living outside the territory guarded by the She-Wolf; the old native noble families and the latest arrivals, all alike looked up to the She-Wolf with the same confidence.

For she was Nature that had fostered Rome, ravenous but free, the Mother who took all sucklings to herself, even young of a totally different kind from her own. She tolerated every foreigner who found shelter within Rome's walls, but turned savagely towards the frontiers: no one should violate the Roman peace! No more motley world existed than that she embraced under her protection and with her motto: Leave for all! Every one his own soul!

In the Forum, the ear-drum of the world where rumours buzzed, there was also a place for Gest, room to sit down on the steps of a temple, among the arcades where Rome's business men and politicians met and all news was spread; near to a cooling fountain in whose basin the children of Rome played with toy triremes; he sat somewhere or other among the statues, himself a mute person but following the vibrations of the place in his distant way.

Talking to anybody was not to Gest's liking; but what cannot a man see, undrowned by his own voice; what does he not find out about men at last, when he draws from other sources than their speech?

So it was not long before the old observer was familiar with all that had happened recently in Rome and in a great part of the world, what took place daily and what would take place, as though he had been a tablet reflecting the shadow-play of humanity, vanished almost before it came to life, image upon image rolling up and passing over into time, as everything passes over into time. He too looked up with wonder at the She-Wolf, in whose sign all the generations of Rome were as though summed up, an imperishable symbol of which changing symbols were formed; what would live, what would endure?

Posterity receives scant written fragments, not much more than the names, which as ever figure in place of the things; but what is not written, what is in the air, that remains for ever in the air; the distant years when Cimberland's Bull drew near to Rome and the She-Wolf, with all four legs stubbornly planted to shield her young, turned her jaws to the frontiers to receive it—they live a shadow-life for all time.

Full of an overpowering anxiety were the years when "the Cimbrian Terror" spread and reached its culmination in Rome.

After Noreia the Cimbrians had made their long march to Gaul, gathering in more allies as they went, a Helvetian tribe, the Tigurini; and when next heard of they had grown together with the Teutons and Ambrones into a multitude beyond all ideas of number, hundreds of thousands, warriors, women and children, cattle and baggage, a swarm that poured onward like an element, demanding land, room for expansion; and they were to learn that nothing is more difficult to get, when the seekers themselves bring congestion with them.

They tried several years in Western Europe, pressed in vain upon the Belgic tribes in the north and were pressed back by them, as they had been repulsed by Boii and Scordisci, they ate up the lands in Gaul and kept the population invested in their fortified towns, pressed them so hard that the unfortunate Celts were forced by famine to eat .each other; they made a wry mouth, the Celts: ill is the taste of one's own kin. But the Celts held out. And now the swarm had turned to the southward and for the second time fell foul of the Roman power, in Provence, the Gallic Province of the Romans.

By degrees the rumour reached the Forum, in vague and incomplete forms, as when one hears of a tempest brewing far away, which darkens the sky but is not yet imminent; beyond the Alps, up in the more or less unknown parts, where barbarians of one kind or another made shift to live and now and then ran together into packs. And the Roman took his late perfumed bath and was carried to the theatre, in an ebony litter covered with horsehair and borne by Ethiopian slaves, all for the colour, and saw the "Sufferings of Orestes," successfully stimulated a craving for the emotional and tragic which everyday life could not satisfy, and got an appetite, lay late at table with Greek-speaking friends and handsome boys, all crowned with vine-leaves: the golden age of innocence, imagined at home in Arcady, which the fashionable world regretted and imitated at great expense. The man of the people gaped in the Circus over gladiatorial games, a tightly packed ring of idlers, toothless from sweet food, but still capable of being gladdened by the sight of murder.

The Republic was in its flower, its prosperity and might still on the increase, the great protracted wars with Carthage concluded, the She-Wolf vanquishing the Elephant, Africa subjected. The Commons of Rome had come out of the duel rich and with absolute power, the great generals and statesmen stood in marble in the Forum, the Republic was irresistible. But its timbers were already worm-eaten. Dissolution had already begun to show itself during the recent Numidian war—the She-Wolf against the Horse, Jugurtha's dangerous cavalry, and the Horse brought low—the austere Roman Knights had clearly sold themselves a little in the Forum and had come near selling the whole Republic too. They had grown too rich, others did their work for them; and Rome's peasants had become an urban mob, the Republic a kept community which lived on the tributes of dependent nations. But at least the predatory instinct was still vigorous, and when Jugurtha had been ignominiously made cold in the Tullian dog-hole, the people breathed freely, as though it was he who was the thief and justice had at last been done.

All this had been done with just as the tempest beyond the Alps began to gather and send forth lightnings. This same Numidian war had brought the name of Marius to the fore, a vulgar person, but not for sale. It would be seen that, when Rome was threatened by an element, she had recourse to elementary Roman qualities in order to meet it.

To begin with the savage strangers did not offer the Romans battle, when they came in contact with their frontiers in the south of Gaul; they asked for land to settle on, a request often repeated at the doors of Europe, and generously offered an alliance; nay, they would take military service under Rome, if they could agree upon the destruction of some third party or other; the Romans gave them a refusal.

On this occasion an embassy was in Rome, consisting of both Cimbrians and Teutons, the only time negotiations took place; and now the parties were able to take stock of each other. We hear nothing of any difference between Teutons and Cimbrians, the Northerners were in general tall, fair, coarse people, coldly regarded by the Romans as phenomenal: an un-Romanly exaggeration of stature, but many negroes were just as tall. Fair they were, of course, with a sheath of straw for hair, like all the rude peoples of the North one had heard about, who lived their lives in forests and eternal shadow and on that account had lost their colour.

Howbeit these fellows of superhuman size were apparently of docile and merry disposition; they smiled from their height upon the little Romans and showed an unreserved delight in all Rome's marvels.

The streets with their shops and taverns fascinated them, they walked in the middle to avoid knocking anything down, planted their big feet cautiously, trying not to smash the paving-stones and mosaics; they looked up and they looked down, wrinkling their foreheads like bulls—by Jupiter, these were the clodhoppers come to town! The simplest things seemed new to them; in the Forum they gaped at the fountains and one of them drank straight out of the basin like an ox. Pipes for the water to come through—wonderful: even the springs were tamed and shut up in iron here! Their hair simply bristled with inspiration when it dawned on them that the *whole* of Rome was paved, miles of slabs, each one of which was worth taking away for a good grindstone—incredible! And the statues, the naked figures! Oh, they were good; the men pretended to cast down their eyes and check themselves, but couldn't keep it in, had to snigger or they would have died. And the laughter came, in huge open roars, as they held each other so as not to fall: nothing concealed here, of either sex!

THE SHE-WOLF OF ROME

Etruscan Bronze from Conservatory Palace, Rome

But the biggest success, almost, was when they caught sight of a donkey with a nosebag on. Evidently the use of nosebags was unknown in the countries these big, clumsy, straggling creatures of innocence came from, for they fell into immoderate transports, stopped and laughed till they roared, shoving each other off their feet: no, this was a bit too much, what would they think of next? There was no getting them away until they had fallen on the ass's neck, finding a brother at last, and kissed it and shown that they could carry it; and the centurion who was showing them through the city got bored and shrugged his shoulders: and these were the fellows that were going before the Senate! Pretty green, weren't they? born yesterday, me Hercule!

Here in the Forum it was that a certain Teuton put his foot in it and found a place for ever in history; the man who was shown a much admired piece of sculpture representing an old herdsman and asked how much he thought it was worth: even if he was alive the Teuton wouldn't give anything for such a useless old slave, was the answer. So much for the ambassadors' knowledge of art—acorn-eating bumpkins!

They showed themselves not altogether without manners when they were brought before the full assembly of the Senate, up in the Capitol, holding themselves very properly and putting aside their laughter for the time being; but of course these illiterates could not express themselves in language; an interpreter had to be sent for, an old seaman or loafer from the riverside who spoke Hyperborean and whom the strangers seemed to know and hold in respect, whoever he might be, from their own coasts perhaps; through him the envoys submitted their case and boldly looked the assembly up and down while it was being translated, like a troop of big thumping boys who had proposed a game and confidently expected the other party to accept with pleasure.

One or other of them gave a sigh and shifted his weight on to the other leg: it was a long way up, they had been taken up thousands of steps, a mountain of steps, right into the sky, through one dizzy pillared court after another; it seemed you had to pass through many chambers before reaching the kernel of Rome. But now at last they were there and could survey the assembly, a whole lot of little old men, surrounded by much marble and themselves frozen in the face, bald, most of them, with polished scalps, the hair all gone; the whole council oppressively still, though there were so many of them, all seated, with one bare shrivelled arm outside the toga and the other in its folds—what could they be hiding in it?

One spoke at a time while the negotiations were going on, not loudly but so that all could hear; on the other hand it was extraordinary to see how the speaker used his hands, moulded his meaning in the air with them, twined his fingers at a difficult point, and flipped himself on the teeth, strewed out invisible things and clutched at his chest, hammered like a smith with one hand on the other, the picture of passion all of it, but without the speaker getting the least excited. Nobody addressed the strangers, nor even the interpreter; the assembly discussed the proposal amongst themselves, not at any great length, and announced the decision through an attendant when it had been arrived at.

The end of it was, then, that the embassy was sent down all those steps again, in and out but down all the time, with a view as they went of all the glories of Rome spread out beneath them. The little old men all sat in silence, relapsed into complete frigidity, after they had drawn up their answer and the petitioners had been dismissed with nothing but a No for their trouble and their journey. One of the old men had taken his left hand out of his toga, and then those of the strangers who had been inquisitive as to what he concealed in it—a knife perhaps,

something sharp?—had a chance of seeing before they left
that it was a long ivory claw, with which the old man
scratched himself. Ah yes, and now he had used it to
rake them off him!

So there they stood in the Forum again and could
stretch their heads back and look up at the high place
where they had been given audience, that and another
high place farther to one side, the Arx, the strong citadel
of Rome, towering with its sheer walls and its temple on
the highest summit like a closed unapproachable shrine.
With contempt for any information the spying eyes of the
strangers might pick up, their guides had chosen to bring
them face to face with Rome's strongholds; now they
might go home and tell of what they had seen!

Crestfallen they were, and many a Roman dryly relished
the disproportion between the size of the braves and their
importance, when they turned their backs—and what
backs!—and took the road out of the city carrying with
them nothing but a certificate of their own insignificance.
Oh yes, the nosebag, no doubt they would introduce that
when they came home. *Habeant!*

The Roman women looked after them with other eyes,
the eyes of curiosity; a pity they were going before there
was a chance of knowing a little of each other: the old
lawless look which implies the warning that a woman is
ready to go over to the enemy at any time, if he proves
himself the stronger. But were not the Roman ladies descended from raped Sabine women?

The doughty champions on their side had not shown
themselves devoid of feeling; they nudged each other when
they saw a pretty woman in the street, drinking in the
lines of her figure, the robe tightly drawn over the breast
and stomach, and turned when she had passed, tightly
drawn at the back too; and they gave each other a forcible
look, as though calling to witness: were such things possible, could one trust one's eyes, so much voluptuousness,

a child of Heaven out for a walk! But could it be the
thing—by herself among male men, slaves and blackamoors
of every kind! How was it she wasn't devoured in broad
daylight, why didn't everybody smash in everybody else's
skull so as to get her for himself and snatch the blankets
out of a house to wrap her in and carry her off! And
with a shake of the head they hunched up their giants'
shoulders, bearing a load of renunciation, and walked on,
unable to conceal a certain smacking of the lips.

Somewhat bowed down under all their disappointments
they made their way out of Rome.

Here they were forgotten in a day for other things.

But they can scarcely have reached their own people
again before the information came to Rome from Gaul that
the Consul of the year, Marcus Junius Silanus, had joined
battle with the Barbarians and had been beaten with his
whole army.

This was the Romans' second defeat and again the Barbarians might have crossed the Alps, this time from the
western end, and invaded the plains of Italy, which lay
unprotected. Instead of that they stayed in Gaul and pil-
laged the countries there to the very bone; and later, when
they had inflicted on the Romans their last decisive defeat at
Arausio, they turned towards Spain and played havoc there
for a time, though without making much impression on the
warlike inhabitants, while the Romans recovered and
collected their forces in the meantime.

Why did they not strike when they could have struck?
Were their leaders in disagreement? Were their plans
more far-reaching? Was it the omens? It was Boierik's
custom to seek important decisions for himself and the
hundreds of thousands who depended on him by sharpening a splinter of wood in the form of an arrow and throwing it up into the wind; the way the arrow pointed when
it came down was the way he took, for that was the will

of the winds; had not the arrow yet pointed towards Rome?

The time came when it did so. After Silanus's disaster the Romans sent fresh armies to Gaul under the Consul Lucius Cassius; he engaged in several actions with the united tribes, but ended in being defeated and himself killed; the remnant of his army was forced to accept peace at the hands of the victors on humiliating terms.

One of the captured officers who was brought before Boierik warned him, with all the authority of Rome in his bearing, against approaching Italy; Rome was not to be attacked, even Hannibal had not ventured it. For answer Boierik cut him down: if the man fell, then the inviolability fell with him!

Finally, at Arausio, in the neighbourhood of the Rhone, the defeat was crushing. This time two generals led the Roman forces, Cneus Manlius and Servilius Cæpio, and they were jealous of each other, Cæpio a man stained by the corruption of Rome; they divided their forces and the Barbarians overcame them in detail. The double defeat is said to have cost the Romans over a hundred thousand men.

In this battle as in the previous ones the Romans were literally howled down by the savages, the legions first scared half out of their lives by the bestial Cimbrian howls and then mowed down. The barbarians acted upon the eye simply by their appearance, horrid bodies leaping high in the air, flesh, tatooing and iron, two-pronged spears like forks, long, heavy one-edged swords like scythes; their slaughter was a piece of harvesting, the enemy pitchforked into the air and laid in swaths; noise was their tactics, suddenness their plan of battle: the whole terrible yelling horde charging at once! And thus the legions were paralysed, the hardy little Roman soldier was disarmed by panic, even before, true to his wont, he had taken his stand and begun to plane away the enemy.

The Cimbrian howls were heard as far as Rome, even in the bedchambers; many lay awake at night after the mourn-

ful news had been received.   The extent of the disaster was
intensified by what was heard of the Barbarians' treatment
of the vanquished; horrible, horrible tidings.

It seems as though these peasants had been seized with
malevolence after the murderous battle of Arausio; Cæpio's
tricks and untrustworthiness had made them disgusted with
Rome; the defeated should be punished and at the same
time the old, cruel gods honoured with a sacrifice that
would be remembered: the prisoners were dispatched, some
of them hanged as offerings to the Wind God, the fruit of
the Hell tree, others slaughtered as a human sacrifice to
their fathers' ancient, greedy Gods of Fire: miserable
stripped Romans by the thousand, a repulsive night work
left to the sibyls.

Fires and the smell of blood ascending to heaven, the
sacred Bull towering in the midst of a reeking abomination,
the moon red and swollen overhead like a mass of entrails
in the sky!   In festal robes the terrible old women stood
upon the shrine, barefooted and in white, heads smeared
with chalk, and drew the knife across the throats of the
victims who were passed up to them; quickly, next man up
—while the blood collected below in the immense sacrificial
bowl and ran over.   In cackling voices they prophesied
from the signs they found in hearts and entrails, good signs,
repeated a thousand times, no doubt of it, the more omens
of that kind the worse it looked for the enemies of the Bull!

Not even the booty would the victors keep, it had been
promised in advance to the gods of the country, in the
knowledge that the battle was a hazardous one.   All the silver and gold was given to the Rhone, which had shown
them favour, together with all the captured arms, armours
and ensigns, and the horses of the Romans; all was sunk
in the river and devoted to the River God.   Many rivers
had they passed, and many yet awaited them; with them
above all they wished to be on a good footing.

Let it be seen whether the Romans could offer the local

gods more than they had now given them!   And truly, they could afford it; there was not a man in the host who was not already carrying about a pig's weight in gold, besides waggon-loads of treasure, bronze vessels and mountings, chains and jewels, all taken by cautious violence, to avoid breakage, from the many peoples whose countries they had passed through.

The battle of Arausio was the first round of the duel, when the Bull had taken the She-Wolf on his horns and tossed her to the sky in such a sweep that she was likely to be fixed there as a constellation.

But she came down again and remained whole; she would come again with a sharp fang.

In Rome the news from the seat of war called to life all the old steady defensive spirit of the Republic.   Every sensible man said to himself that the threat to Rome's existence was now imminent, if this human avalanche poured down from the Alps over Italy.

To begin with the gods gave them a respite; the sinful city had looked to its own profit but had never neglected to sacrifice to the gods, and *they* too had revenues to lose. Rome breathed again when the tempest, with a tempest's opulence and absence of plan, drew off elsewhere, clouding the sky of Spain for a couple of years; in the meantime the Romans were busy.   When the pause was over, the Cimbrians and Teutons again on the march and on their way to the Alps, it was known that this time they would cross them. But in the meantime Marius had been getting ready for them.

In the hour of need Rome had recourse to the man with the simple, certain instincts, Marius the man of the people, in whom no refined or complex line of thought checked initiative.   The old gentlemen of the Senate were wise enough to set aside their own feelings in order to choose a nature repellant, openly hostile, to themselves, to do the work of saving Rome; you do not grasp the scorpion with bare hands.

The occasion was an extraordinary one; since Hannibal crossed the Alps Rome had not been in such serious peril, and he was after all an enlightened man who knew bounds; this time it was boundlessness itself that was coming, the Senators were clear about that and showed considerable active disinterestedness; all considerations but that of meeting the danger were swept aside; straight to the goal: Marius at the head of the State! He was elected Consul out of the ordinary course, and re-elected year by year contrary to law, until the campaign was concluded.

Afterwards they would be able to wash themselves free of him. A strong smell of stables clung about him, he bragged of having the habits of a common soldier, after his unquestionably useful service in Africa, and he was insolent and scornful about the hereditary nobility: hadn't they risen from the ranks in the beginning, like himself, he would like to know? He couldn't keep his mouth shut and shouted in the popular assembly about the venality of the Senators, as though everybody didn't know it, and thus secured the votes of the mob; of course he was himself incorruptible, never took money for political purposes, *he* bribed! He was brutal, put down vice without regard for the pet sins of many; while he himself was so ugly that he had to take his caresses to women of the coarsest type, preferably in the dark, and pay them well; no Greek graces of face and limb or amiability about that man! No, few were less Greek than he, for he did not speak the language of the gods, like Rome's men about town, and is even said to have boasted of it, certain of the applause of the ignorant, and to have declared that he scouted a learning derived from libertines and slaves. A soul like his was an offence to Rome, but now he would have to be used, there was need of a rasp.

Marius's frank primitiveness makes one think of that

Teuton who was shown the statue and his remark about it: in reality a judgment on decadent Rome, the peasant leaving art for nature, back to the beginning!   For Marius was the old strict agrarian spirit of the Republic over again; instinctively Rome summoned her lower orders to meet an outbreak of nature from beyond her bounds.   A bust which is said to represent Marius, and is in any case a portrait of a citizen of the Republican period, seems to conceal in its rough-hewn features the memory of a woman buried beneath them: the mother, the harsh Roman woman, practised in self-sacrifice, who brought him up and kept order in the home he came from, with the taste of a working woman and a dog's fidelity to her race, one of the mothers of the Republic: the devotion and the ferocity of the She-Wolf!

And it looked as though the memory of ancient discipline, an almost forgotten rod of punishment, reformed the morality of Rome for the time; the nobility could do nothing themselves but they knew what energy was.   And intrigue they were skilled in, concocting a plan, and fear goaded them on, they were afraid, a delicate flush suffused the cheeks of enfeebled old Senators; they worked, the Senate sat day and night.   The city buzzed about their ears in an audible panic, clients came up to them as they left the council chamber, wringing their hands: the big business men were in a fever, the brokers glowed like copper with a green sweat, could not keep their food down, terror and doubt upsetting their stomachs: should they be bulls or bears?   The wealthy freedmen looked petrified, like the statues in the Forum: what about the interest on their capital, their house property, villas, the mausoleum they had built on the Appian Way, would they have a use for it too soon?   Or would some unworthy outsider get buried in their marble instead of them?   Was the government taking the right line for them?   Had the Senate made the right choice?   Ought they to go to a common person to save the country?   Yes, a common man was just what was wanted. The language itself would be all the better for a change of values.

Everywhere the terror was general and was never afterwards forgotten. Augurs and soothsayers were quite wrinkled in the forehead from worrying over entrails and the flight of birds; up on the Arx, Rome's ancient look-out round the horizon, the universe was studied early and late: what was to be read in the stars? Rome's householders dared scarcely put their foot over the threshold when they came out of the atrium in the morning with slaves bearing rolls and documents behind them; what would they meet, would they stumble, what kind of birds were in the air?

The braying of an ass, earthworms above ground, the sight of a hare, even in a poulterer's shop, all were interpreted as fateful omens. Rumours of portents flew from one end of the city to the other; a gulp had been heard in the Cloaca Maxima underneath Rome, a weeping in the city's foundations—ah, drivers and water-carriers told each other of it in the street, shivering in the middle of the summer day. Never had the air been so charged with fate; almost tangibly, in a woman's shape, the destiny sent from above was felt leaning over the city.

The Roman ladies, the defenceless ones, shuddered. Would it really befall them to be dragged off by the big, hairy savages? They remembered that the envoys they had seen had a thick golden nap on the back of their hands, like bears walking on their hind-legs; a wantonness as of new-born gods sported in their locks; and the Roman ladies sank into their chairs like hens all rumpled at the thought. Who could read what was in their minds? What omens did *they* take, when the legions marched out of Rome for the seat of war, the compact little Romans in full marching order with their packs on their shoulders, braced up, hardy as ants, our own brave fellows—but didn't one know them in and out, down to the very birthmarks on their bodies? Hush! And the Roman lady went home to her mirrors and her women slaves; it was obvious that whoever it was that came back, she would keep herself anointed and dainty, all ready for the triumph. The apprehensions of the Roman ladies were divided, when Marius set out with his army *versus septentrionem*.

But they regained their balance and showed the correct attitude, as ever before, towards the vanquished, when Marius had annihilated the Barbarians; first the Teutons at Aquæ Sextiæ, then the Cimbrians in the Raudian plains.

IV

THE BATTLE

THE horde had agreed to divide itself: the advantage the Romans had given them at Arausio by dividing their forces, they now resigned to their enemies.

The object of it was dangerous enough; the plan was to hem in the root of the peninsula, when each body had crossed the Alps at its own end: the Bull closing on Rome with a horn on each side. But the upshot was that Marius broke off first one horn, then the other.

The whole horde at once he could scarcely have mastered; each half by itself gave him plenty of work.

At the very beginning he applied the technical methods of Rome, the science of war first, then war itself; he put in hand elaborate engineering works on the Rhone, the gateway towards Rome where the enemy was expected on his return from Spain; and when he arrived he found Marius entrenched in an impregnable camp, while at the same time he had regulated the outlet of the Rhone, dug canals and assured his transports and supplies, an immense piece of work at which he kept his troops to drive the idle habits of Rome out of them.

They were a new military material which he could shape as he pleased, the population of Rome drafted into the army irrespective of class, not as before exclusively the old free citizen class to whom war was a privilege. Marius introduced recruiting, a far-reaching measure which affected both the aristocracy and the common people, downward on one side, up on the other, and which contained the

germ of the autocracy to come: the army increased in power
and at its summit the dictatorship. A year or two after
these events a child was born who was to grow into a man
and give his name to this apex: Cæsar. Begun as a roping-
in of the people, the establishment of the new army ended
in placing the yoke of a single man on the necks of all
classes in Rome and of a great part of the world; few men
have disposed of the life of so many generations as the re-
morseless Marius.

Besides turning his troops into diggers, doubtless not
without a sinister hint as to who was going to be buried,
he trained them with an iron hand in obedience and discipline, taught them to suffer, made them artisans of war;
he thought out a nasty improvement of their arm, the *pilum*,
the Roman lance, the nails of which he had taken out, so
that the head might stick fast like a harpoon and eat its
way in better. He took methodical steps to accustom his
soldiers to the appearance and howls of the barbarous
warriors, arranging a sort of school or theatre where, from
the ramparts of the camp, the men were daily confronted
with the enemy, themselves under cover for the present, and
thus got the panic gradually rubbed out of their eyes.

And the Barbarians, without knowing it, lent him a hand,
were quite pleased to show themselves; it was their amusement to ride up to the ramparts and challenge the Romans
—poor little souls who shut themselves in so carefully and
shunned the open field! It was not *their* way to take advantage of a better position than their opponents', an equal
chance was reckoned among them as one of the rules of war.
Shouldn't they have a little fighting these fine days?

The plain was black with their hundreds of thousands,
and the Romans' blood began to boil at being unable to
stop their ravaging the country and at their boastfulness;
they could quite well stand the look of the enemy now and
were hardened to the yelling. Skirmishes took place before
the ramparts, the Romans were blooded and wanted to fight,

railed against their general, were not inclined to sit still and be laughed at. And Marius nodded to himself in his tent, now they would soon be right.

But he did not accept the Barbarians' challenge. First he waited till they had divided themselves into two hosts and the Cimbrians had left at last to march over to their position on the eastern side of the Alps, where the other Consul, Catulus, was posted to meet them. And then he still waited while the remainder, the Teutons and Ambrones, in their own words grew old and regarded the idea of fighting as a distant improbable legend. Marius waited and played the coward for weeks and months; the Teutons rode up every morning to ask after his health, yawning like big tired dogs, crying out with boredom; and the Roman soldiers' bile was stirred.

At last the Barbarians lost patience, since it was evident that the Romans had settled for life in this entrenched camp, the soil within the ramparts must have an attraction for them; well, they might squat there till they were over head and ears in their own filth, the Teutons were bound for Rome—ridiculous that they hadn't gone on at once, all they had to do was to march past the Roman fortifications!

And they did so. As their braves rode up to the ramparts for the last time on their way to the Alps they gave the Romans the benefit of their high spirits and asked if they had no messages to send home to their wives, for they would soon be seeing them. It was an ill-advised thing to shout, and the Romans had no retort; with pale lips they followed the march of the multitude, towards the Alps, towards Rome.

The march past lasted six days. For six days the vast mob was moving past, infantry and cavalry, carts and baggage-waggons, cattle, women, thralls and children, slowly advancing, the heavy oxen with their heads bent down by the yoke, the wheels bumping behind them in the dust, a sluggish river of waggons; but on it moved, irresistibly, beyond the horizon, like the thread from a spindle in the inexhaustible camps of the Barbarians. Finally the last column of waggons disappeared and the horde left behind it a broad ploughed-up track under a veil of dust, as though a landslide had passed over the country; the last crack of the whip, the last shout died away. For six days the earth had trembled beneath this black human stream; the Romans looked after it, in silence, speechless from what they had seen.

But now Marius broke camp and followed the horde: across the Alps they should not pass. Cautiously, always in fortified camps at strategically favourable points, he followed at their heels, until reaching Aquæ Sextiæ, the place of hot springs near the foot of the Alps. Here, half by chance, but a chance utilized by Marius with careful calculation, it came to a fight. The accounts give details, the sum of which is that Marius won a complete victory, by good luck, by the fact that the enemy was again divided, and by surprise tactics skilfully carried out.

The Ambrones were beaten first, and as the Romans pursued them to their waggon-camps they came upon howling women, we are told, who with axes and swords attacked not only their own men in flight but the pursuing Romans, grasping their naked swords barehanded and "abiding with an invincible courage to be hacked and mangled with their swords." [1]

Plutarch gives the account. After the defeat of the Ambrones the Romans passed a critical night; they still had the Teutons to deal with, in immense numbers, and the camp was unfortified. All night long they heard the Teutons uttering "loud cries, which were nothing like men's lamentations and sighs, but rather like wild beasts' bellowing and roaring. So that the bellowing of such a great multitude of beastly people, mingled together with threats

[1] The quotations from Plutarch are here given in North's translation.—Tr.

and wailings, made the mountains thereabouts and the running river to rebound again of the sound and echo of their cries marvellously: by reason whereof, all the valley that lay between both, thundered to hear the horrible and fearful trembling. This made the Roman soldiers afeard, and Marius himself in some doubt: because they looked to have been fought withal the same night, being altogether troubled and out of order."

But the Teutons let the opportunity slip, and Marius had time to lay his ambush. It was significant of the Barbarians' ideas of warfare that the Teutons' leader, Teutobod, offered to fight Marius in single combat, a duel between the two strongest was to decide the matter on behalf of the armies. Teutobod was about seven feet high and according to tradition could leap over six horses. Marius declined his offer. When at last the armies came to close quarters the Teutons in their rage threw away an advantage and charged from the plain against the higher ground occupied by Marius; an outflanking division of the Romans took them in rear, and it was all over with them.

Teutobod fell into the hands of the Romans alive. All the tents and waggons, the whole property of the migratory people, were captured, the Teutons wiped out as a nation, killed or taken prisoner.

So many fell that the inhabitants of the region afterwards fenced their vineyards with the bones of the slain, as Plutarch relates in his Life of Marius, adding that the soil became so fertile from the putrefying bodies and from the heavy rain of the following winter that in the spring it gave an extraordinarily rich crop. The chronicler does not vouch for the excellence of human manure, though it is asserted by the Greek poet Archilochus; he quotes others who claim to have observed "that of ordinary after great battles there falleth great store of rain. Either it is by mean of some god that pouring down pure rain doth purify, wash, and cleanse the ground, defiled and polluted with man's

THE BATTLE OF THE CIMBRIANS

Drawing from Sarcophagus in Capitoline Museum, Rome

blood: or else it happeneth by natural cause. For that the overthrow of so many dead bodies, and of the blood spilt, engendreth a moist, gross, and heavy vapour, which doth thicken the air. . . ." He thus leaves it undecided whether the carrion or the rain benefits the soil. However this may be, wine grew of the Barbarians' bodies, sweetness of slaughter.

While Marius was occupied in arranging a sacrificial pyre of the shields and spears of the vanquished, a messenger arrived announcing that he had been elected Consul for the fifth year. A few days later news reached him from the eastern theatre of war: Catulus had guarded his passes so half-heartedly that the Cimbrians *had* crossed the Alps and were now in Italy. Marius then postponed his entry into Rome and was afterwards able to turn two triumphs into one.

Plutarch's ancient prose sounds like a fairy tale of giants and goblins, a piece of early Gothic viewed with the amazed eyes of the sober classical historian: "Now, these barbarous people had such a glory in themselves, and disdained their enemies so much, that more to show their force and boldness, than of any necessity that compelled them, or for any benefit they got by it: they suffered it to snow upon them being stark naked, and did climb up to the top of the mountains, through great heaps of ice and snow. And when they were at the very top of all, they laid their long broad targets under their bodies, and lay all along upon them, sliding down the steep high rocks that had certain hangings over of an infinite height."

Clearly enough glad winter memories of home had had a refreshing effect on the spirits of the Cimbrians, oppressed by the heat of the South, and they could not resist a boyish desire to roll in the drifts and sledge down the steep snow-slopes of the Alps. Like a band of noisy lads they came sliding down the roof of heaven into Italy!

Catulus had taken up a position behind a river, the Adige,

with the intention of checking them there. And then the Cimbrians "came to camp near unto the Romans by the river side, and considered how they might pass it over: and began to fill it up, tearing down (like giants) great hills of earth which they found thereabouts, brought thither great trees which they pulled up whole by the roots, threw great pieces of rocks which they brake, and whole towers of earth after them, to stop and break the course of the river. But besides all this, they threw great timber into the river, which being carried down the stream, came with such a force, and hit against the post of the bridge so violently, that they shaked the Romans' bridge marvellously."

Catulus was forced back from the Adige and evacuated the country as far as the Po. The first encounter, moreover, had been accompanied by all the courtesies of war; the Cimbrians had taken prisoners but generously set them free again, and so good was the impression the Romans made on them that they confirmed the safe conduct they gave them by oaths and laying of hands on the sacred Bull. Possibly another alliance might have been offered, in all amity, if they had had only Catulus to deal with.

For the present they spread over the plains between the Adige and the Po, occupied the land as if it was their own and liked it well: plenty of room, if the people who lived there already squeezed up a little; excellent arable land, kept in very good order by the natives, who could go on with that and bring the corn as tribute; on the whole a tempting place to stay in.

During this breathing-space Norna Gest saw them. He appeared one day at their camp with his swinging, unhurried gate, and was recognized by the Cimbrians and well received; but he had no long talk with any one of them, they were too restless for that; for news from the North, where they might imagine Gest to have been, they never asked; they were full of their own affairs and had been too long away. But they were glad to see the old man and let him go about the camp as long as he liked and where he liked.

But this time he had no audience of Boierik. You now had to pass through three ramparts of waggons, one inside the other, to reach his tent, which showed up in the middle with crimson trappings and a long banner waving from the top; but Gest got no farther than the first.

The ranks had become higher of necessity; true, all were equal as members of free and equal tribes, but the Cimbrians, who formed the core of the avalanche and had given it their name, preserved a central position, and their leaders had become dukes, Boierik a prince. He lived in the innermost ring, and admittance to him was gained through the mediation of the dukes, who occupied the second; they could be approached, though with difficulty, by one who had good connections in the outer ring, where the Cimbrians' trusted chiefs of clans and most valiant champions were gathered together; beyond them Norna Gest did not succeed in penetrating during the time he stayed in the camp.

Now and then he saw the leader of the army ride past, but at a distance, the body of horsemen who formed his escort were so thick about him that only a helmet was to be seen towering above the rest, apparently of gold with a huge crest of fiery red feathers. He rode at a smart pace, and the escort with him; a thunder shook the ground and they were gone in an instant, every man silent, with wild boars or gaping beasts on their helmets, the two-pronged spears lowered at the charge, and the whole troop moved like one body, with a drumming in the horses' bellies and a blowing in their throats.

These were the same little horses they had ridden from home, but the next generation; for about a horse's age they had been on the move, Gest reckoned, and the men he had known as lads of twenty would soon be elderly;

children that had watched the start from their mothers'
arms were now grown up. Many, many had been born on
the trail and had known nothing but travel. They had
grown into quite another people than that which had set
out. Even those who had been mature before the migration had greatly changed. Well, what is it they expect,
thought Gest, if they are no longer the same on reaching
their journey's end!

The tone of the camp was still set by the braves, the
young crowd which was constantly being renewed from below as the boys passed into the men's circle. Their intercourse was marked by the transitional age, the rough tone,
the grating laugh, coarseness and a bold front, heat and
impatience; but the tone had become coarser under the
influence of the life they had led and the knowledge acquired by contact with all kinds of people.

It was extraordinary to see the fellows' vanity and contempt for death, which had reached a pitch of fanaticism.
If they counted the lives of others no higher than their
own, then Woe to the rest of the world! So highly did
they rate themselves that they threw away what one would
have expected them to cling to, life itself; no one, not
even the gods, should have the power to give them anything! They shed each other's blood without cause; a
quarrel came of what was hardly a difference of opinion,
the ghost of a suspicion that a man was capable of fear,
and they went for each other like fighting-cocks, death for
one or both of them, hale young fellows bursting with life
hacking at each other; and the stricken one laughed, could
not help it, with the blood gushing from his mortal wound
as from a vat, died on his feet and laughed, a hearty laugh,
was still laughing as he lay, till his gums turned white and
he groped blindly in the air. So dear to them was honour,
though when all was said and done it was only based on
a weakness for what others thought. But then their lives
were their own.

The men drank. They had taken to it inevitably in the wine-producing countries they had scoured. The cellars were the first thing when they stormed and sacked a town, and they were in such a hurry to get drunk that they kicked in the great earthen jars and slobbered up the wine from the floor. Their old Northern habits were forgotten, as their homes were forgotten, spring water was no longer a gift of the gods, curds, herring and barley were no longer their staple food, they had acquired a taste for seasoned dishes, frowned upon any fare but rarest dainties and paid for their luxury with toothache. Men who had once stood winter nights in the open under a cowhide now slept in the South behind hangings in fringed tents.

Gest was scandalized. He turned his eyes to the women; they could hardly have grown womanly! They were more outspoken and headstrong than before, hardened by the hard field life and marked by the precariousness of their existence; the mothers dried-up and lean, but blazing with courage. The young girls were handsome as before, even handsomer; a wild new generation had grown up that had known nothing but a wandering life, limber young heifers with the creak of the wilds in their joints, blue-eyed and blithe, strong, powerfully built and upright; flocks of them, a wonderful breed fostered by the open air, with all the gentle capability of the race in reserve. What a future they bore within them for a nation!

But chiefest and most beautiful among them all was the priestess Vedis. She was now in the flower of her age, at the summit of exuberant womanly maturity, very tall, and the brightest being any one had ever seen. She was like the rosy blush of love, but was never to see her own blood repeated in a new generation; she was love itself for all generations. She was to remain alone and shine upon all as their hearts' most beautiful dream.

Strange it was to see with what sacred feelings she was regarded; all the young men, every one of them, looked up to her with unmixed reverence, nay solemnity; their grimaces vanished as soon as they saw her or even heard her name. They retired into themselves, found their real self in the radiance of her being. They worshipped her as a soul, without earthly thought, but deep down within them they were aflame for her; how could they help it! And she, she loved them all. She was betrothed to all these wild lovers, dedicated to her people, but was never to become a mother.

This could be seen in her; she was in the radiance of her youth but shone alone, like the morning star; a motherly light was on her maidenly features, she felt for all her big distracted erring children; she had become the protectress of the camp, to whom all looked for spiritual comfort; but she was alone.

And the most fervent wish of every warrior was to protect her, to surround and bear her in a ring of steel safe and untouched for ever through the world!

Not long could the Cimbrians rejoice in the good pastures of the plains of the Po and the fair prospects they offered to a settled agricultural population. Just as they were beginning to get on quite well with the worthy Catulus, Marius arrived with his troops from Gaul.

He did not come to hobnob with them or get a testimonial from them; the grim Marius cared nothing for what others thought of him, did not even trouble about his fame with posterity. Nor had the army he had trained any intention of marrying the enemy. Whether they showed bravery or covered themselves with honour was all one to them, so long as they got their knife in before the other man and could get back to the circuses and shady quarters of Rome. They were long since hardened to the sight of the monsters, even to indifference; their *moral* had almost passed to the other extreme, contempt. They had swallowed the Teutons, now for a dish of Cimbrians!

But the Cimbrians avoided battle with the combined forces of the Consuls, showing deliberation for once; better after all to wait till the Teutons came! They were touchy about taking an advantage—a thing a warrior *could* not do—all the same there was no sense in exposing one's self with half one's forces when it was just as easy to wait for the other half to come up. In the mean time they sent envoys to Marius and asked leave to remain on the land they had taken, or to be allotted other lands broad enough for themselves and their brothers. Refrain: land.

Marius: What brothers?

The envoys: The Teutons, of course. (Aside: The density of these Romans!)

At this all present began to laugh, like the entrance of the Chorus in the ancient tragedies. But Marius replied that they need not trouble about their brothers the Teutons; they had already got as much earth as would lie upon them.

The envoys then saw that they were being made fools of and became rude: this should be avenged, it was an insult to the majesty of the Cimbrians as well as the Teutons; the Romans should smart for it as soon as the Teutons came.

Marius: They are here *now*.

And on a sign from him Teutobod and the other Teuton chieftains were brought forward in chains.

Dumb show, a few words exchanged in undertones between the Barbarians in their own tongue, and the prisoners nodded, mournful as the grave, like messengers from the realms below; yes, it was true, they were all dead.

Then the flap fell in front of Marius' tent-door, the Cimbrian envoys were gone, and the laughter of the Chorus broke out behind them in a peal.

Then the Cimbrians offered instant battle, advancing in battle array and challenging the Romans.

Marius stayed in his camp, disregarding the sneers at

his cautiousness. But it was now that he had the pins taken out of his soldiers' lance-heads, so that they might stick faster in the enemy's bodies.

As Marius did not leave his camp, the Barbarian Prince, Boierik, rode up to it in person and challenged him to name his own time and place for a fight which was to decide which of them should possess the land.

So then they had a chance of seeing him, and terrifying was the look of his person, tall and huge as a tree, with his feet almost touching the ground as he sat on his horse, which however was only of moderate size, his breadth of shoulder almost eclipsing his height; on his head he wore a helmet with bull's horns and above it a crest of red cock's feathers, but his face was bare, fierce with the murderous red moustache on his lip, an unwonted sight to the clean-shaven Romans; scowling eyes of icy blue and cruel brows drawn over them, his whole expression full of wrath, head thrown back; and his dread arms completed the picture, a sword of super-human size at his side and the fork in his hand; a drastic weapon, but was it not apt to defeat itself by penetrating no farther than the length of the prongs? His shield was not strikingly large, for in this particular courage showed itself in a neglect of protection; it was white, as though chalked, and could be seen a long way off; its barrier did not seek invisibility in battle!

Boierik was accompanied only by a few horsemen, an insane exposure of a man on whose life the fate of hundreds of thousands depended. Marius could have had him seized and hanged, and the Barbarian knew it, but the Roman let him ride back unharmed, crowned with his savage halo; if the whole welfare of the hostile army was bound up with this one man who acted for them all, Marius may sarcastically have thought, then he should surely live!

He accepted the challenge, not without taunting the Barbarian with the un-Roman form in which it had been

MARIUS

delivered, and the battle was fixed for the third day following, the place the Raudian plains near Vercellæ. Here,
then, the Cimbrians were chastised at the time and place
they had themselves proposed.

The sun and the heat of the day were the chief cause of
the fall of the Cimbrian nation. In a literal sense the sun
fought on the side of the Romans; Marius had taken care
that the position gave him this advantage; and even if he
had not thought of it, the Barbarians would certainly have
yielded it to him, in their anxiety to avoid the reproach
of a lack of bravery.

In Plutarch's words: "The heat and the sun which was
full in the Cimbre's faces, did the Romans marvellous
pleasure at that time. For the barbarous people being very
hard brought up to away with cold (because they were
born and bred in a cold country, shadowed altogether with
woods and trees) were to the contrary very tender against
the heat, and did melt with sweating against the sun, and
gaped straight for breath, putting their targets before their
faces: for it was also in the heat of summer, about the
seven and twenty day of the month of July, that this battle
was given, and this dust also made the Romans the bolder,
and kept them that they could not see the innumerable
multitude of their enemies far from them. And every man
running to set upon them that came against them, they
were joined together in fight, before that the sight of their
enemies could make them afraid. And furthermore, they
were so good soldiers, and so able to take pains, that how
extreme soever the heat was, no man was seen sweat nor
blow."

Another writer uses the mythical expression that the
Barbarians dissolved like snow in the midday heat; the
right image, that of the Ice King who had ventured south
of his own dominions and melted away.

Before the attack, when the two armies were drawn up in
front of each other like vast human tidal waves conjured

up on the plain—the united armies of the Consuls to the
number of over fifty thousand, that of the Cimbrians un-
numbered, but their order of the battle, which was in the
form of a square, is said to have measured three miles each
way—Marius performed his devotions, as Plutarch witnesses: "Marius having washed his hands, and lifting
them up to heaven promised and vowed a solemn sacrifice
unto the gods of a hundred oxen. . . ."

What a moment! On earth the armies, drawing towards
each other with their infinite tramp, the plain spread out
on every side, fair and open in its verdure and dotted with
the homes of men, and above it in the north the long
snow chain of the Alps hovering like a mirage in the sky,
the rampart which the invaders had scaled; but above
armies and earth and heaven-seeking mountains the eternal,
unapproachable heaven itself, the *day*—and then this snarl-
ing pitiless Roman raising his hands in all simplicity to
Heaven, like a child begging its mother to be lifted up, a
gesture whereby the very sternest seeks to escape from the
earth, whose pollution is near. . . .

And then the armies begin to get in touch with one another, tuba and lur roar with hoarse throats against each
other—the She-Wolf and the Bull! The wild predatory
howl of the She-Wolf when she sits on her haunches and
fills the night with her blood-song before going out to
hunt for her young, that is the note the long, straight tuba
sends to every part of the horizon; the roar of the rutting
aurochs in boundless echoing forests is heard again in the
curved neck of the lur. Slaughter and destruction hang
over the world.

From the compact masses a flight as of swarming bees
shoots obliquely into the air and down again in an arch,
with a thousand flashes of steel as it goes, the first volleys
of arrows let off at once, hosts of barbs falling upon the
hosts, and a great raw reek from one army meets its fellow from the other, sweat and stench given off by the charg-

ing masses in the immense crush and heat of the day.

And the war-cry is raised from the stormy sea of the Cimbrians, the howl with which they strike the enemy's soul before they reach him and excite themselves, the vast roaring of a host.

And with high leaps in the air the warriors can be seen charging on, already in the blazing delirious frenzy which possesses them in battle and makes them insensible to wounds, superior to life and death, thrilled through with a terrible form of soulfulness, like the element of fire.

On thunders the cavalry in scattered swarms, each acting for itself, the horsemen leaping on and off their horses, as is their tactics.

But the Roman cohorts stood close and firm as walls; with cool head the soldier muttered to himself the instructions he had been given, like a lesson he would he heard in, grasped his *pilum* and sniffed quietly.

A cloud of dust hid the hand-to-hand fighting, like a curtain heaven drew before its face, so thick that men lost their way in it, whole divisions roamed about without being able to find each other. Beneath this curtain the slaughter was accomplished. Marvels of valour were performed by the Cimbrians, a fire dance, the topmost pitch of crazy joy, and in that they died. Their long heavy swords they used like artists, and now and then succeeded in cleaving a Roman soldier to the groins, but nearly always they were brought down first; the lithe little marten of a Roman went in under his shield and made two, three and four thrusts with his short, two-edged *gladius* while the scythe was in the air; he worked.

Boierik came on, his bull's crest foremost amongst the fighters, blowing from his nostrils like a bull, all his mad animal forces flashing from his heavy sword; he was now in the fire his terrible heart desired, and in it he would be consumed. As a warrior he knew no bounds, he would have gone against the Roman army quite alone, mowed it down with his own hand, going up and down among the swaths till the field was bare. But the Romans stung, he did not feel that one lance after another struck him, breaking in the shaft, while the point bent and hung in him like an anchor; at last he was heavy with anchors whose barbs ate into his flesh; as in a fog he dragged himself on with all the crooked irons in him, sweeping the air with his weary scythe, and his shoulders sank, the bull's horns went down like the sickle of the moon in a sea of fighting-men and weapons. A howl closed over him. Howling the remnant of his army rushed to their death.

Plutarch: "So were the most part of the barbarous people, and specially of the best soldiers, slain in the field. And because they should not open or break their ranks, the foremost ranks were all tied and bound together with girdles, leather thongs, and long chains of iron: and they that fled, were chased and followed into their camp by the Romans, where they met with horrible and fearful things to behold. For their wives being upon the top of their carts, apparelled all in black, slew all those that fled, without regard of persons: some their fathers, other their husbands or their brethren, and strangling the little young babes with their own hands, they cast them under the cart wheels, and between the horses' legs, and afterwards slew themselves. And they say, that there was a woman hanged at the end of a cart ladder, having hanged up two of her children by the necks at her heels. And that the men also, for lack of a tree to hang themselves on, tied slipping halters about their necks, unto the horns and feet of the oxen, and that they did prick them afterwards with goads to make them fling and leap so long, that dragging them all about, and treading them under feet, at the length they killed them. Now, though numbers were slain by this means, yet were there three score thousand of them taken prisoners, and the number of them that were slain came to twice as many more."

The Romans must have been fighting against odds of about three to one, and when it is considered that their enemies as individuals were both bigger and stronger, they might claim to have used their other advantages with honour.

Roman training and technical skill had asserted themselves *splendide* against the overpowering physical gifts of a primitive people. But had they not been forced by these same people to return to ancient Roman virtues, and had not the vigorous invaders learnt slackness of them, amongst other things?

The sun went down over the Raudian plains after the battle, red and round like a bloody shield from the dust which still hung in the air as after a volcanic eruption, and crows and birds of prey were already beginning to glide down from every quarter of the sky in the cool twilight—what a battlefield! Far and wide lay thousands and thousands of young warriors who had risen hale and rosy-cheeked the same morning, Romans and Cimbrians in confusion, some in each other's embrace, and now stiff corpses every one!

The evening was more than still, after the immense war-cries of the day were silenced, and the shrieks of the women had died away, shrieks of despair, shrill and penetrating like the birth-cries with which they had once brought into the world all those who were now dead. Still was the evening after all the shouting, as still as the surviving women when they were led away to captivity and humiliation.

But when the sun had gone down and dusk had fallen, the chain of the Alps still glowed with a distant unearthly glory. A shadow from the battlefield turned towards it —Norna Gest, the Lonely, the Long-lived, who was here with his sorrow, always among the dead!

Before now he had seen vigorous new peoples come down

over the Alps, and none of them ever returned. When would the next wave come? How long would the conflict last, before the combining power of Rome and Northern nature, more pristine but as yet undeveloped, were merged in productive unity?

The battlefield lay with all its dead, and among them Boierik, a prostrate form among the rest—yes, it was the Bull that had fallen. The She-Wolf had got her teeth into his entrails from below and torn them out. And now the Bull lay with broken horns and crushed limbs upon the ground.

V

VÆ VICTIS!

IMMEDIATELY before Marius took the field against
the Cimbrians and Teutons he had concluded the
Numidian war and celebrated his triumph by a solemn
entry into Rome and a pageant of booty and chained prisoners along the Via Sacra to the Forum and Capitol. Of
this Plutarch records:

He showed "that to the Romans which they thought never
to have seen: and that was, King Jugurthe prisoner, who
was so subtil a man, and could so well frame himself unto
his fortune, and with all his craft and subtility was of so
great courage besides, that none of his enemies ever hoped
to have had him alive. But it is said, that after he was
led in this triumph, he fell mad straight upon it. And
the pomp of triumph being ended, he was carried into
prison, where the sergeants for haste to have the spoil of
him, tare his apparel by force from off his back: and because they would take away his rich gold ear-rings that
hung at his ears, they pulled away with them the tip of
his ear, and then cast him naked to the bottom of a deep
dungeon, his wits being altogether troubled. Yet when
they did throw him down, laughing he said: *O Hercules,
how cold are your stoves!* He lived there yet six days,
fighting with hunger, and desiring always to prolong his
miserable life unto the last hour: the which was a just deserved punishment for his wicked life."

As it befell the Kabyle, so should it befall Teutobod
and the other Barbarian chiefs; they decorated Marius's
triumph; afterwards the chronicle is silent about them, the
only mercy that was shown them.

311

Did the Romans consider the rank of the vanquished and the extent of their misfortunes, were they generous towards their enemy, did they measure their magnanimity by the bravery of a worthy opponent? Oh no. On the contrary. All the deeper, all the more perceptible was his degradation. But had not the vanquished themselves, when they were powerful, slaughtered Romans after the battle of Arausio?

The vanquished lost not merely life and liberty, they lost their character; this was in the hands of the victor, posterity sees it in the mirror of revenge, unless it has the means of going behind this. The posthumous fame of the Barbarians became part of the Romans' stock of abuse, lost itself in proverbial phrases, a few striking traits engraved in the memory of the people: a Teuton was a furious person, a Cimbrian a yelling one. With their names they created a notion, as Cæsar afterwards made absolute power synonymous with his name for all future time, when the name of King was too small to fit him; but Cimbrians' and Teutons' names were used to debase the notion of their report, they explored a new dimension for contempt. The synonym for bogey-man, ogre and tosspot was an Ambronian, but then it was notorious that the Ambronians had been drunk at the battle of Aquæ Sextiæ. Certain bestial ideas were associated with all three names, so that the verdict of history could be summed up in a *graffito* on the street corners of Rome:

> Teutons raging
> Cimbrians howling } Swine.
> Ambronians foaming

You Cimbrian! was the cry in Rome's taverns, when one fuddled slave abused another over their cups, and the man turned pale; you Teuton! and he was on his feet; Ambronian you are! and the limit was reached, the slave felt degraded, a box on the ears rang out, and a scuffle followed. When feared images fall the mud gets to them at last.

So much for their fame; in their lifetime the vanquished, all the thousands of prisoners, were punished as severely as a Roman overseer, most likely a freedman who had been a slave himself and *learnt* ill-treatment, could lay it on.

First the shame and spiritual torment of having to walk the Via Sacra in front of Marius's triumphal car, barefoot and loaded with chains, between two living walls of the Roman mob, who with drooping eyelids aped the nobles' way of looking at this human scum and in their greasy togas shrugged their shoulders in the most superior style, when they did not give way to their own instincts and fling dirt in the faces of the bound captives.

Colder than ice upon the mountains was the chill with which Knights and Senators looked down on the procession from their litters or from the balustrades of the Capitol; these noble gentlemen had made no mistake in mobilizing the Plebs; you want rabble to keep down rabble. (Later, there was no end to the trouble they had with Marius, whom they had spoilt.)

The ladies of Rome watched the procession, wrapt in grace and distinction from top to toe, showing no more cruelty than was becoming, with the sweetest look of disgust and a silvery laugh at the sight of the fettered brutes; for them of course the pageant was a chance of being seen.

It might be that here and there a glance fell on the big red bristly fellows, recalling a memory of having seen the captive before: the hairy back of the hand, the bold, powerful carriage—but now it was broken; and the Roman lady's eyes shifted from the prisoner to the little Roman soldiers who were marching with wreaths on their brows, armed to look after the fettered captives, noses in the air; strange how it struck her that they had grown broad, compact, strong, campaigning life had almost made strangers of them, though she knew them so well; and her finger went up to her mouth, and she threw them a hasty kiss, while her great dewy eyes gleamed and filled with tears.

With the red bear she had an account to settle, and when the prisoners were sold and she had got one of them in her house as water-carrier, and he appeared in the bath-room with his yoke, strong as a bull and useful, she was just undressed, but took no notice of his presence—what did it matter to a lady if a slave saw her naked, his eyes were nobody's; but with her sense that nothing escaped she felt that the slave was shaking with agitation, his bellows stopped blowing and water splashed on the mosaic floor; he was allowed to go without so much as a fibre of her Aphrodite's body betraying the fact that he existed. The Roman lady could never forgive a Barbarian for having been, in a moment of vertigo, the object of her desire, when he was free.

But worse things, inconceivable things, are at work in her feline soul. A long, carefully calculated look at the water-carrier, on a ripe opportunity, and he draws himself up, she has *seen* him; an occasional meditative look at him, a pensive sigh, and he grows bold, for he was once a free man and worshipped beauty; and if one day an exclamation escapes him, a homage not to be restrained, but distant, the joy of the child of nature in loveliness— why, then she breathes lightly through her nose, looks round and beckons to the slavemaster, points, and the gigantic Nubian hurries in fuming; and then the leaded scourge whistles over the back of the unfortunate water-carrier. He smiles, holds himself erect under the blows, he has been misunderstood, and he smiles again; but then the negro seizes his yoke and knocks his teeth down his throat, more hurry in and he is held and bound, ten men are not too many, two or three for each limb. With hands and feet tied together he is given a dose of the cat on the floor; the Roman lady looks on with little pensive eyes; then she turns and retires to her apartments.

Some other day when she has forced him to shed tears, though it takes long, she will perhaps take him into her alcove and enjoy his crippled body.

Sure enough, the young Cimbrians' superfluous laughter, both their frank merriment and their loutish larking, was turned to groans; they were kept up to the collar and felt the lash.

Some of them went to the treadmill, which they had thought so funny the first time they saw it; that was from the outside, inside it meant aching feet and a gradual brutalization.

Others had work in the fields; that was in the open air, but under supervision, with frequent blows from a man of lower worth than they had been; chained at night in cellars together with other rabble, their food all kinds of offal.

But the toughest customers were sent to the gladiatorial schools and trained to manslaughter. They thought they knew all about it but had a lot to learn, all the airs and graces and dexterity, the various tricks, according as they were put to fighting with helmet and dagger and called a Thracian, or were sent naked into the ring with a net and a fork, like a merman, with the name of *retiarius*, or again whether they had to face lions in the arena or were expected to slay each other. They had to learn Latin and say *puls* for porridge and *aqua*, like a croaking frog, when they meant water.

They were condemned to bodily torment, from the day the red-hot iron branded them with the mark of the school and they smelt their own roast flesh, until they were turned out as finished bruisers and had had most of the bones in their faces broken and mended again; they were brought up to nothing else but death. A roundabout death, of course, full of artistry and long drawn-out; and when it came there was form to be studied, a fine gesture, one should breathe one's last to a burst of clapping. More than one of them, when he had murdered a brother, tasted the applause of the amphitheatre's connoisseurs. Occasionally, from certain considerations, they were spared, since it would not do to exterminate the gladiators all at once, there would be none left.

Thus they found their places, as men do who have left the land of their childhood and are no longer boys, have entered a regulated community and are harnessed to some calling or other, in which they are to die.

The Bronze Bull was captured at Vercellæ, and Catulus is said to have had it set up at his villa.

But on the day of the triumph it naturally formed part of the procession, rocking on its strange barbaric car, on which it had been brought from Thule through thousands of miles of Hercynian forest and across the wildest mountains along the Via Sacra towards the heart of Rome—but it was not thus that its entry into Rome had been imagined by the captured chieftains, some of whom were driven in cages in the procession, gone mad from grief and ill-treatment, with festering sores on their limbs from the fetters, and teased like apes by the Roman boys who prodded them through the bars with sticks.

Then from the sunny haze surrounding the Capitol the She-Wolf could look down at the Forum, where the Bull was being driven up amid the scoffing of a happy mob.

The pontiffs versed in the mysteries and service of the gods afterwards examined it from curiosity: barbaric workmanship, yet marked in certain details in a striking way by enlightened taste. The solar sign on its forehead puzzled them, not its interpretation, but the fact that a barbarous people had got hold of this highly-developed symbol. Had the light of Rome really penetrated so far to the North? A stolen Southern work, some thought, the whole image had been carried off, with sacred signs and all. But concealed in a chamber in the interior of the Bull they found an ancient idol, certain features of which reminded them of the most holy image both of Rome and Greece, transmitted through the ages, which only the highest initiates had ever seen, for it would strike ordinary mortals with blindness, though the augurs retained their sight, the Palladium itself—was it not strange? The same fire at the very bottom of the sacred conceptions of all peoples? The worship of Vesta; and what had they been told about the fire-priestesses of the foreign barbarians? Yes, it was strange.

In Catulus' garden the Cimbrians' Bull was soon forgotten. And afterwards it disappeared entirely. The She-Wolf was preserved to posterity, but of the Bull nothing is known; doubtless it ended as old metal and went into the melting-pot again, the best thing that could happen; it had been a failure, and new rallying-signs would be found for the forces of which it was a symbol.

And as the Bull was lost in oblivion, so were the Cimbrians. Of the terror a memory was preserved in Rome, but the terror itself was worn away, like so much else, in the mills of Rome; the Civil Wars and the days of the Empire raised many other bug-bears.

When the Roman mother wanted to get her little son to bed in the evening and he took his stand in his scant shirt a long way from the door and would not come in, she had once been used to say, Now the Cimbrians are coming, and instantly the little man toddled across the street and buried his head in her lap; now he broke into a shrill audacious laugh when such nursery tricks were tried on him and he had to be threatened with newer terrors— Now the Germans are coming! That did it.

Yes, the Cimbrians and Teutons had only been one egg that had been loosened from the great ovary of the North; Rome was to be allowed no pause.

But the advanced guard of the Cimbrians ate the bread of captivity and punishment until they died under the far-famed Southern sky.

There was a small second generation—even slaves are permitted to propagate—a smaller third one; the remainder were lost among the heterogeneous bastards of the Roman people. The first unhappy generation of captives wore their chains smooth in the slaves' quarters of many a Roman establishment, till age, affliction and harsh treatment put an end to their sufferings.

Those who had been children when they fell into captivity had to support their misery longest. Of this youngest brood, and perhaps of some descendants of their elders, we hear something thirty-six years later, when the slaves' revolt broke out in Italy and for a time became a very dangerous threat to Rome.

Its leader Spartacus was a Thracian, of a hardy, half-savage race which afterwards gave the Romans a great deal to do; together with a crowd of other gladiators he had broken out of the fighting school at Capua and spread the fire of rebellion among all slaves, so that he had soon collected an army of over a hundred thousand men and beat the Roman troops in several pitched battles. His army was composed of prisoners of war from all quarters of the world; to enumerate them was to draw the map of the Roman empire, every country round the Mediterranean which they had despoiled, men of every tongue and every colour, all under the yoke; and among them it is said that no small part was the remnant of the captive Cimbrians.

Spartacus had the intention of going northward, across the Alps, with his horde, with a sound feeling of getting away from Rome and doing the reverse of what the Cimbrians amongst others had come to grief over; but the elements of his swarm were too dissimilar, they all wanted to go home, which meant to all points of the compass, from which they had been scraped together; his army could not be led towards any definite goal. The Romans exerted all their forces to put down the revolt, and their Consul Crassus, which being interpreted means the fat man, hunted them until he had got them surrounded right down in the toe of Italy's boot. Here and elsewhere the slave army was beaten and taken prisoner; Spartacus fell.

The Romans submitted his dead body to torture. The right of property in human flesh, beasts of burden born of women, was assured. On the highway between Rome and Capua a horseman might enjoy riding along on an avenue of six thousand crucified slaves.

Among them some of the last of the Cimbrians expired, nailed up in the blazing sun.

Aqua . . . they croaked, like frogs perishing in the dust, *aqua* . . . but they got flies in their mouths instead.

An imposing incident was connected with the servile war. Spartacus and his band at one time took up a position on Vesuvius, which was then extinct and covered with vines to its summit; the crater itself formed their fortress, and the Romans besieged the fissure through which they had reached it.

A fine view they had, over the Mediterranean and beautiful Italy, a promised land; but just as the human skin does not look its best under a magnifying glass, so they found the beauties of the landscape increased by distance; they had climbed as high as they could go, right up the world's chimney, to enjoy a brief rest.

They were starved out. At last, when the Romans thought all was very quiet within, they advanced through the cleft, but were much surprised to find not a soul. The slaves had made ropes of vines and let themselves down the sheer outer wall of the crater on the other side; thus there was a leak in the trap that time.

But the wrath of Vesuvius was roused. For it was no less a person than one of the brothers of Gunung Api him-

self they had outraged, walking on his hat and making war
on his very scalp; he disliked this and broke into eruption, and a century and a half later, for mountains measure time by a bigger scale than men, and burned the vineyards and vermin from his sides, slobbered lava and
boiling mud upon the country round, strewed cinders on
top, and buried another generation altogether, the great
grandchildren of the transgressors; at any rate both Pompeii and Herculaneum were overwhelmed.

It was the end of the world to those who witnessed it.
A Græco-Roman author, Dion Cassius, described the eruption in these words: "Many men of immense size, sur-
passing all human stature and even our conceptions of
giants, appeared now upon the mountain, now in the surrounding country and in the towns, both by day and night,
wandering about on the earth and passing to and fro in
the air. And afterwards terrible droughts suddenly occurred and mighty earthquakes, so that the whole plain
seethed and the mountains leapt; and sounds were heard, as
of thunder underground and a roaring above the earth, and
the sea roared, and the heavens answered again. And there-
upon there was suddenly a fearful crash, as though the
mountains were overthrown, and instantly there leapt into
the air first stones of immense size, so high that they
reached the topmost summits, and then much fire and an
infinite mass of smoke, so that the whole atmosphere was
overshadowed and the sun completely hidden, as in an
eclipse; thus there was night instead of day and darkness
instead of light. And some thought that it was the Giants
that had risen (for many such gods continued to show themselves through the smoke), but others thought that the
whole universe was about to be engulfed in chaos or in fire."

Yes, it was the ancient fire, Gunung Api, also called
Lucifer, or Loki, it was his red lads that had left the mountain to play and stride about the sky.

HOWLING, THE REMNANT OF HIS ARMY RUSHED TO THEIR DEATH

See page 308

When the eruption was at its height it appeared to those
who were never to see another day rather as though fire was
bursting out everywhere, from the mountain, from the
clouds, the glare of fire came from the sea, fire burst out
of the earth, stones and trees became fire, flames formed in
the houses' foundations, as though a fire beneath was forcing its way up; tongues of fire ran along the roofs, the air
they breathed turned to fire, and in that fire they sank
down, gasped and expired, like fire-illumined worms upon
the earth.

But it was no more than a brief blaze and a short rumbling; in reality the fire was confined, Vesuvius had only
flashed out through the bars. Afterwards he smoked for
centuries, to keep his crater clean.

The world did not come to an end; it has to last yet,
with its yearnings and its troubles. A couple of towns were
destroyed, and the heirs of the dead—oh, they were rum-
maging for their places before they were in the ground—
built towns above them. Later on they were dug up, and
eighteen centuries-old moment was brought to light, petrified by an eruption, a resurrection of the Roman and his
belongings as though scarcely an interval had elapsed.

A gladiatorial barrack was excavated at Pompeii with
everything pertaining to slaughter and punishment, arms,
armour, scourges, down to the smallest details, the prisoners' rude drawings on the walls, and they were pretty
broad; the smell of their sweaty bodies was not far from
being dug up again.

In one of the cells where the slaves were locked in at
night a heap of big skeletons was found linked together in
the hardened ash, a squad of prisoners that had not been
able to get out or that some one had omitted to release;
they had huddled together in their chains like dogs, while
the cinders rained down from above and closed over them,
finally stopping nose and mouth. How the last mouth

struggled for the last breath of poisoned air, shaking the
ash away once more and opening its lips, a breathing-hole
among the ashes, still hoping; but the ashes fell.

There may have been great-grandchildren of the Cimbrians among them, born as captives of captive parents,
Romanized by now and perhaps with nothing left but their
size to recall the Northman. And that is the last there is
to be told of the great, happy, mad boys of Cimberland.

But what of the women?

There was a fair in the slave market in Rome.

It lasted many days, for there was only room for a small
part of the female slaves that were to be sold. But there
was plenty of time.

After a war, the brief white heat which welds the changes
of history and decides in a moment the fate of hundreds of
thousands, it is surprising how long the years are, ages can
be spared for dividing the spoil.

The number of the captive women was legion, but each
one was accurately valued, there was bargaining and hag-
gling, over and over again, about the price per head, before they were all sold and carried off by their new owners.

The goods were all young. The old and useless had been
killed, they were not worth transporting; most of them had
done it themselves, the Barbarians' terrible female soothsayers and butchers, who had raved both at Aquæ Sextiæ
and Vercellæ and fired the other women to murder and
suicide, a fearful sort of creatures who as they died had
bitten the soldiers' fingers with their toothless gums, as
they were taking off their necklets; ugh, the soldiers dried
their fingers and shuddered, it was as though a far worse
death had sucked at them than that which raged about them
in battle. These tortoise-like hags they had stabbed or trampled to death, but besides them there were young priestesses,
of very good appearance; these they had taken alive, they
would fetch a price.

One of them indeed was noticeable for a kind of barbaric beauty, such heavy tresses had never been seen, nor so fair; the woman's skin too was very white, reminding one even of the chryselephantine Minerva; she was a rarity and would undoubtedly reach a high figure.

It goes without saying that the soldiers offered no violence whatever to the captive girls, however tempting they might be and in spite of the forced abstinence of war-time; for otherwise they would have been unsaleable.

Most of the mothers had killed themselves, or had been dispatched. The children could be sold, those of them that were whole. In any case mothers and children were separated, as were all other relatives, where kinship could be established; for association among slaves was always a thing to be avoided.

Among the Barbarians themselves there was said to have been a difference of rank, some of the young girls appeared to have been of nobler birth than others, a kind of knighthood was spoken of, degrees of birth ranging even to princes, on an uncivilized scale, so there were possibly princesses among the girls; they did not show it, all were alike able-bodied and they were sold as they came. Almost without exception they were fitted for men's work, the hand-mill, carrying fuel, heavy outdoor and indoor jobs, being big and hardy; but for that matter they might be applied in just as many ways as there were buyers and buyers' tastes.

Intacta! cried the slave auctioneer, getting hoarse as the day went on, over every single female individual who was pushed to the front of the platform on which the sale took place; age, so many years, at a rough guess; and in this they were often out, for compared with the Roman women the Barbarians might be much older than their looks; very muscular, fit for manual labour; hale and sound, no visible blemishes!

The slave-dealer had a wit and added spicy remarks, men laughed, a whinnying chorus passed over the square now and then, like a flock of birds taking wing. And the market had a smell of many warm human beings.

The poor creature was exposed, for they did not sell a pig in a poke, and there she stood twisting her body like the pink worm a human being is, but had no hole to creep into. Rome gazed at her, in silence, a coarse pause which decided her fate; then the slave-dealer threw her garment over her again—the view was not to be a long one, for it was part of what was offered for sale and would become the property of the purchaser.

Most of the buyers were women, the matrons of Rome who had a place for another slave-girl and were carried to the market; their purple-lined litters stood on one side with the slaves sitting on the shafts—perhaps two couples of newly acquired prisoners from the male supply, Teutons or Cimbrians like the females who were being sold, some of them personal acquaintances, it might be; but the new porters showed no sign of sympathy, they looked tired, sitting with bowed heads, and the red pompons with which they had been decorated trailed towards the ground.

A fight started among the porters, origin obscure; they were of many nationalities and in the Babel of voices nobody could make head or tail of their explanations; but it was a Teuton who had flown into a rage over the slave-market and it had taken twenty men to settle him; he had begun it . . . well, the Tiber was very handy, and the corpse was pitched into it.

The Roman matron was noted for economy; the ladies moved about the market-place with their tunics daintily gathered over their feet and examined the slaves, who stood in bunches or lay down on the platforms, a human crust on the pavement with narrow passages between for purchasers to move about and inspect them. The Roman ladies had good eyes, they could spot what they wanted at a distance and pushed along sideways through the crowd, scanned the

girl and buried a bejewelled hand in her shoulders to feel
if they were firm, examined her breasts, had she had a
child? pulled her hair, was it her own? and pursed their
lips: far too attractive, these sluts! They resembled each
other like ingots of gold, cast in the same mould and bearing the same stamp, all these country wenches, an offen-
sively good-looking breed. Handsome serving-women were
by no means desirable in a Roman lady's household; they
went for the rougher, more begrimed but useful sort, and
these were sold first.

But the rest found buyers too, often after keen bidding
by many fanciers, who sent up the price and delighted the
slave-dealer. It was men who were bidding, unblushing
rakes, whose money-bags, however, made decency superfluous. Nor did they put in an appearance till after dusk,
when possible female relations or acquaintances had gone,
between theatre time and the bacchanal, perfumed they
came, humming a verse of Theocritus; and so they made
their choice.

Slowly, one by one, but all in their turn, the young forsaken daughters of Cimberland were sold and crossed off
with a chalk mark on the forehead, to be fetched or delivered according to agreement. Could any punishment be
too hard for the vainglorious bankrupts who should have
protected them?

The defenceless ones passed to thraldom and humiliation
in many forms. Not worst of these was the lot of the wash-
erwoman, loaded with burdens and standing to her waist in
the waters of the Tiber; nor yet that of chambermaid to one
of the rich Roman ladies, who were said not to shrink from
stabbing their slaves to death with hairpins when they were
in a bad temper; nor grinding flour, head downwards for
a life-time, nor weeding and clearing stones on an estate
—the company they were condemned to, the world of their
fellow-slaves, was worse.

And worst was the fate of the fairest, who attracted the hot attention of sin; the rapid fall, a long step down, and ever down; their path cannot be traced.

But no complaint of theirs has reached posterity. The hardest lot a brutal tyranny, into whose hands they had fallen, could impose on a woman, was not hard enough to make them wince.

Many an inhuman lot has a woman made bearable by her devotion. Nor is every master harsh. Perhaps many of them carried an unspoilt heart into a new, precarious existence, even if no one had a heart for them.

VI

BESIDE THE TIBER

A MAN in a clay-stained cloak, straight from his workshop, but otherwise with the look of a well-to-do Roman, was hurrying anxiously through the streets of the city, paying no heed to his surroundings, like one who has received an urgent message and whose only thought is to arrive in time. But many of those who saw him turned round with a respectful look and nodded to each other: Cheiron the sculptor—and in a hurry!

He was hastening to the slave-market. A strange thing had happened. He held in his hand a letter which he had just received; a hired messenger had brought it to his studio outside the city with no other explanation than that it was to be delivered into his own hands, and without being able to describe from whom it came. It was a folded papyrus, and on it an unskilful hand had traced a drawing which was evidently intended to be a rough plan of Rome. At a spot which could only be the slave-market an object was drawn which after some deciphering proved to be nothing but a beetle . . . and in a flash the meaning was clear to Cheiron: the slave-market and the Northern prisoners of war who were just now being sold . . . the scarab . . . and *Inge!* A powerful memory of old days burst upon his soul . . . the land far, far away where he had once been a prisoner, was he to find it here? Now flushed, now pale, Cheiron hurried through the streets of Rome . . . could it be true? If only he was not too late!

He arrived just as Vedis was led up to the platform to be sold. . . .

327

Cheiron in the market! All faces turned that way, with a friendly murmur: well, naturally, the sculptor was on the look-out for a model, had evidently come straight from his work for that purpose; and with Roman politeness they made room for him among the bidders. The figures were already high, it was a wonderful woman, but everybody gave way to Cheiron and the slave was knocked down to him on the spot.

He left the market at once with his purchase; they saw him take off his cloak and put it over the slave's shoulders as though to screen her from the eyes of the crowd. She was taller than he, and many a man smiled: how keenly he had been set upon buying that magnificent barbarian woman; he had at once given a gold ring in pledge to clinch the bargain. . . . Oh, the great Cheiron was not so very old yet!

For the first few days she was perfectly dumb, sitting on the floor petrified and lifeless in a dark corner like one who has lost her wits.

She started as though expecting a blow when any one came near her, quivering under the eyes, with patches of white on her cheeks as though she had already been struck; and her hands trembled, she shook all over, big and strong as she was, but all in a state of listlessness, the spasms of a creature quite benumbed.

Food she accepted readily and gladly when it was given her, in her famished condition, but wept at the kindness shown her, wept as she ate and moistened her bread with tears—and her tears got the upper hand, she buried her head in her hair and wept, in long and violent fits; all her sufferings and misfortunes overwhelmed her again, but she checked herself with all her might and tried to stifle her weeping, writhed in her pain and shed rivers of tears, was almost choked and gasped through her hair like a drowning woman; her grief completely crushed her.

And afterwards she sat with wet, blue lips, panting and drawing her breath with difficulty and in hiccups; with long intervals, but again and again, a convulsive sobbing came from her heart.

At last she got over it and sat still, painfully disfigured and swollen, with dimmed eyes, flushed and bathed with tears, looking like a calm after a deluge—all the dripping trees and the heavy sky, exhausted with weeping, which can rain no more.

In a little while she slept; her head drooped and she slept for many hours, rolled in her hair, quivering slightly even in her sleep, with convulsive starts that shot through her bosom.

When she was not sitting shy and bewildered, or weeping, she slept and slept, and Cheiron let her sleep, made a bed for her in her corner and left her in peace.

She was in a miserable, neglected state after many weeks' transport on the roads and detention in prisoners' camps; her hair was a matted mass caked together with dust and rain and tears, her skin streaked all over with dirt, livid blue spots on her limbs from blows and kicks; and she was emaciated, scared out of her wits, completely shattered by terror and despair. And yet neither dirt nor distress could conceal her exquisite features and her youth, the wonderful lines of her tall, sweeping, intensely womanly figure; she remained noble, and with the eagle eye of the sculptor Cheiron detected her form through the outer show.

That it was not Inge, but must be a daughter of hers, Cheiron saw at once, with wonder and the deepest emotion.

In her features she might have been mistaken for her mother: the long face and long, delicate nose, with quivering nostril's full of life like a horse's; but she was still fairer and of bigger build, with an addition of strength from another kin, her father's. It was as though Cheiron's lost devotion of years ago had come to life before his eyes, but transfigured and greater, as a devotion is transfigured by memory. But now she was unhappy, torn out of her existence by the roots like a plant, trembling like a blind girl left alone, with all hope gone, distressed as the only survivor of a world that was destroyed, and lost in a new one.

The scarab hung round her neck; her mother must have given it her, and, though she had lost all else, she still had that. Only a goddess could have guided her destiny as it had been guided; the goddess whose picture was on the scarab, the compassionate Venus.

From whom had the letter come? That she could not have sent it herself was clear from the state she was in. And then Cheiron had given the scarab, many years ago, to the old minstrel in the land of the Cimbrians, expressing the hope that it might come into Inge's hands—it was the night he was to have been sacrificed and had been set free by the minstrel, at the prompting of the lovely May Bride, to whom he had scarcely dared to raise his eyes, and whom he was never again to see. Was it the old minstrel who had sent the letter? Was he then in Rome? Who could understand the workings of the Goddess of Love? Ah, that strange old man . . . when he had given him his freedom and told him which way to take to reach safety, he had carried his kindness so far as to bestow a fish-hook on him at parting, that he might not suffer want on the journey, and had laid stress on its being a good hook! And in fact Cheiron had fished his way through many an inhospitable country with it.

But now the scarab had come back, and with it a girl who was almost Inge herself! Did it mean that Inge had had a warm feeling for him and now sent her image in her stead? But *she* did not know him, seemed not to see him even. What would happen now? The ways of the Goddess were inscrutable.

After sleeping and weeping, sleeping and weeping, for two days and two nights, Vedis got up. The woman in her

conquered, and one morning Cheiron found her changed;
she had composed herself and bathed, had washed and
combed her hair, a labour of hours, and had put on a
simple garment that had been laid out for her, instead of
the ragged sackcloth of the slave. She looked up with
clear, but impenetrably lonely eyes, when she became aware
of her master's presence, dropped them again at once and
waited for an order, to be set to her work.

And he set her to work. Oh yes, she was to be a model.
She bent her head. As a model she would oblige him by
taking her clothes off. She did so. After a pause, during
which he was studying her, she heard him give a snort.
Then he seized the clay, gave it several hard punches and
began to model.

Cheiron lived beside the Tiber above Rome, in a big
house which shut out the view of the road beyond; on the
other side a garden, enclosed by walls, ran down to the
river. The place lay quite by itself, cut off from the outer
world, though the turmoil of Rome hummed in the air at no
great distance. The spacious house had several courts
with arcades and fountains; both it and the garden were
full of statues and works of art, and the garden was shady
with old and leafy trees. Cheiron worked in the house
with his servants and pupils; but when he was modelling
Vedis it was always in the garden, under the open sky.

And by degrees, as the work progressed, she began to
look about her and come to life; she noticed the trees, the
river, and formed ideas of her own, day by day a sense of
well-being came over her. It was pleasant in the sunshine,
in the caress of the ever-warm air; she raised her eyes to
the trees and was as it were renewed by the sight of them,
her bosom expanded and remained full, her eyes became so
blue, she was like the awakening of a day.

It was her youth asserting itself. Her health had come
back, her limbs were rounded, fuller than before, the blood

showing through her clear skin; and when she had wholly
recovered herself Cheiron felt that the earth had never
borne a more beautiful, faultless and radiant female form.
She was beauty, she was youth itself.

But Cheiron—he was not so young. His age was double
hers, he knew it. And he was not going to hide it from her.
The sculptor turned to his model with an old man's manner,
added several years to his age, was strict and short with
her; she had to work long hours for him, standing in the
garden while he struggled with his figure; and he was ob-
stinate, made a long tussle, over and over again till he got it
as he wanted it; and then it was not what he had in his
mind.

Sometimes he would have a strange wild fit when at work,
with a forceful look from the model to the figure and back
again, and he walked round it fiercely, breathing only in
snorts; at other times he burst into song, was lord of heaven
and earth; but it always ended in his throwing up his work,
frowning deeply and dragging himself away from the figure
like a beaten man, when his day's courage and strength
were exhausted.

When they were not at work she never saw him, he left
her absolutely alone; she had a room entirely to herself.
Others attended to the housework, that was no employment
of hers; she had her arduous duties in standing as a model.
No one else ever entered the garden.

She still had relapses, hiding herself with her sorrow
when it broke out again, and Cheiron heard the sound of
inconsolable weeping from an arbour in the garden; so
she was thinking of her brothers again, of all the poor
warriors she had seen killed or dragged away to captivity;
and after a long while she came out with red eyes.

But the flowering of her nature could not be repressed.
Her nature was joy, sweetness in the blood, and joy burst
out of her like springtime, when the winter of her grief was
spent. A warmth was born within her; rosy and sensitive,

happy in her solitude, she looked up into the trees of Cheiron's garden, listened contentedly to the river, was ready with a gesture of delight when she saw a bee, played with kittens, was never so happy as when she was alone.

With trees she had a way of her own, an inborn familiarity; she would stand beside them with no other wish than to be near them, they were like sisters together. She decked herself with flowers, without a thought of pleasing, and seemed to play with them, her lips moved as though she were talking to the flowers or to herself, entirely lost in the companionship of green things.

Early in the cool morning she rose and plunged into the Tiber, emerging from it like a nymph and drying herself and her hair in the morning breeze; she walked in the garden among blossoming almond-trees, in dew and perfume, and would lose herself in a tree, standing in its arms, hidden among the white blossoms which shaded into the most delicate pink, herself as white of hue as the blossoms and as rosy as the dawn, her long, rounded limbs like newly grown stems with faultless bark, her hair like a shower of light from heaven; in light and fragrance and colour she vanished in the tree like its soul, the dryad that was there and not there.

She plucked many, many flowers, seized with insatiability, and held them all in her embrace. She gave the rose a kiss, alone with it among the bushes, a big greedy kiss, and blushed with it. She loved the garden and grew brighter and brighter the more she was alone.

But Cheiron was gloomy. He had begun to work on his statue in marble, and it gave him trouble: all his short-comings were chiselled in the imperishable material.

But he finished it, for everything must have an end, both hopes and failures. And then he walked away from it backwards, when the last polishing strokes had been given and acknowledged to be hopeless, since no one comes up to Nature;—walked from it backwards as it stood shining in the garden, into his house, as though he wished never to see it again.

But it was a good statue. While Vedis had again become human and a woman and had regained her cheerfulness, all the overflowing vigour and carelessness of youth, Cheiron had immortalized her suffering and distress in his everlasting marble.

The image of suffering womanhood was there preserved for ever. It was the strange captive woman, understood by none, as she stands in silent despair, bound and exposed for sale, numb beneath the eyes of the buyer, immersed in a lost world, the doom of a nation which she has witnessed, the death of her whole race, all her kin; a picture of the deepest inward grief which even coarse spectators and the prospect of degradation cannot change to terror, for all her thoughts are turned inward; an expression of the dumb grievance of her sex against the people she belonged to and whose disasters she has seen.

It was the doom of Life, perpetuated in a work of art. To distant generations it would convey the accusation: womanhood outraged and crushed, and the cause of it, the violence of the brutal man of war.

But when Cheiron had gone into his house, and Vedis saw his affliction, as though his work was wasted and he had gained nothing, she went after him and found him in his room, among works of art which depressed his spirits, sitting idly and tired, his tired hands dusty with marble: the statue had refused to come right for him, he thought . . . and the model would not come right for him either. . . .

Then she stretched out her hands to him, in an unconscious, wonderfully beautiful and simple gesture, with anxiety in her face, his trouble reflected in love's mirror, an expression lovelier than he had ever seen in any other. And look—now Cheiron smiles, a great light breaks forth,

as when a child is given what it has been crying for. And
they both laugh, impossible to say which of them laughs
first.

It had come, her joy had welled over so that she could
no longer bear it alone, and now it had turned naturally to
him who had allowed it rest to grow. And he—he was so
glad, since, if in Art he could not attain what no one ever
attains—Life gave it him instead!

It was the first time she had seen him smile, but it was
a smile that had once lured many maidens to a certain
smithy in a certain far-off land, where a sooty lad fascinated the natives with his Southern air and his white teeth,
in spite of his being only a thrall. And his eyes were
radiant now, anything but tired, absent sculptor's eyes; he
flashed up with an artist's power of instant transformation
and rejuvenation. A moment before it was as though
Vedis's sorrow and all the sorrow he had put into his work,
the statue's sorrow, the world's sorrow, rested upon him;
now Cheiron smiled, a smile which melted and dissolved
much loneliness.

Hand in hand they went out and both looked up to the
sky, a great day, the day of their happiness; hand in hand
they wandered through the garden to a grove where Cheiron
had a statue of the Goddess of Love, a piece of the noblest
Greek work. A fine thread of smoke rose from the altar
before it among the laurels; Cheiron and Vedis offered
incense together and poured out wine upon the earth, both
holding the same bowl, before the face of the Goddess.

How inscrutably she had confused their paths and guided
them for the best! Had not Vedis lost her freedom they
would never have met, and she would have remained a
vestal all her days and never been human and a woman,
as she was now to be. Had not Cheiron been a thrall in
exile he would never have raised his eyes to the unattain-
able and remained in solitude, alone with his dream, until it came to fulfilment.

But to the dead woman who had given both of them life they twined garlands in a silence of deep reverence, and offered them, knowing no better, to the river, watching them silently till the stream carried them out of sight.

Ah, the marbles of the garden recalled Vedis's most sacred memory: her dead mother and the frozen blossoms on her cheeks.

The growth of the garden, great evergreen bushes and trees, looked like the fortunate ancestors of the poor stunted evergreen scrub of the heath that Vedis had played with in winter as a child, and they exhaled the same hidden fire; in a strange way the most elusive scent of her childhood combined and made one with her happiness in a distant Southern land.

And great was their happiness. She expanded in all the heavenly joy of her bright nature, and he enveloped her always with his enraptured gaze, which was so strong that she felt its warmth upon her face, blushing and shielding herself with her hand as though from a scorching fire.

A vanished world, her whole soul imprisoned in regret and growing with her growth, came back to her: childhood, a child of their love, a little Cupid with dark hair, but blue-eyed; and Cheiron modelled the dearest little Eros with sparrow's wings, the life of the past that had come flying to them, doubling as ever its happiness, life repeated and immortalized in an image.

For her first-born Vedis made a song in her own wild language, such as the Cimbrian mothers used to sing over their little ones, as they swung them to sleep in a sheepskin hung to the branch of a tree:

> My leaf, my little tree,
> Grow green, grow close to me!
> Swing him, ye branches,
> Sing him to sleep,
> All little warblers!

The springs around thy foot,
Earth's blood, shall feed thy root.
　　Swing him, ye branches,
　　Sing him to sleep,
　　　　All little warblers!

The high Gods walk the air,
Waving thy crown of hair.
　　Swing him, ye branches,
　　Sing him to sleep,
　　　　All little warblers!

Gather both sun and snow,
Take warmth as well as woe!
　　Swing him, ye branches,
　　Sing him to sleep,
　　　　All little warblers!

Let thy leaf feed the deer,
Cheerful his mouth to cheer!
　　Swing him, ye branches,
　　Sing him to sleep,
　　　　All little warblers!

Eagles, thy heights among,
Shall feed their noisy young.
　　Swing him, ye branches,
　　Sing him to sleep,
　　　　All little warblers!

Squirrels with timorous glee
Build their green bowers in thee.
　　Swing him, ye branches,
　　Sing him to sleep,
　　　　All little warblers!

Live on, my stem, increase!
Life comes of growth in peace.
　　Swing him, ye branches,
　　Sing him to sleep,
　　　　All little warblers!

But make thy seed to fly,
Bounty shall never die!

Swing him, ye branches,
Sing him to sleep,
    All little warblers!

My leaf, my little tree,
Grow green, grow close to me!
    Swing him, ye branches,
    Sing him to sleep,
        All little warblers!

Another Cupid fluttered into the garden and was petted
and modelled, and now Vedis had recovered her world just
as when her two little brothers were strutting about the
floor and grabbing at everything with little honey hands;
but these two little ones were her own, it was she who was
the mother, and the world she had got back was wilder and
sweeter than the lost world of regrets. Dark they were, her
little ones, each bearing a little night upon his head, but
they did not live in the depths of a winter house; they
were in a garden under the open sky, in everlasting summer.

As Vedis had recognized her childhood's most secret
fragrance in the myrtle and oleander of the South, she
merged in an expansion of the soul the great Southern
trees of the garden with deeply buried memories of the
North, almost forgotten—the sanctuary where, as a child,
she had been so powerfully impressed.

She still seemed to hear their moaning over her head,
the tall old trees of the sacred grove; the ash with the
spring below its roots, the holy water with its border of
ochre and a film over it of all the colours of the rainbow;
the airy tree-top full of bees and sunshine in the brief
summer; the apple-tree with its sacred life-giving apples,
the mistletoe high up on a bough of the oak, the holiest
of things, the lightning's infant nurtured by the oak; this
and a luxuriance of her own, for she herself was like a
plant, all this she blended together with the sunny trees of
Cheiron's garden, and the Tiber, and the bees, which here

again loomed out of the noonday fires, and the columns
of the courts, and marble and pictures and music and
song; of all this she made a world about her and within
her and about those she loved.

After Cheiron had modelled Vedis as a tragic figure he
had thoughts of working from her in the free, sublime
style, and was in doubt whether it should be a Flora or a
Mænad, a Pomona or an Aphrodite, or Demeter, or Minerva; but he ended as time went on in modelling her as
all of these.

First as Pomona, since he had seen how she loved trees
and flowers: the wild young girl of the woods awaking
when for the first time she sees a man and stretches out
her hands to him with innocent impetuosity.

As Aphrodite he raised an imperishable memorial to
her beautiful, faultless form, nudity transfigured.

And the sweetness in her blood, throbbing to a tempestuous joy of life, he portrayed as a Mænad, with garments
in wild disorder, thyrsus in hand.

But more beautiful he made her as the flower-strewing
Flora, Spring with her cool, fragrant gifts, her light step,
her great open eyes, all her careless newborn wealth.

Demeter—here she was at rest, the ripe reposeful corn,
broad, motherly, beautiful growth, the swelling abundance
of Summer.

And in a colossal Minerva he set up a monument to her
clear, upright, sound good sense. Clay or chisel was
never out of his hands.

In Cheiron's garden, that world raised above all other
worlds, a secret little Hellas, a Greek island between walls,
Norna Gest found his charges, when he came fishing up
the Tiber and made fast his little craft to the bank by the
happy house.

What a difference in the Tiber above and below Rome!

Here the pure water from the mountains; there the out-flow of Rome's drains, fish muddy about the gills, and the fish-hook brought up corpses of babies smothered at their birth. The world of Rome bent on achieving its own de-struction, but fresh new streams ever on the way to the She-Wolf's city!

And Norna Gest nodded in his wise beard; it was his consolation that the seed which he had helped to sow in this happy garden would prove the forerunner of what later ages possibly might bring to fulfilment: the union of beauty-worship and feeling, the nuptials of Antiquity and the young nations of the North.

Cheiron and Vedis stayed by the Tiber. But Norna Gest would not linger when they bade him, he never stayed long; and one day he took leave of them, he was setting out on a journey; they watched his back as he slowly dipped his paddle and glided with the stream down the Tiber, past Rome and to seaward.